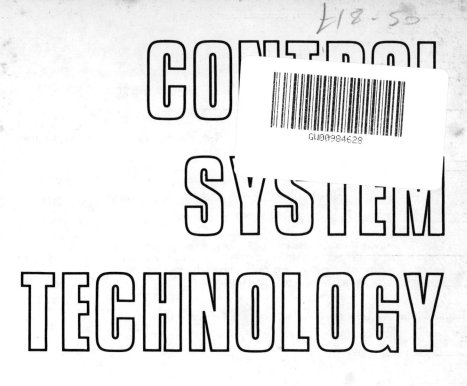

CONTROL SYSTEM TECHNOLOGY

C.J. CHESMOND

Senior Lecturer in Control Engineering,
Queensland Institute of Technology.

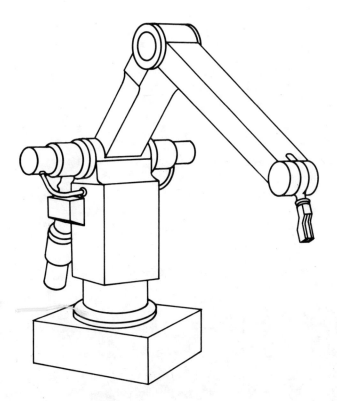

Edward Arnold

© C.J. Chesmond 1982
First published by Q Search, Queensland Institute of Technology, Brisbane, Australia

First published in Great Britain 1984 by
Edward Arnold (Publishers) Ltd, 41 Bedford Square, London WC1B 3DQ

Edward Arnold, 3 East Read Street, Baltimore, Maryland 21202, U.S.A.

Edward Arnold (Australia) Pty Ltd, 80 Waverley Road, Caulfield East, Victoria 3145, Australia

Reprinted 1986

ISBN 0 7131 3508 5

Printed in Great Britain by Butler & Tanner Ltd, Frome and London

PREFACE

Having taught Control Engineering for many years, I have formed the strong opinion that an engineering student, of whatever category, should be instructed how to create a practical control system before being expected to learn how to analyse, in detail, its behaviour. Certainly, when the student eventually becomes either an engineer or an engineering associate, the bulk of his working life will be devoted to practical engineering with analysis, of whatever complexity, occupying only a small proportion of his time. Thus, the educator has a responsibility to introduce the student to the principles involved in the creation of practical engineering systems.

As the bibliography appended to this volume testifies, there is a wealth of reference material available in the fields of instrumentation and automatic control. What, to my mind, has been significantly lacking has been a comprehensive *textbook* dealing with control system technology, and this volume is an attempt to fill this void. The book has evolved from a far more modest publication entitled *Control System Hardware.*

Control System Technology has been written with professional and para-professional engineering students in mind, be they enrolled in courses in electrical, mechanical, chemical, mining, aeronautical, nuclear, or production engineering. To satisfy such a wide market, I have tried to present the material in as readily understood a form as possible; however, in order to limit the book to a reasonable size, it has been necessary to assume that the reader has a prior knowledge of such fundamental fields as basic electrical and electronic circuits and components, elementary mechanics, fluid dynamics, thermodynamics, system analysis, etc.

This book is intended to complement the multiplicity of texts available for the study of control system analysis, many of which are listed in the bibliography: the two types of book should be used concurrently. In order to avoid producing an encyclopaedic type of reference work, it has been necessary to limit the coverage devoted to each topic: the book at least indicates all of the alternatives available to the practising engineer, and the bibliography provides sources for further, more detailed, information.

I have tried to provide a balanced coverage of the field. The book includes a comprehensive survey of transducers; servomechanisms and process control systems have been given equal emphasis; there is a comprehensive treatment of signal conditioning and data conversion; construction, testing, and commissioning of control systems have all been covered; computer interfacing and on-stream analysers have been included in order to reflect their increasing importance in control engineering.

I have yet to read a text which has not contained omissions or errors of fact and have, alas, little reason to expect this volume to be flawless. I should be grateful if the reader would draw my attention to those areas deserving of alteration or elaboration, so that any subsequent edition may be an improvement.

I am deeply indebted to many of my colleagues at the Queensland Institute of Technology for the assistance which they have given me in the preparation of this material: they are too numerous for it to be practical to list their names here.

Colin Chesmond
Brisbane
October 1982

CONTENTS

1

CLASSIFICATION, TERMINOLOGY AND DEFINITIONS

1.1   NATURAL CONTROL SYSTEMS

Feedback control systems exist in nature, to a considerable extent. The simple action of a human picking up a pencil typically involves two feedback paths: firstly, visual feedback data enable the current positions of the fingers to be signalled to the optical system and hence to the brain; secondly, having located the pencil, feedback data are transmitted to the brain, via the nervous system, to signal the amount of pressure currently being applied by the fingertips to the pencil.

The objective of the brain is to establish the desired positions for the fingers and the desired degrees of finger pressure, to compare these desired values with the actual values being transmitted back to the brain, and to use the results of these comparisons to compute an appropriate course of action which will then be implemented, by appropriate body muscles, upon receipt of suitable signals from the brain.

Systems such as this, which employ feedback data, are termed Closed Loop Control Systems. The converse of these are termed Open Loop Control Systems, such as would result, in the example under consideration, if the person involved were blind and had finger tips insensitive to skin pressure: it is still conceivable that the pencil could be picked up, but the probabilities would be high for missing the pencil altogether, failing to grip it, subsequently dropping it, or snapping it! Thus, with Closed Loop action there is the potential for considerably improved quality of control, compared with Open Loop action.

The contents of this volume are concerned with automatic control systems, in which the functions alluded to so far are implemented by hardware, with the function of the human operator reduced to the task of establishing desired values, or goals, for the automatic systems.

1.2   HISTORY

One of the first automatic systems to be documented was constructed in pre-Christian times, to open the doors of an ancient Greek temple. The lighting of the fire on an altar caused water to be driven by pressure into a bucket and the resulting additional weight was used to actuate the door opening mechanism. This was inherently an open loop system, because there were no feedback data supplied to the hardware to indicate the actual position of the doors.

The first significant closed loop control system was James Watt's flyball governor, developed in 1788 for the speed control of a steam engine. Minor developments occurred from time to time (for example, in windmills and machine looms), but the real watershed for control engineering was triggered by the Second World War and has continued ever since, accelerated until recently by the space programs. Initial progress was made in single loop systems, which contain a single feedback channel, but the technology has been extended to embrace multi-loop systems, which contain two or more feedback paths: thus, in a modern transport aircraft, systems will be present to automatically control such variables as altitude, rate of climb and descent, Mach number, air speed, airport approach trajectory, cruise flight path, etc., in addition to the more straightforward variables such as attitude and rotational velocity, and these are implemented with a hierarchy of feedback control loops.

1.3 THE FUTURE

In the aerospace field, it can be anticipated that there will be progressive improvement in the degree of sophistication of the control systems used. Precision guidance of space probes, the wide range of operational modes of the space shuttle, and the ability, remotely from Earth, to manoeuvre vehicles traversing areas of the surface of planets all require a high level of complexity for the control systems involved.

In the industrial field, repetitive production line operations are increasingly being taken over by robots, which can be designed to operate in the most hostile of environments and which can function for twenty four hours per day without exhibiting fatigue. Progressive improvement in the control of product quality can be expected to result from improvements in instrumentation hardware.

Control engineering techniques are being adapted to be applied to fields such as environments, economies, company management, and resource management.

In many instances, it is becoming necessary to interface the control systems to on-line digital computers, in order to cope with the complexity of the systems under control. Indeed, the application of computers is often rendering it logical to employ digital hardware for the control systems themselves: note that, although the digital hardware is very different in nature from its analog counterpart, the control principles employed are changed little by this modified approach.

1.4 GENERALISED SINGLE LOOP CONTINUOUS FEEDBACK CONTROL SYSTEM

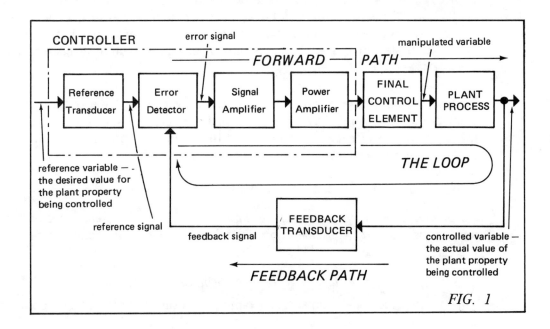

FIG. 1

Figure 1 is a generalised representation which is valid for any single closed loop continuous control system. Notice that the plant process forms an integral part of the control loop: the implications from this are, firstly, that the performance of the control loop is heavily influenced by the performance of the plant process and, secondly, that the control engineer will need to have a fairly intimate knowledge of the details of the plant process being controlled.

A transducer is a device which is capable of converting the value of a data variable into a signal whose magnitude and sense are representative of the magnitude and sense of the data variable. Typically, the feedback transducer, which is measuring the actual value of the variable being controlled, is mounted directly on the plant under control, whereas the reference transducer is mounted on a control station (for example, a console) which may be remote from the plant; the reference transducer indicates the desired value (which typically is selected by an operator) of the variable under control.

The error detector performs the function of computing the error signal, which is the difference between the reference and feedback signals and therefore represents a measure of the difference between the desired and actual values for the controlled variable. Obviously, then, a perfect control system is one in which the error signal is held at zero at all times, so that any departure from this condition represents a performance degradation from the ideal.

The final control element is some actuating device physically integral with the plant and which is capable of manipulating the plant in such a way that the controlled variable is, in fact, capable of being adjusted. Because of the input signal requirements of the final control element, stages of signal and power amplification generally are necessary, in order to boost the error signal strength appropriately.

Typically, the amplifiers and the error detector join the reference transducer in the control station; when mounted together as a single unit, they generally are referred to as a Controller. The Controller may be remote from the remainder of the loop elements, even to the extent of being connected by telemetry link, in some cases.

Because of the nature of the hardware, the power level at the output from the plant typically will be many orders of magnitude greater than the power level at the input to the reference transducer, so that it may be possible to control MW of output power with mW of input power, for example.

1.5   CLASSIFICATION OF CONTROL SYSTEMS

Automatic control systems may be classified in many different ways and these are outlined below. Any one control system obviously will relate to several of the categories listed.

A.   Open Loop versus Closed Loop Continuous Control

Figure 2 represents an elementary example of a simple open loop speed control system, using a separately excited DC motor.

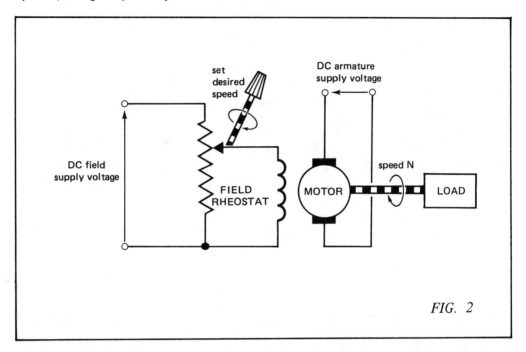

FIG. 2

The speed of the output shaft will be set manually, by adjustment of the field rheostat, so that, in theory at least, there will be a given specific speed for each position of the rheostat slider, which therefore may be calibrated in terms of equivalent shaft rpm.

The accuracy with which a particular desired speed is actually attained will be impaired by the following factors:

●   changes in the supply voltages;
●   variations in the resistances of the rheostat, field winding, and armature winding, resulting from temperature changes due to self heating or fluctuations in ambient temperature;
●   variations in the characteristics of the load;
●   magnetic hysteresis in the motor, which will cause the value of speed attained to depend upon the recent past history of variations in desired speed setting.

The degree of precision with which the speed is obtained may be improved considerably, by monitoring the shaft speed with a suitable instrument (a velocity transducer) and requiring a human operator to make appropriate adjustments, to the rheostat setting, in order to correct for any drift in the measured speed away from the desired value. This arrangement represents an elementary form of closed loop control, with the operator serving as the error correcting part of the loop, so that the quality of control will depend largely upon the manual dexterity and mental concentration of the operator. The system may be automated, by employing hardware based on the block diagram of Figure 1, so that the quality of control should now be consistent. Figure 3 represents a typical closed loop arrangement developed from the open loop configuration of Figure 2.

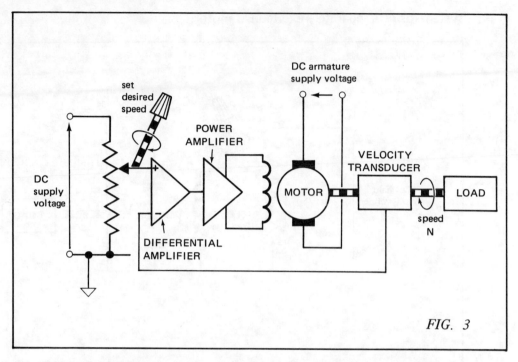

FIG. 3

Generally speaking, the properties of an open loop system are as follows:

Advantages	*Disadvantages*
Relatively simple, resulting in cost, reliability and maintainability advantages.	Relatively slow in response to demanded changes.
Inherently stable.	Inaccurate, due to lack of corrective action for error.

Generally speaking, the properties of a closed loop system are as follows:

Advantages	*Disadvantages*
Relatively fast in response to demanded changes.	Relatively complex.
Relatively accurate in matching actual to desired value.	Potentially unstable, under fault conditions.

Instability is a condition, with feedback systems, whereby control is lost and the actual value ceases to track the desired value. Typically, but not inevitably, the output oscillates and these oscillations progressively increase in magnitude. With adequate design, instability can only develop after an equipment failure has occurred. Obviously, the effects can be catastrophic (for example, in aircraft or nuclear reactors) so that, in these situations, it is necessary to detect failure and to disable the control system as rapidly as possible: inevitably, this will introduce further complexity.

B.   Classification by Type of Plant being Controlled

This is self explanatory: examples are power generator control, boiler control, air conditioning control, aircraft control, ship control, space probe control, etc.

Where the function of the plant is the manufacture of a product in a more or less continuous process, the control in this context is referred to as Process Control. In these applications, a wide range of off-the-shelf controllers is available commercially, and these are referred to as Process Controllers. The method of implementation of control, together with the terminology used, has tended to differ from the practice in other areas of application.

C.   Classification by Type of Process Variable being Controlled

Again, this is self explanatory: examples are considerable and include displacement, velocity, acceleration, force, torque, tension, temperature, pressure, mass, liquid and gas flow rate, humidity, liquid level, chemical composition, pH, voltage, current, frequency, neutron flux density, altitude, air speed, Mach number, rate of climb and descent, etc.

In a closed loop system, it is desirable that the feedback transducer should provide a direct measure of the variable being controlled. In a limited number of instances, no suitable instrument is available, so that the feedback data have to be generated by computation from measurements, by suitable transducers, of related process variables. It should be appreciated that a closed loop system is only as good as its transducers, so that accuracy of control cannot be better than the accuracy of the transducers (it will often be significantly worse). It should also be noted that, if a process variable cannot be instrumented, then it cannot be controlled in a closed loop arrangement; in other words, the feedback transducer should be measuring that variable (or property) of the plant process which one desires to control.

D.   Servomechanisms versus Regulators

A Servomechanism is a closed loop continuous control system in which the plant output is mechanical in its nature; the function of the system is to cause the actual value to track as accurately as possible changes (which may be rapid) in the desired value. Representative examples would be position control systems for aircraft control surfaces (ailerons, elevators, rudders, etc.), robotic arms, nuclear fuel rod loaders, and graph plotters and speed control systems for mine winders and steel mill rollers.

A Regulator is a closed loop continuous control system, the function of which is to hold the actual value at a constant level, determined by a preset desired value (or "set point") in the presence of fluctuating operational conditions. Representative examples would be automatic voltage and frequency control systems for electric power generators, temperature and liquid level control systems in breweries and oil refineries, and pressure control systems on steam generating plant.

In practice, the distinction between a Servomechanism and a Regulator can be imprecise, especially where speed control is involved. In any case, the principles involved in the construction, analysis, and design of the two categories of system are identical.

E.   Classification by Type of Control Signals being Employed

In this context, the system is defined by the nature of the signals involved, and will therefore be electrical, mechanical, hydraulic, pneumatic, or combinations thereof.

F.   Analog, Digital, and Hybrid Control Elements

With Analog elements, the output signal will vary in a smooth, continuous, manner when the input signal is varied in a smooth, continuous, manner. Most electrical elements and virtually all non-electrical elements are inherently analog.

With a Digital element, the output signal (or signals) take the form of a pattern of voltages (or currents) and this pattern (usually in a suitable binary code) is representative of the value of the output data. In the case of Serial transmission, one data channel is used and the pattern is transmitted as a time sequence of pulses; in the case of Parallel transmission, there are as many data channels as the code word length (that is, the number of binary digits in the pattern) and all of the bits in the word are transmitted concurrently.

Hybrid systems, which contain some analog and some digital elements, are referred to as Sampled Data control systems. Since almost all plant processes are inherently analog, it follows that any continuous control system using digital control elements is a sampled data system.

The majority of electrical analog elements use a varying DC voltage or current as the control signal. In some instances, however, the value of the data being represented is used to amplitude modulate a sinusoidal carrier (typically at 50, 60, 400Hz, 1, 2, or 4 kHz) and a system using this type of device is known as an AC-Carrier control system.

G.   Linear versus Nonlinear Continuous Control Systems

A linear control system is one entirely composed of elements which exhibit a straight line relationship between the data value represented by the output signal and the data value represented by the input signal, under steady state conditions of calibration.

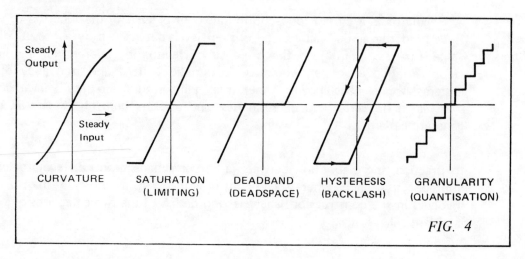

CURVATURE   SATURATION   DEADBAND   HYSTERESIS   GRANULARITY
                   (LIMITING)   (DEADSPACE)   (BACKLASH)   (QUANTISATION)

FIG. 4

A nonlinear control system is one containing one or more elements which do not exhibit such a straight line relationship, and examples are shown in Figure 4. It is important to appreciate that no element is completely linear since, for example, it must be driven to some practical limit if the input signal is sufficiently excessive, and also that most apparently nonlinear elements, in fact, exhibit approximately linear behaviour, for relatively small input signal excursions about a nominated quiescent operating level.

H.   Single versus Multiple Loop Continuous Control Systems

Many systems involve more than one feedback element and therefore contain a multiplicity of feedback loops. Moreover, localised ("minor") feedback loops often are placed around individual system elements or small groups of elements: one function of such a feedback is to "disguise" any nonlinearity in an element in the forward path of that loop, and this is said to result in a "linearising" effect.

I.   Sequence Control Systems versus Continuous Control Systems

A sequence control system is a system of electronic, electrical, or pneumatic digital logic elements, arranged to make on-off decisions at prescribed instants in time. Such a system may be used on its own, with on-off final control elements, in processes involving repetitive operation: feedback may be involved, in the form of on-off signals from limit switches. Alternatively, the sequence control system may be used (in conjunction with continuous control systems) for performing such functions as controlled start-up and shut-down, up-dating of controller set points, etc.

1.6   CHOICE OF SYSTEM HARDWARE

It will be relevant to indicate here the types of factor which will need to be taken into consideration when selecting control hardware.

A.   Feedback Transducers

For some types of process variable, the range of alternative transducers commercially available may be considerable: examples are displacement, flow, liquid level and temperature instrumentation. In other cases, the range is extremely limited: examples are velocity, humidity, chemical composition, and neutron flux density instrumentation. The possession of a detailed knowledge of the alternatives available obviously is essential for the creation of viable systems. Bearing in mind that the transducer is to be associated intimately with the plant, the factors which could be relevant to the selection of a suitable device are:

- cost
- availability
- ruggedness, in respect to the plant environment
- range
- accuracy
- linearity
- repeatability
- speed of response
- reliability

- maintainability
- life
- power supply requirements
- physical compatibility with the plant
- signal compatibility with the controller
- signal-to-noise ratio.

Chapters 2, 3 and 4 deal extensively with the more common types of transducer.

In some instances, the output signal may be incompatible with the input requirements of the controller and then it is necessary to interpose signal conversion and/or signal conditioning hardware. Some examples of this would be:

- square-root extractors to compensate for the square law relationship inherent in some flow transducers;
- air-to-current converters to enable transducers generating pneumatic signals to be interfaced to electronic controllers;
- digital-analog converters to enable digital transducers to be interfaced to analog controllers;
- analog-digital converters to enable analog transducers to be interfaced to digital controllers;
- demodulators to enable AC-carrier transducers to be interfaced to DC controllers;
- noise filters to remove parasitic noise from corrupted signals.

Chapters 10, 11 and 12 provide extensive coverage of signal conversion and signal conditioning hardware.

B.   Final Control Elements

To a major extent, these are either control valves (globe or butterfly types, with pneumatic, electric, or hydraulic actuators), heaters, or motors. The factors which could be relevant to the selection of a suitable motor, for example, are:

- cost
- availability
- ruggedness, in respect to the plant environment
- load details: inertia, friction constants, torque loadings
- maximum and minimum velocity
- maximum acceleration
- duty cycle
- reliability
- maintainability
- life
- mounting and coupling requirements
- power supply requirements
- input signal characteristics.

Chapters 5, 6 and 7 describe the commonly used types of final control element.

C.   Controllers

These complete the feedback loop, accepting the feedback signal as an input and generating, as an output, the input signal required by the final control element. The controller may be custom built or it may be an off-the-shelf commercial item.

Particularly in the custom built cases, the production of the controller may involve considerable design, development, manufacturing, and commissioning effort. The performance of the plant process, feedback transducer and final control element to a large extent are predetermined, for a particular situation, so that it is necessary to have flexibility in the controller characteristics, in order to obtain satisfactory performance from the completed control loop.

Chapters 5 to 12, inclusive, cover the wide range of hardware likely to be encountered in both custom built and off-the-shelf controllers. In addition, Chapter 2 contains descriptions of the most common reference transducers.

2

TRANSDUCERS — DISPLACEMENT, REFERENCE AND VELOCITY

2.1   INTRODUCTION

The range of devices available to provide transduction of displacement (rectilinear or angular) is considerably greater than that for any other variable. Moreover, many of these displacement measuring devices form the secondary element in transducers for other variables, such as temperature, force, torque, acceleration, tension, liquid flowrate, liquid level, liquid density, etc.: in this role, the function of the displacement measuring device is to enable the transducer to generate an electrical output signal.

Representative applications of displacement and velocity transducers as primary feedback transducers in closed loop control systems would include the following:

- recording instruments;
- machine tool position and speed control;
- steering of tracking aerials (antennae) for telecommunications, weaponry, and astronomy;
- paper mill and steel mill control;
- industrial robot control;
- control and guidance of aircraft, satellite launchers, missiles, ships, and submarines;
- control of transportation vehicles.

Because of the considerable range of devices in these categories, space will permit discussion of only the more commonly used types. In the measurement of motion, it is necessary to make a distinction between rotational and translational movement: transducers for measuring rotational motion are said to be "rotary" or "angular", whilst those for measuring translational motion are said to be "rectilinear". The last named word is preferable to "linear", when describing the type of motion, because the word "linear" is best reserved for describing the calibration graph for the transducer. Thus, linear is the antithesis of nonlinear, whilst rectilinear is the antithesis of rotary: a transducer may be rectilinear and nonlinear; alternatively, it may be rotary and linear!

Displacement Transducers, which are known also as Position Transducers, are used primarily as feedback transducers in position control systems, which are called, alternatively, Servomechanisms or Servosystems. However, other versions of these may be used as reference transducers for a wide variety of control systems, especially where the reference variable value is to be set manually.

Velocity Transducers, which are known also as Rate Transducers, are used mostly as principal feedback transducers in velocity (speed) control systems and as secondary feedback transducers in position control systems. In the latter case, the velocity transducer signal is a measure of the rate of change in the displacement transducer signal, and is used principally to modify the dynamic behaviour of the position control system, a process known as "damping".

2.2   DISPLACEMENT TRANSDUCERS

2.2.1   Servo Potentiometers

Servo Potentiometers are distinguished from conventional potentiometers in that they are manufactured to far superior specifications; these can involve:

- a close tolerance on the linearity of the wiper voltage versus wiper displacement characteristic;
- a close tolerance on the resistance of the track;
- the use of high grade bearings, to minimise friction;
- the use of a high quality precious metal brush, for the wiper, to minimise friction, wear, and contact resistance.

The track of a servo potentiometer may be wirewound or it may be manufactured from homogeneous material such as carbon composition, high conductivity metal or metal composition film, or conductive plastic. Most servo potentiometers are wirewound, because of the high degree of linearity which can be obtained with this type of construction; however, a disadvantage which results is a granularity effect, due to the fact that the voltage at the wiper must increment by an amount equal to the voltage dropped across one turn of the winding, when the wiper is moved. The wirewound construction also lends itself to the addition of fixed tappings, the use of which is discussed in Sections 9.2.7 and 11.6.

The law relating wiper voltage to wiper displacement sometimes is made deliberately nonlinear, which is discussed in Section 11.6: one method for achieving this is to graduate the cross-sectional area of the track and, with wirewound types, a stepped form of nonlinear function can also be achieved by using wire of different diameter along different sections of the track.

Rectilinear potentiometers are constructed with lengths of travel ranging typically from 1mm to 6 metres (with 1cm to 15cm common), track resistances ranging from 20Ω to 200 kΩ (with 100 Ω to 10kΩ common), and linearity errors ranging from less than 0.1% (with 0.1%, 0.5%, and 1% common). Typical resolution for wirewound potentiometers ranges from 70 to 200 steps per cm. More than one track may be mounted within the case of the device, in order to provide multiple data channels. Rectilinear potentiometers will be destroyed if overdriven mechanically, so that mechanical limits must be placed externally on the input displacement. Life of these potentiometers may be short, due to problems experienced with trying to maintain a good contact between the wiper and the track.

Rotary potentiometers are manufactured in single turn and multiturn versions. Single turn types use a toroidal former for the track and the usual need for a deadspace, to provide electrical isolation between the two ends of the track, means that the useful input travel is less than 360°, and typically ranges from 320° to 355°. (Note, however, that Section 9.2.7 describes a toroidal potentiometer which represents an exception to this situation). Usually, no mechanical limits to travel are included in the device, so that it will not be damaged if the wiper should be driven into the deadspace: if such limits are not incorporated into the input drive, then the feedback signal generated by the potentiometer will be lost, whenever the wiper is driven into the deadspace. When this occurs, the load connected to the wiper terminal will be presented with an open circuit signal source.

The typical track resistance range is from 50 Ω to 200 kΩ, with linearity errors extending down to 0.01% and resolution (for wirewound types, and dependent upon the diameter of the toroidal former) extending down to 0.04%. Toroidal potentiometers may be "ganged" together, on a common shaft, to provide multiple data channels.

Multiturn potentiometers use a helical former for the track, and the wiper assembly is designed so that the brush simultaneously rotates and advances axially, as the input shaft is rotated. These potentiometers are made with as many as 25 shaft revolutions for full travel, with 5 and 10 revolutions being the most common. They will be destroyed, if overdriven mechanically, so that external mechanical limits must be incorporated into the input drive. The typical track resistance range is from 10 Ω to nearly 1 MΩ, with linearity errors extending down to 0.02% and resolution (for wirewound types, and dependent upon the number of shaft revolutions for full travel) extending down to less than 0.01%. Multiturn potentiometers sometimes are ganged together on a common shaft, to provide multiple data channels.

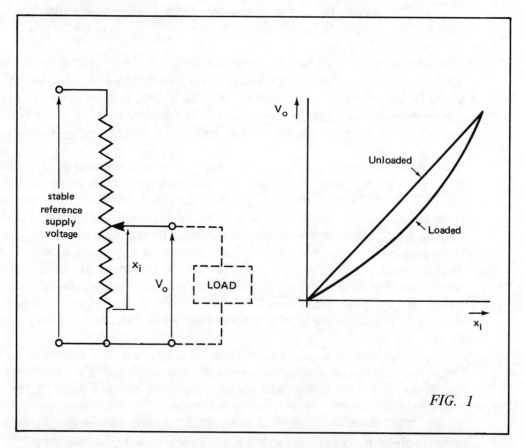

FIG. 1

Figure 1 shows the most common method of connection for a servo potentiometer, which is connected as a potential divider supplied from a stable voltage reference source, which usually is DC but occasionally may be AC. In some applications, the voltage supply will be distributed symmetrically about signal common and, in this case, it is preferable to use a centre tap on the potentiometer track and to connect this tap to signal common, thus establishing a rigid electrical datum at the mid-point of the shaft travel: this mid-point would then also be used as the mechanical datum, for calibration purposes.

Figure 1 also shows the distorting effect that the presence of significant load current can have on the calibration of the potentiometer, with the deviation between the loaded and unloaded characteristics being greatest at mid-travel: loading can readily degrade the linearity of a potentiometer, so that, where necessary, a precision buffer amplifier should be inserted between the wiper and the load, in order that negligible current will be drawn from the wiper.

The merits and demerits of potentiometers, in comparison with alternative displacement transducers, are seen to be as follows:

Advantages	*Disadvantages*
Relatively inexpensive.	Limited life.
Rectilinear and rotary versions are available.	High breakaway force/torque.
The law can be modified, if tappings are available (see Section 11.6).	Uneven wear of the track will result in a degrading of linearity.
DC or AC operation.	Poor brush contact will result in parasitic noise generation.
Requires no special power supply, usually, provided that the available supply is stable.	Relatively low reliability, due to the use of electrical contacts moving over a relatively rough surface.
High sensitivity.	Limited travel, with the possibility of destruction, if overdriven.
Reasonable accuracy.	Sensitive to loading effects.
Available in a wide range of resistance values.	

2.2.2 Differential Inductors and Transformers

Increasingly, these devices are replacing potentiometers, mainly because of the superior reliability associated with the former. They can be subdivided into four categories:

LVDI — Linear Variable Differential Inductor
LVDT — Linear Variable Differential Transformer
RVDI — Rotary Variable Differential Inductor
RVDT — Rotary Variable Differential Transformer.

The LVDI and LVDT are rectilinear transducers, whereas the RVDI and RVDT are rotary. The rotary versions have a very limited travel (typically ± 60°) and sometimes are referred to as "Rotary Pick-Offs". The rectilinear versions are by far the more extensively used, mainly because they are available with a wide range of travel. The inherent reliability associated with these inductors and transformers arises because they do not involve the use of any moving electrical contacts: in fact, there need be no physical contact whatsoever between their moving and stationary component parts.

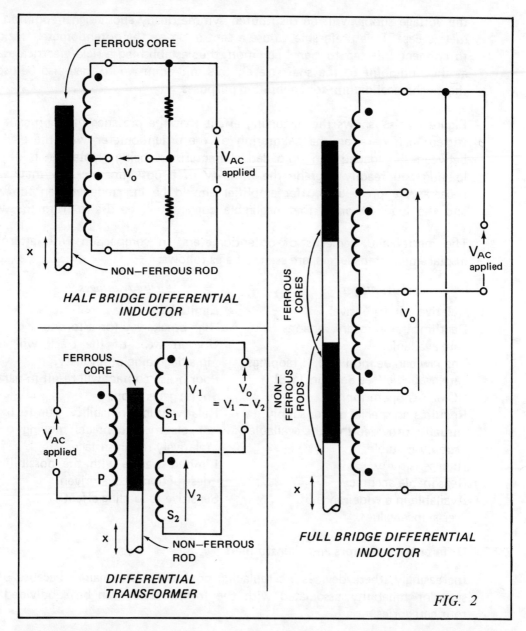

FERROUS CORE

V_{AC} applied

V_o

x

NON—FERROUS ROD

HALF BRIDGE DIFFERENTIAL INDUCTOR

FERROUS CORE

V_{AC} applied

P

V_1

S_1

V_o = V_1 − V_2

V_2

S_2

x

NON—FERROUS ROD

DIFFERENTIAL TRANSFORMER

FERROUS CORES

NON— FERROUS RODS

V_{AC} applied

V_o

x

FULL BRIDGE DIFFERENTIAL INDUCTOR

FIG. 2

Figure 2 shows the electrical circuits for half bridge and full bridge differential inductors and for differential transformers. In each case, the applied AC voltage is sinusoidal and has a frequency which may lie between 50 Hz and 20 kHz but which usually is in the 1 kHz to 5 kHz range. In the case of the differential inductor, the device is connected in an AC Wheatstone bridge arrangement, which is balanced electrically at the null position for the core(s), so that $V_o = 0$; as the cores are offset, by input displacement x, the self and mutual inductances of the windings vary, so that the bridge becomes unbalanced and V_o changes. In the case of the differential transformer, the two identical windings are connected in series-opposition so that, when the core is in the null position, $V_1 = V_2$ and $V_o = 0$; when the core is offset by input displacement x, the magnetic coupling with the primary increases for one secondary and decreases for the other, so that V_o changes.

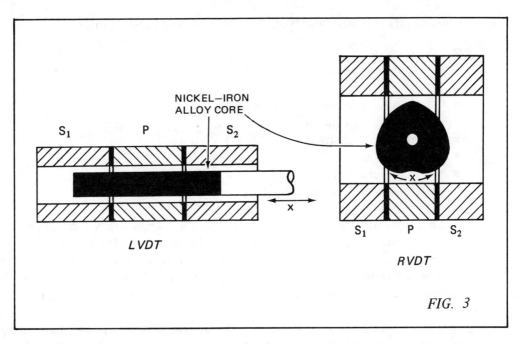

NICKEL–IRON ALLOY CORE

S_1 P S_2

S_1 P S_2

LVDT

RVDT

FIG. 3

Figure 3 indicates the type of construction used for the LVDT and RVDT, and comparable configurations are used for the LVDI and RVDI respectively. As can be seen, the moving member need make no physical contact with the fixed member, since magnetic flux linkages form the transducing medium.

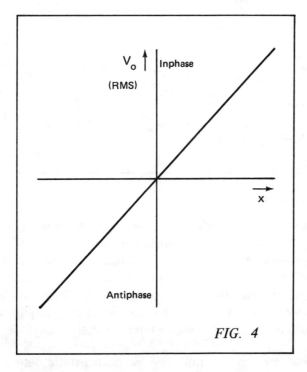

V_o (RMS)   Inphase

x

Antiphase

FIG. 4

Figure 4 shows the type of output voltage versus input displacement characteristic obtained with all of these devices. Typically, V_o will nominally be in phase with V_{AC} for positive values of x, and nominally in antiphase with V_{AC} for negative values of x. In practice, due to the effects of magnetising current, core losses, and winding impedances, there will be small parasitic phase shifts present, so that the phase of V_o will not be precisely 0° or 180° relative to V_{AC}. In addition, the presence of ferrous material in the magnetic circuit will cause a small amount of harmonic distortion in the output voltage waveform.

The rectilinear types are constructed with travels ranging typically from 1 mm to 30 cm, although this range has been extended to 0.1 mm to 250 cm in certain devices. Linearity errors as low as 0.1% are achieved relatively easily, whilst the resolution is infinite, because the V_o vs x characteristic is stepless.

The advantages with these transducers are seen to be as follows:

- rugged;
- zero breakaway force/torque;
- stepless characteristic;
- relatively insensitive to loading effects;
- virtually infinite life;
- maintenance free;
- linear law;
- high sensitivity;
- relatively inexpensive.

These properties make these transducers appear to be virtually ideal for displacement measurement. However, one must also take into consideration the fact that the useful travel is extremely limited with rotary types, that a special AC reference supply is required, and that the output signal is alternating and therefore requires conversion to DC (see Section 10.5) before it is usable in most control systems.

Manufacturers have recognised these last two limitations and have introduced completely self-contained DC versions, as shown in Figure 5; these require an external DC power supply and generate a bipolar DC output voltage proportional to displacement x.

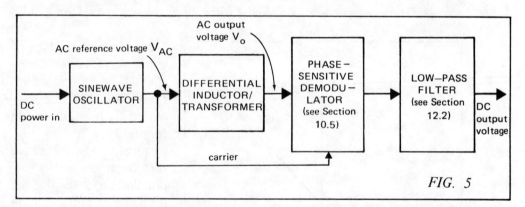

FIG. 5

2.2.3 Capacitive Displacement Transducers

In recent years, manufacturers have introduced a small number of devices which can be regarded as the electrostatic equivalent of the electromagnetic differential inductor and which possess comparable advantages. These capacitive transducers are available in both rectilinear and rotary versions and are capable of very fine resolution: for example, rectilinear types have been made which can detect displacements in the μm range. In addition, they can operate in highly hostile environments, including both extremes of ambient temperature.

The alternative principles which can be employed for electrostatic detection of displacement are:

A.   The introduction of a body into an electrostatic field, resulting in a change in dielectric constant.

B.   The alteration in the separation distances between capacitance plates.

C.   The alteration in the effective area of capacitance plates.

In each case, the variation in capacitance can be made to be proportional to the displacement of the input medium. To sense this variation, the capacitor (or differential capacitors) typically would be connected to form the arms of an AC Wheatstone bridge, so that an oscillator and means to convert the bridge AC output voltage to an equivalent DC voltage would normally be required, in order to establish a viable measuring system, just as was the case with the electromagnetic transducers of Section 2.2.2.

2.2.4   Synchros

Synchros are very small single phase rotary transformers, which evolved from now obsolete ranges of transducers known as Selsyns and Magslips. Synchros are supplied in cases with nominal outside diameters ranging from 0.8 inch (size 08) to 2.3 inches (size 23), with sizes 11, 15 and 18 being the most commonplace. Usually, they are manufactured to military specifications, although some commercial versions are available.

Synchros have a cylindrical outer stator and a concentric inner rotor. The stator resembles a miniature slotted and laminated three phase induction motor stator and carries three star-connected distributed windings. The rotor is laminated, skewed, and may be cylindrical, slotted, and carry one or more distributed windings, or it may have an H-shaped cross section and carry a single concentrated winding.

Normally, electrical connection between the case terminals and the rotor winding(s) is made by means of precious metal brushes running on slip rings mounted on the rotor shaft. However, some manufacturers make a few brushless models, which employ a set of rotating transformers to couple magnetically between the terminals and the rotor winding(s). Typically, each transformer would have a turns ratio of 1:1 and the cylindrical secondary would be mounted coaxially on the rotor shaft and would be surrounded by the cylindrical primary, which would be part of the (stationary) stator assembly: the magnetic coupling would be constant and independent of the shaft angular position.

Synchros seldom are operated singly: usually, they are connected in "chains" of two or more different types of synchro device. When the ultimate output from a synchro chain is a mechanical displacement, the synchros are said to be "torque synchros", which are represented by the letter T as the first of a two or three letter code. When the ultimate output from a synchro chain is an AC voltage, the synchros are said to be "control synchros", which are represented by the letter C as the first letter in the code. Torque synchros normally are used for remote signalling of angular data, such as might be required in ships, aircraft, factories, railways, etc., although this does not preclude their use in feedback control systems: for example, the mechanical output displacement could be used to actuate a hydraulic servovalve (see Section 6.2.1) in an electrohydraulic servosystem. Control synchros are used specifically as reference and feedback transducers in feedback control systems.

Figure 6 shows the electrical stator and rotor circuits for all of the alternative synchro types, together with the function of each. Manufacturers' data sheets should be complied with rigorously, when selecting combinations of synchros for the construction of a synchro chain.

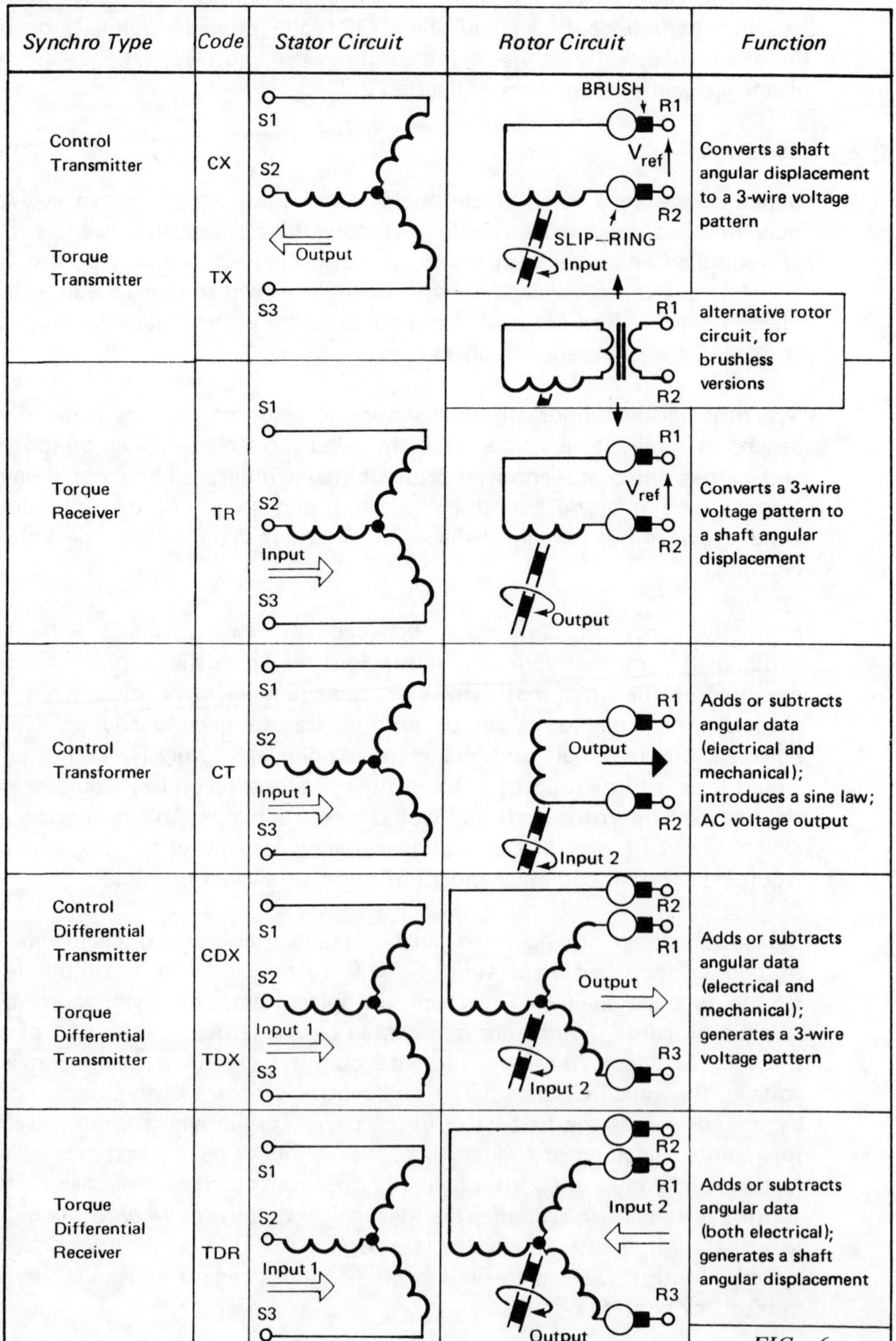

Synchro Type	Code	Stator Circuit	Rotor Circuit	Function
Control Transmitter	CX		BRUSH R1, V_{ref}, R2, SLIP–RING, Input	Converts a shaft angular displacement to a 3-wire voltage pattern
Torque Transmitter	TX	S1, S2, Output, S3		
			R1, R2, alternative rotor circuit, for brushless versions	
Torque Receiver	TR	S1, S2, Input, S3	R1, V_{ref}, R2, Output	Converts a 3-wire voltage pattern to a shaft angular displacement
Control Transformer	CT	S1, S2, Input 1, S3	R1, Output, R2, Input 2	Adds or subtracts angular data (electrical and mechanical); introduces a sine law; AC voltage output
Control Differential Transmitter	CDX	S1, S2, Input 1, S3	R2, R1, Output, R3, Input 2	Adds or subtracts angular data (electrical and mechanical); generates a 3-wire voltage pattern
Torque Differential Transmitter	TDX			
Torque Differential Receiver	TDR	S1, S2, Input 1, S3	R2, R1, Input 2, R3, Output	Adds or subtracts angular data (both electrical); generates a shaft angular displacement

FIG. 6

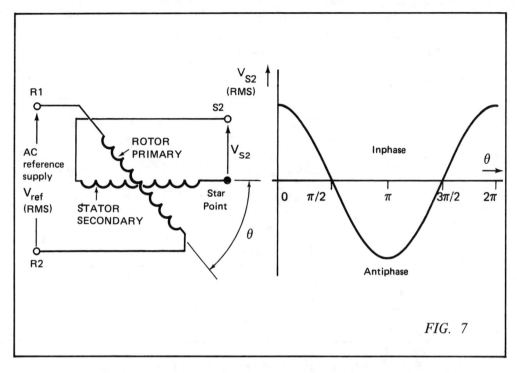

FIG. 7

In the case of a synchro transmitter, the rotor winding and any one stator winding behave as a single phase transformer with variable magnetic coupling, as shown in Figure 7. If the alternating rotor flux is resolved into two components, one in the direction of the axis of the stator winding and the other perpendicular to it, then it is the former component which will be responsible for the generation of the AC e m f in the secondary winding. Thus, in terms of RMS values and ignoring losses,

$$V_{S2} = \frac{1}{k} V_{ref} \cos\theta,$$ where k is the turns ratio and θ is the relative angular

displacement of the rotor. It follows that, for instantaneous values,

$$v_{S2} = V_{S2_m} \sin\omega_c t = \frac{1}{k} V_{ref_m} \cos\theta\sin\omega_c t,$$ where ω_c is the frequency, in rad/s,

of the reference supply and subscript m denotes maximum (peak) value. When θ lies between $\pi/2$ and $3\pi/2$, the phase of V_{S2} will be the reverse of that which exists when θ lies between $-\pi/2$ and $\pi/2$.

Thus, the RMS value of V_{S2}, taken in conjunction with the phase of V_{S2} relative to V_{ref}, is a measure of the value of θ; however, the data would be ambiguous because, for any specific magnitude and phase of V_{S2}, there are two alternative corresponding values for θ, except when V_{S2} is at a positive or negative maximum. Fortunately, when the voltages (V_{S1} and V_{S3}) at the other two stator terminals are also taken into consideration, a specific combination of the three voltages will represent unambiguously a single value for θ. Note that

$$v_{S1} = \frac{1}{k} V_{ref_m} \cos(\theta + 2\pi/3) \sin \omega_c t$$

and $$v_{S3} = \frac{1}{k} V_{ref_m} \cos(\theta - 2\pi/3) \sin \omega_c t.$$

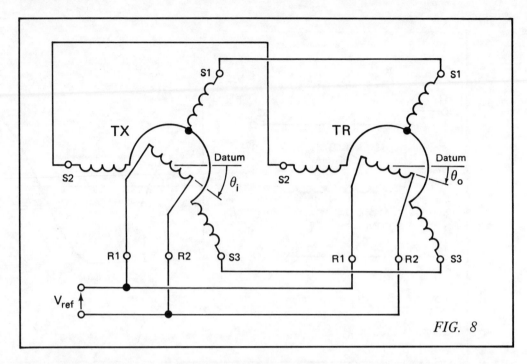

FIG. 8

Figure 8 shows a typical torque synchro chain. The pattern of voltages on terminals S1, S2 and S3 of the TX will be a measure of the value of θ_i set in, and these voltages will circulate a set of alternating currents through the stator windings of the TR. It can be shown that the alternating flux pattern established by the TR stator currents will have an axis which has a spatial alignment displaced by angle θ_i from datum. Whenever θ_o is different in value from θ_i, the TR rotor flux will react with the stator flux to produce motoring action and the torque generated will drive the TR rotor to align the rotor winding axis with the axis of the stator flux. Thus, in the steady state, θ_o will be a replica of θ_i and the shaft of the TR rotor will duplicate variations in displacement of the shaft of the TX rotor. The system therefore is useful for signalling angular data; the effect of the length of the transmission path on the accuracy of angular data transmission is not of primary significance.

In practice, the TX and the TR will tend to "fight" one another for dominance: this effect can be resolved by mismatching the stator winding impedances of the two machines and by designing high friction levels into the TX rotor shaft drive. In addition, some torque receivers use a rather different construction from that described here: these are known as Torque Indicating Receivers and are incapable of generating transmitter action. In such devices, all of the windings are static, with the star-connected windings on a cylindrical outer stator and the fourth winding on a concentric, cylindrical, inner stator. The rotor element now is part of a thin cylindrical metal shell which is free to rotate between the two stators. The torque developed is significantly less than that with a conventional Torque Receiver.

Figure 9 shows a typical control synchro chain. Similarly to the torque synchro chain, there will be an alternating stator flux pattern established in the CT, with its axis aligned with a displacement θ_i measured from the direction of the S2

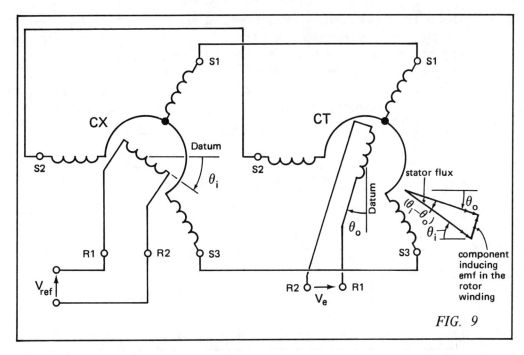

FIG. 9

axis. By transformer action, this alternating flux will induce an alternating e m f in the CT rotor winding and the magnitude of this e m f will depend upon the relative angular alignment of the CT rotor winding with the axis of the CT stator flux. By measuring the CT rotor displacement from a datum normal to the direction of the S2 axis, the inherent cosine relationship is converted to a sine relationship yielding

$$V_e = \frac{1}{k'} V_{ref} \sin(\theta_i - \theta_o) \text{ for RMS values,}$$

and $\quad v_e = \dfrac{1}{k'} V_{ref_m} \sin(\theta_i - \theta_o) \sin \omega_c t \quad$ for instantaneous values, where k'

represents the combination of turns ratios.

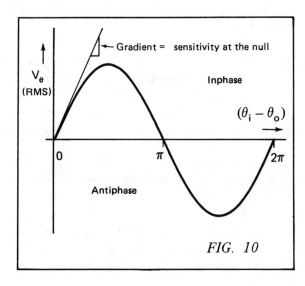

FIG. 10

The calibration curve for the CX-CT combination is shown in Figure 10. The value of V_{ref} has been standardised to two alternatives: 26V and 115V RMS. A "26V" synchro pair will yield a gradient of 22.5V per radian at the origin of this characteristic, so that the maximum value of V_e will be 22.5V RMS; a "115V" synchro pair will yield a gradient of 57.3V per radian (1V per degree) at the origin, corresponding to a maximum value for V_e of 57.3V RMS.

This synchro pair normally would be used in a closed loop control system, with the CX serving as the reference transducer and the CT performing the dual roles of feedback transducer and error detector. Figure 11 shows a typical servosystem using control synchros. The sine relationship inherent in the V_e vs $(\theta_i - \theta_o)$ characteristic means that such a system will be highly nonlinear in its behaviour, except in the vicinity of the true null $(\theta_i - \theta_o = 0)$ and the false null $(\theta_i - \theta_o = \pi)$.

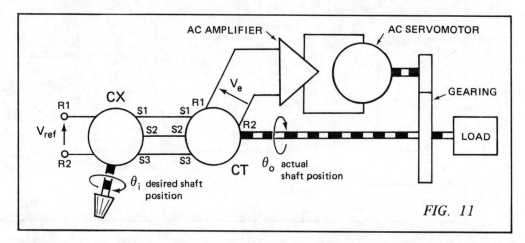

FIG. 11

The motor will be connected to drive in a direction to increase θ_o whenever V_e is inphase, and to decrease θ_o when V_e is antiphase, with the result that the steady state always will correspond to the vicinity of $\theta_i - \theta_o = 0$, so that $\theta_o \cong \theta_i$, as required. $\theta_i - \theta_o = 0$ then represents a stable (true) null, whilst $\theta_i - \theta_o = \pi$ is an unstable (false) null.

The waveform of V_e will be represented by the expression, for the instantaneous

value, $v_e = \dfrac{1}{k'} V_{ref_m} \sin (\theta_i - \theta_o) \sin \omega_c t,$ which implies a sinusoidal carrier

$\dfrac{1}{k'} V_{ref_m} \sin \omega_c t$ being amplitude modulated by the instantaneous

value of $\sin (\theta_i - \theta_o)$. Refer to Sections 10.4, 10.5, 12.5 and 14.9 for further discussion about amplitude modulation.

The value of the synchro supply frequency has largely been standardised on two alternatives: 60 Hz and 400 Hz. However, other supply frequencies (such as 50 Hz and 1100 Hz) occasionally are used. A higher frequency is preferable because, when the synchros are in motion, V_e also contains a parasitic component arising from generator action: this component is proportionally smaller for higher supply frequencies.

The accuracy obtainable with a synchro chain is in the order of 10 minutes of arc per synchro, which is equivalent to 0.046% of a full revolution. In practice, V_e will be subject to small parasitic phase shifts and will contain small components at frequency harmonics of ω_c, due to the effects of magnetising current, iron losses, winding impedances, and mechanical manufacturing tolerances. These phase shifts can be corrected, using power factor correction techniques employing, for example, the addition of small capacitors at strategic points: a common technique is to connect three identical capacitors in delta (mesh) across the synchro stator terminals.

The differential synchros in Figure 6 can be used for the summation and subtraction of additional angular reference data, as indicated in Figure 12. In each case, the operation of the differential synchros may be deduced by referring to the data presented in Figure 6.

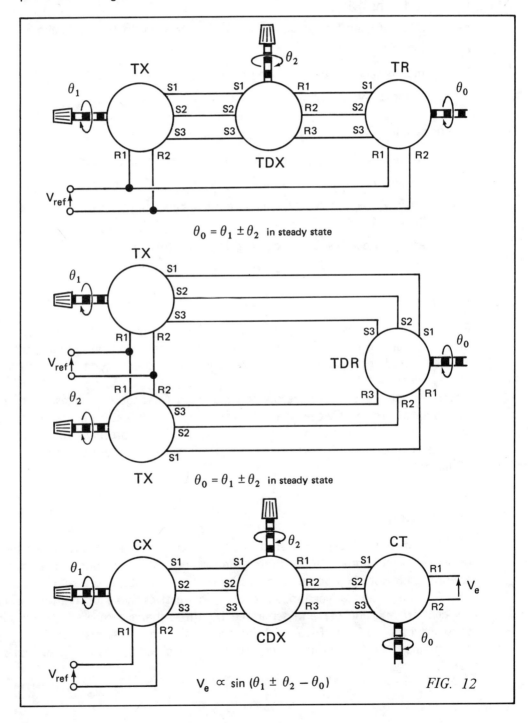

$\theta_0 = \theta_1 \pm \theta_2$ in steady state

$\theta_0 = \theta_1 \pm \theta_2$ in steady state

$V_e \propto \sin(\theta_1 \pm \theta_2 - \theta_0)$

FIG. 12

The advantages with synchros, when contrasted against alternative angular displacement transducers in control system applications, are:

- rugged;
- breakaway torque is low or, with brushless versions, very low;
- stepless static characteristic;
- accuracy is relatively insensitive to loading;
- high sensitivity;
- 360° of useful rotation, with no discontinuity in the static characteristic;
- long life;
- maintenance is low or, with brushless versions, very low;
- moderately expensive.

The principal disadvantages are:

- highly nonlinear static characteristic, except near the null;
- require a special AC reference supply for the CX rotor;
- error voltage is AC and may require subsequent conversion to DC (see Section 10.5);
- error voltage is subject to parasitic phase shifts;
- not available in rectilinear form.

2.2.5   Resolvers

Resolvers operate using the same principles as conventional synchros, but in most cases are constructed with the stator and rotor each having two, electrically isolated, windings distributed to resemble a two phase type of construction.

Resolvers can be used for resolving data from rectangular (cartesian) to polar co-ordinate form and vice-versa, and this type of application explains the name given to these devices. They can also be used for co-ordinate rotation and in place of the CX, CDX, and CT in data transmission and control chains. Figure 13 illustrates these various applications.

2.2.6   The Inductosyn

The Inductosyn principle is based upon that of a resolver transformer and the device is manufactured in both rectilinear and rotary versions. The windings are printed in copper, bonded to a glass or metal substrate, and assume a "hairpin" form. In the rectilinear version, a short member carries two short hairpin windings, adjacent to one another and separated by three-quarters of a winding pitch, as shown symbolically in Figure 14; in addition, a long member carries a single, continuous, hairpin winding having the same pitch as the windings on the short member.

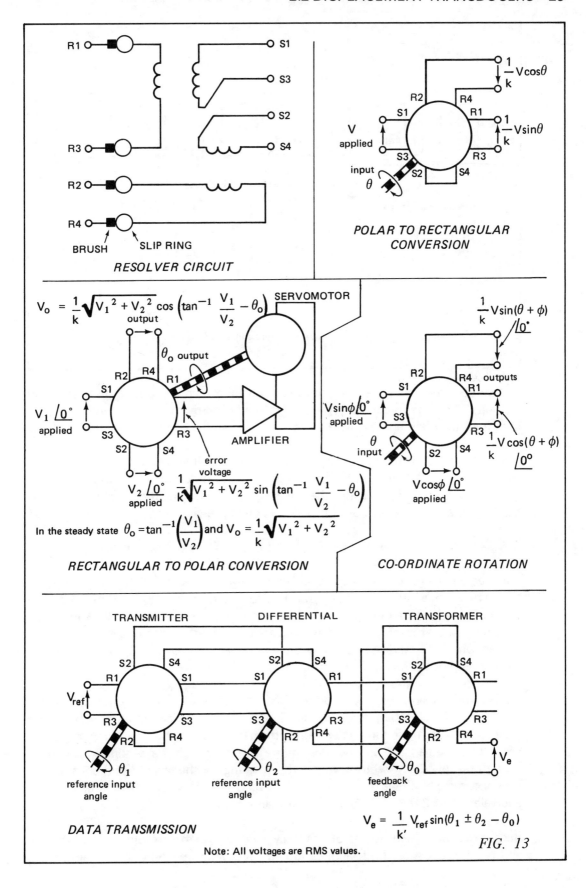

RESOLVER CIRCUIT

POLAR TO RECTANGULAR CONVERSION

$$V_o = \frac{1}{k}\sqrt{V_1^2 + V_2^2}\cos\left(\tan^{-1}\frac{V_1}{V_2} - \theta_o\right)$$

$$\frac{1}{k}\sqrt{V_1^2 + V_2^2}\sin\left(\tan^{-1}\frac{V_1}{V_2} - \theta_o\right)$$

In the steady state $\theta_o = \tan^{-1}\left(\frac{V_1}{V_2}\right)$ and $V_o = \frac{1}{k}\sqrt{V_1^2 + V_2^2}$

RECTANGULAR TO POLAR CONVERSION

CO-ORDINATE ROTATION

DATA TRANSMISSION

$$V_e = \frac{1}{k'}V_{ref}\sin(\theta_1 \pm \theta_2 - \theta_0)$$

Note: All voltages are RMS values.

FIG. 13

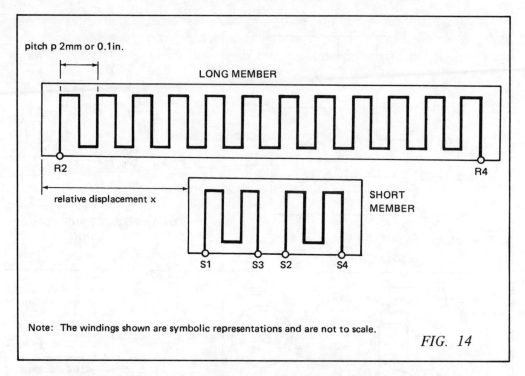

pitch p 2mm or 0.1in.

LONG MEMBER

R2

R4

relative displacement x

SHORT MEMBER

S1   S3   S2   S4

Note: The windings shown are symbolic representations and are not to scale.

FIG. 14

In practice, the short member sits over the long member but is just separated from it. The long members typically are made in 25 cm lengths, which may be mounted together end-on, whilst the short member typically is 10 cm long.

When the short member is excited with a pair of voltages similar to those which would be generated by a resolver transmitter, the Inductosyn behaves as a rectilinear resolver transformer and the winding on the long member generates an AC output voltage with an RMS value given by an expression of the form

$\frac{1}{k'} V_{ref} \sin(\theta_i - \theta_o)$, where $\theta_o = \tan^{-1}(x/p)$.   The excitation voltages can have

any frequency from 200 Hz to 100 kHz, with 400 Hz being typical, and normally they are synthesised using the type of circuitry described in Section 2.3.3. The Inductosyn alone cannot unambiguously interpret axial displacements in excess of $\pm$ p/2, so that it must be used in conjunction with other transducers, as discussed in Sections 2.2.9 and 13.4.2. Accuracies in the order of $\pm$ 2.5 μm are claimed for the rectlinear types.

Rotary Inductosyns employ two flat circular members, the pair having alternative diameters of 7.5, 10.5, and 15 cm. The hairpin windings in this instance are orientated with their long sides radial from the disc centre and occupy the full 360°: the disc carrying the twin windings is printed with the windings divided up into a multiplicity of sectors, whilst the winding on the other disc is continuous. The accuracy of these devices can be as high as $\pm$ 0.5 second of arc, which is equivalent to $\pm$ 3.9 x 10^{-5} % of one full revolution.

Because of their high degree of accuracy, and even better resolution and repeatability, Inductosyns find application in precision machine tools, automatic inspection systems, theodolites, tracking aerials, inertial navigators, etc. Their life is almost infinite, reliability is very high, and the maintenance required is negligible. Other advantages and disadvantages will be similar to those which apply to synchros.

2.2.7 Shaft Encoders

Shaft Encoders (which sometimes are called Digitisers) are digital rotary displacement transducers which are manufactured in electromechanical, optical, and magnetic versions. Shaft encoders may be of the "absolute" variety, which generate parallel digital data, or the "incremental" variety, which generate serial digital data typically in the form of pulse trains. Figure 15 shows a 4-bit absolute electromechanical encoder, in which the disc is rotated by an input shaft and the brush-gear is attached to a surrounding case.

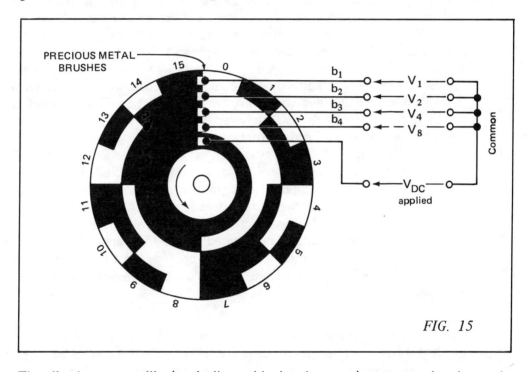

FIG. 15

The disc has a metallic (typically, gold plated copper) pattern printed onto it, using precision printed circuit techniques, and the pattern represents angular data in some form of binary code: normally, metal corresponds to binary 1 and insulation corresponds to binary 0. A DC voltage is applied to the metallic pattern, by means of a brush running on a printed concentric slip ring. Thus, the radial line of brushes detects the presence or absence of the DC voltage and, in so doing, the set of output voltages indicates the current angular position of the input shaft, in terms of the binary code inherent in the metallic pattern.

The least significant track always is placed outermost, in order to maximise the resolution, which is limited by the dimensions of the brush contact surface and by the diameter of the disc. In order to keep the diameter of the case to reasonable proportions, single disc shaft encoders normally are not manufactured with a word length greater than 10 bits, corresponding to a resolution of 1 part in 1024, which is marginally better than 0.1% of a full revolution. By gearing together two discs, word lengths corresponding to the order of 1 part in 10^5 (0.001%) are achievable in practice, being limited by the precision of the gearing. The combination of two discs to generate composite output data represents a digital application of the "coarse-fine" technique discussed in Section 2.2.9, with the low-speed disc (which is mounted directly on the input shaft) providing the coarse channel data: in other words, the more significant data byte.

If the binary code is chosen such that the same numerical value is assigned consistently to a particular bit, then the code is said to be "weighted". A problem which can exist with all discs having weighted codes is that of "ambiguity", which arises at every alternate transition in the "natural binary" coded disc pattern of Figure 15: this phenomenon occurs because of the finite width of the brushes and the manufacturing tolerances on the alignment of the brushes and on the disc production. Thus, when the set of brushes is bridging sectors 1 and 2, 3 and 4, 5 and 6, etc., the pattern of voltages may represent a value completely different from the values represented by the bridged sectors. For example, with the disc in the position shown in Figure 15, the voltages could represent any four-bit pattern of 1 s and 0 s, depending upon which brush is in contact with metal and which brush with insulation. The solution found to this problem is to allocate two staggered brushes to every binary channel except the least significant, and the alternative techniques using this principle have been given such names as "V-Scan", "U-Scan", "2-P-Scan", "V-Disc", etc. The two brushes in any particular channel are gated, using suitable logic, by the state of the output of either the next less significant channel or the least significant channel, depending upon the technique adopted. The gating is such that no brush, except the least significant, can be addressed whenever it is in the vicinity of a transition: the output data generated by the logic are unambiguous, except during the nanosecond duration switching process. Most commercially available encoders of this type incorporate the logic hardware within the case of the encoder.

Other types of binary code which are used quite frequently in encoders fall into the class of unweighted codes, which description applies to Gray, cyclic progressive, and reflective codes. These have the distinction that, at every transition, there is a change in state in only one output channel. Table 1 shows the difference between natural binary and Gray code, for the equivalent decimal values ranging from 0 to 15. Inspection of the Gray code shows that, at every transition, either bit b_1 or b_2 or b_3 or b_4 changes state: this means that, irrespective of the width of each brush and the precision of its alignment and of the disc pattern (provided that the combination does not exceed the width of one least significant bit in the pattern), the output data can only represent either the numerical value just being left behind or the numerical value just being approached. This property is true for all codes in this particular class, as is the characteristic that any particular bit has no consistent numerical value, which is the meaning of the term "unweighted".

TABLE 1.   COMPARISON OF NATURAL BINARY AND GRAY CODES

DECIMAL VALUE	NATURAL BINARY CODE				GRAY CODE			
	b_4	b_3	b_2	b_1	b_4	b_3	b_2	b_1
0	0	0	0	0	0	0	0	0
1	0	0	0	1	0	0	0	1
2	0	0	1	0	0	0	1	1
3	0	0	1	1	0	0	1	0
4	0	1	0	0	0	1	1	0
5	0	1	0	1	0	1	1	1
6	0	1	1	0	0	1	0	1
7	0	1	1	1	0	1	0	0
8	1	0	0	0	1	1	0	0
9	1	0	0	1	1	1	0	1
10	1	0	1	0	1	1	1	1
11	1	0	1	1	1	1	1	0
12	1	1	0	0	1	0	1	0
13	1	1	0	1	1	0	1	1
14	1	1	1	0	1	0	0	1
15	1	1	1	1	1	0	0	0

b_4 — most significant bit b_1 — least significant bit

In Section 9.3.1 it is shown that, in digital controllers, the processing of data should be undertaken using a weighted code, because of the relative simplicity of the logic required to implement the arithmetic. It follows that, whenever a shaft encoder generating an unweighted code is to be used, the output data must be converted to a weighted format before they can be processed by the controller. The user of the encoder will need to provide the necessary conversion logic, the design of which is discussed in Section 10.15.

All of the encoders described so far will require additional logic in some form, either integrated into the encoder case or added externally to the encoder. In every instance, erroneous output data of nanosecond duration will be generated whenever the logic changes state and the controller must be designed so that these transients are insignificant.

All of the encoders described so far have also been of the "absolute" variety: this implies that the output data format is parallel and that the output data word will be restored correctly, immediately power is restored following an interruption in supply. An alternative category of encoders is referred to as "incremental", in which the output signal takes the form of either a pulse train, a squarewave, or a sinewave; the set of output signals typically would take one of the following forms:

	OUTPUT A DATA	OUTPUT B DATA
Form 1:	Increments in displacement irrespective of direction.	Current direction of motion.
Form 2:	Clockwise displacement increments.	Counterclockwise displacement increments.

Incremental encoders are manufactured using the same techniques as are used for absolute encoders, with the principal difference being that far fewer tracks are required for the incremental types, so that the case diameters tend to be significantly smaller. Figure 16 shows a typical disc pattern for generating a squarewave representing increments in displacement but not indicating direction. In this case, the Schmitt trigger changes state whenever brush x senses V_+ or $0V$, but it is unaffected by an open circuit input.

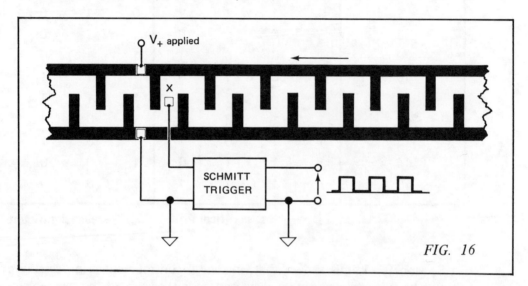

FIG. 16

With all types of incremental encoder, the output signals must usually be processed by a reversible counter (see Section 10.14) before the data can be used by the controller. The effect of the counter is to convert the serial data generated by the encoder into the parallel data format required by the controller. The principal problems with such a technique are that the count is lost whenever the power supply is interrupted and that the counter may respond to noise spikes on its input lines. When the count is lost, the counter must be zeroed electrically and the encoder drive must simultaneously be zeroed mechanically.

The manufacturing techniques described so far have involved an electromechanical type of construction. A commonly used alternative, which is significantly more expensive, involves optical techniques with which the encoder disc is made from glass and the pattern is printed to form alternate clear and opaque areas. The brush system is now supplanted by a system of photocells which are excited by a light source and lens system. A few manufacturers have developed an electromagnetic alternative, based on comparable principles, in which the disc is now metallic and presents to a set of magnetic sensors a sequence of alternate areas of high and low magnetic reluctance.

The merits of the various shaft encoder types, which are available commercially for measuring only angular displacement, are listed below.

Absolute Shaft Encoders

- data restored when power supply is restored;
- require anti-abiguity logic, which usually is integral, or code conversion logic, which usually is external;
- noise insensitive;
- usually coded for positive data values only;
- relatively bulky;
- require a relatively large number of output connections.

Incremental Shaft Encoders

- require an external counter, in most applications;
- data lost when power is interrupted;
- noise sensitive;
- relatively compact;
- require a small number of output connections.

Electromechanical Shaft Encoders

- low maximum speed;
- limited life;
- poorer reliability and maintainability;
- relatively high breakaway torque;
- output current must be very small (μA) to avoid brush arcing, which will destroy the disc pattern;
- limited maximum resolution per disc;
- relatively lower cost.

Optical and Electromagnetic Shaft Encoders

- high maximum speed;
- almost unlimited life;
- good reliability and maintainability;
- low breakaway torque;
- disc cannot be damaged due to output loading;
- greater maximum resolution per disc (optical types);
- relatively higher cost.

Compared with other displacement transducers, shaft encoders of comparable resolution are very expensive and this disadvantage has tended to preclude their widespread use; this is despite the obvious merit associated with the digital nature of the output data. In addition, rectilinear versions are not commonplace, except in the form of Diffraction Gratings, which are described next.

2.2.8   Diffraction Gratings

These form the basis of transducers which employ an optical principle of operation and which are directly competitive with the Inductosyn. Like the Inductosyn, gratings are manufactured in both rectilinear and rotary versions; unlike the Inductosyn, gratings do not require to be incorporated into a coarse-fine measuring system in order to create a viable transducing arrangement.

The rectilinear version of the transducer involves a long grating, which usually is the moving element, and a short grating, which usually is the stationary element. The short grating, which typically is about 2 cm square, is made from glass and has ruled upon it a series of parallel straight opaque lines, between which will remain a series of parallel straight clear lines. On a "coarse" grating, the lines would typically be pitched 10 or 40 to the millimetre whilst, on a "fine" grating, they might be 400 to the millimetre.

The long grating would typically be 25 cm long by 2 cm wide and further gratings would be abutted end-on whenever travels in excess of 25 cm are required. The long grating is made from steel, for light reflecting versions, and from glass, for light transmitting versions; this grating also is ruled with parallel lines having the same pitch as the lines on the short grating.

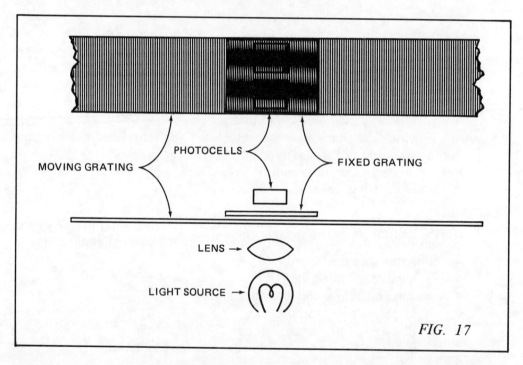

FIG. 17

Figure 17 shows how the two gratings would be mounted relative to each other, with the optical system shown for a light transmitting version. With the light reflecting type, the light source and photocells would both be mounted above the short grating. Note that the lines on the short grating are inclined, relative to those on the long grating, and this results in a set of light and dark bands, each typically about 0.5 cm wide, running lengthwise (that is, perpendicular to the lines on the long grating).

When the long grating is displaced by one half of one line pitch, the bands move across the grating, with a light band now replacing a dark band and vice-versa: the direction of movement of the bands reverses whenever the direction of motion of the grating reverses. The photocells, by sensing the presence of a light or dark band, with the associated circuitry can sense a displacement typically of one quarter of one line pitch: that is, 0.6μm in the case of fine gratings. Special versions have been developed which can resolve down to one tenth of one line pitch. The photocells will average the light distribution across many lines, so that imperfections in individual lines will be of no significance.

This measuring technique, which here produces optical magnifications of up to (say) 4000:1, uses a phenomenon known as "Moiré fringes". In the case of fine gratings, optical "interference" results in enhancement of the light and dark bands produced by these fringes, so that the discrimination by the photocells is improved.

The fixed and moving gratings are mounted in close proximity without being in physical contact, so that frictional forces are zero. The output signal from the photocell circuits usually will be a pulse train, together with a second signal indicating the direction of motion; alternatively, some commercial products generate sinusoidal output signals having a phase relationship which is a measure of the grating displacement. In the case of the digital output versions, the outputs typically will be applied to a reversible digital counter, with the output count representing the nett displacement of the moving grating occurring since the counter was last zeroed: the data will be lost whenever the power supply is interrupted and also can be corrupted by impulsive noise induced in the inter-connections.

Angular diffraction gratings are manufactured using the same principles, with the moving grating being a circular disc and the fixed grating a sector of a circle having the same diameter: the lines are radial, nominally, but slightly inclined to the radius in the case of the fixed grating, and are ruled within an annular band.

Life, reliability, and maintainability of diffraction grating transducers will be of a high order, due to the complete absence of electrical connections in motion and of parts subjected to wear.

2.2.9 Coarse-Fine (Dual-Speed) Measuring Systems

The accuracy and resolution of a measuring system may be extended, beyond that obtainable with a single feedback transducer, if a second and even a third feedback transducer are added to the system. Figure 18 shows a displacement measuring system in which the reference and feedback transducers are duplicated and geared to their counterparts.

In the vicinity of the null ($\theta_i - \theta_o = 0$), the fine channel, in which the output data change at N times the rate at which the output data in the coarse channel change, generates error data having N times the sensitivity (with respect to the error $\theta_i - \theta_o$) of that of the error data generated by the coarse channel. Thus,

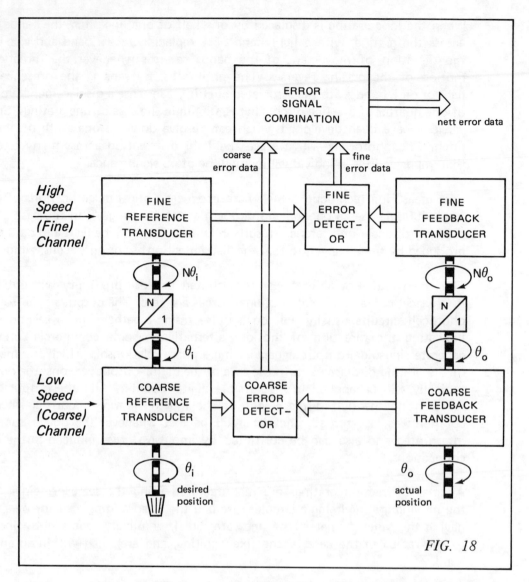

FIG. 18

if the two feedback transducers are identical, the improvement in measurement accuracy and resolution should be N-fold: note, however, that often there is no specific requirement for these two transducers to be identical.

The two reference transducers may not be geared together, if it is desired to be able to independently set each by hand, with the setting of the fine transducer acting as a vernier augmentation of the setting of the coarse transducer. Alternatively, and especially if the requirement is for digital reference data, it may be possible to generate both components of reference data using a single data generation system.

The error signal combination hardware will have to generate nett error data from the combining of coarse and fine channel error data. In the case of digital data, this may simply be an instance of combining end-on the two error data words, with the fine error word generating the less-significant byte and the coarse error word generating the more-significant byte of the nett error word. In the case of analog data, the signal combination hardware is required to monitor the value of the coarse error signal so that, close to the null, the nett error signal is generated primarily from the fine error signal; away from the null, the nett error signal is derived primarily from the coarse error signal.

The upper limit on the value of N is determined by the precision and resolution of the coarse feedback transducer in combination with the precision of the gearing itself. If the practical upper limit on the value of N is inadequate for the specification of the measuring system then consideration must be given to the addition of a further ("superfine") channel.

2.2.10 On-Off Displacement Transducers

In many applications, there are requirements for sensing whether a displacement is less than, or exceeds, a specific value. It would be very wasteful to use the transducers so far described for such applications, because there are many simpler devices which provide on-off sensing.

One of the simplest and cheapest on-off sensors is the Microswitch. This is a snap action type of electromechanical switch which normally is fully enclosed and may be activated by either a lever or a plunger mechanism. Being electromechanical, the low cost must be weighed against the limited life and reliability, plus the operating force required and the contact bounce which inevitably ensues.

Far greater life and reliability can be achieved using "proximity switches", which operate without physical contact being made with the switching mechanism, so that the operating force required will be negligible or zero. There are many techniques for detecting the proximity of a body without making physical contact with it, and amongst these would be included the following:

- the introduction or removal of a magnetic field;
- the change in reluctance of a magnetic circuit;
- the change in permittivity of the dielectric of a capacitor;
- the change in physical dimensions of a capacitor;
- the change in back pressure within a nozzle supplied, through a restriction, with compressed air (see Section 6.1.2);
- the change in reflection, refraction, or transmission of a light beam;
- the change in reflection, refraction, or transmission of an ultrasonic beam.

The details of the proximity switches which are available commercially would occupy a large catalogue and the user is best referred to suppliers' data books for this type of information. The types of parameter which would be relevant when making a choice for a specific application would include:

- physical size;
- limits on physical clearance;
- mounting details;
- suitability of the enclosure for the plant environment;
- operating force requirements;

- power supply requirements;
- output signal characteristics;
- settling time;
- possibility of interference with, or by, the operating medium.

2.3   REFERENCE TRANSDUCERS

Whilst it may seem to be illogical to include a discussion on reference transducers in a chapter devoted principally to feedback transducers, the justification for this is based upon the fact that many reference transducers are similar to the displacement transducers described in Section 2.2, especially where there is to be manual setting of the reference data.

The most commonly used devices for setting manually the reference variable are:

- potentiometers
- synchro and resolver transmitters
- rotary switches
- pushbutton, key, and toggle switches.

Where a digital computer is to be used for establishing the reference data, there often is a requirement for the data word generated by the computer to be converted to a form (analog or digital) which is appropriate for the control system, and the reader should refer to Chapters 10, 13 and 16 for discussion on this topic.

2.3.1   Potentiometric References

Reference potentiometers generally are required to have an accuracy similar to that associated with servo potentiometers. The existence of a deadspace and/or limits to travel no longer presents a problem, however, and a reasonably high level of friction often can be a definite advantage. Loading errors can be as significant a problem as with feedback potentiometers, so that unloading buffer amplifiers should be incorporated wherever necessary.

There is no requirement for the voltage supply for the reference potentiometer to have a high value, whatever the maximum value of the feedback signal: refer to Section 9.1 for discussion on this. Theoretically, almost any voltage supply level can be used; in practice, the level should be sufficiently high to maintain high signal/noise ratios but not so high as to generate significant heating of the potentiometer circuit or to render the supply hardware unnecessarily expensive. There is a definite requirement for the supply voltage to be stable, because the stability of the reference transducer sensitivity depends upon this: a possible exception would be a system in which the reference and feedback transducers are to use a common voltage reference supply: the reference and feedback transducer sensitivities would then change by comparable factors, should the supply voltage change, and the system loop gain also would change by a similar factor.

TYPICAL REFERENCE NETWORK FOR A POSITION CONTROL SYSTEM

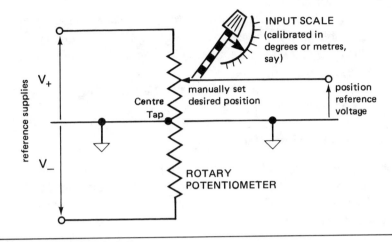

TYPICAL REFERENCE NETWORK FOR A SPEED CONTROL SYSTEM

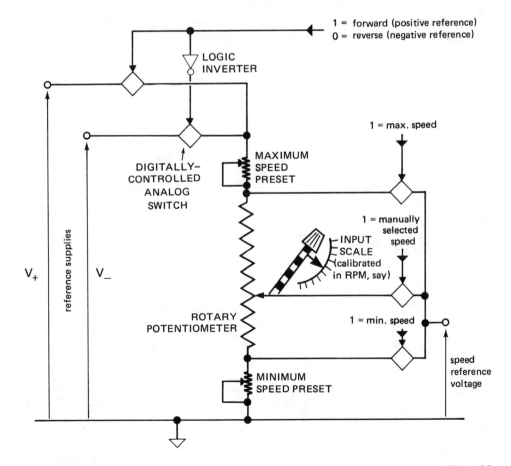

FIG. 19

Figure 19 shows typical reference networks for position and speed control systems. Notice that:

- for a precise electrical null, it is preferable to relate zero reference to signal common potential;

- if V_+ and V_- are not carefully matched in value, preset trimmer potentiometers should be included especially, for voltage balancing purposes — this will not apply to undirectional systems, which only require a unipolar reference;

- the input dial preferably should have a linear scale and be calibrated in terms of desired value.

2.3.2 Synchro and Resolver Transmitters

Where synchros, resolvers, or Inductosyns are to be used as feedback transducers, it is commonplace to use comparable synchros and resolvers as the reference transducers. In these cases, it may be advantageous to build additional friction into the reference shaft bearings, to prevent the setting from being moved by vibration. The dials normally would carry linear scales and be calibrated in terms of desired position.

There are some applications in which it is preferable to synthesise electrically the pattern of AC voltages, representing reference data, presented to the feedback transducer. Refer to Sections 2.3.3, 10.9, and 10.12 for further information.

2.3.3 Rotary Switch Networks

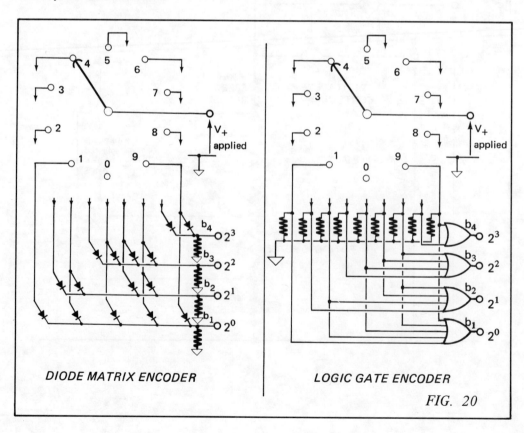

DIODE MATRIX ENCODER

LOGIC GATE ENCODER

FIG. 20

Where the reference variable is to be set manually using rotary switches, it is normal for each of these switches to have ten positions (representing 0 − 9), so that one switch would be allocated to each decimal digit of the desired value.

When the requirement is for digital data, the usual procedure is to encode each decade separately into natural binary code, so that the overall format for the reference data becomes binary-coded-decimal (B C D).

Figure 20 shows two commonly used alternatives for generating natural binary code for one decade of the B C D word. Some manufacturers will supply the switches with integral logic hardware.

Since most digital control systems do not process B C D data, it frequently becomes necessary to convert the reference data to the code of the processor: refer to Section 10.15 for further discussion on this topic.

When the requirement is for analog data the switches are arranged differently, and two examples are shown in Figure 21.

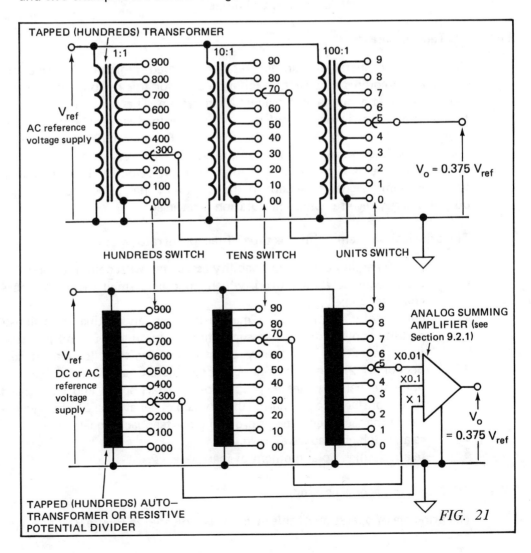

FIG. 21

When the requirement is for bidirectional data to be generated by rotary switch networks, it is necessary to make special provision. One method is to include a sign switch and to cause the selection of (say) a negative sign to complement the digital data (which must now include a sign bit), sign-invert the DC output voltage, or reverse the phase of the AC output voltage, as the case may be. One alternative is to offset the calibration of the reference switches and feedback transducer, alike, so that each datum now is represented by (say) the mid-range output data value of the associated network or transducer: thus, for example, nineteen-way switches now might be used for the reference network, with the central setting of each representing zero.

2.4 VELOCITY TRANSDUCERS

The choice of transducer to measure velocity is very limited, in comparison with the range available for displacement. This is true particularly in the case of rectilinear velocity, for which there are few devices of any significance manufactured commercially. The commonly used analog angular velocity transducers are electromagnetic machines, whilst digital angular velocity transducers employ either electromagnetic or optical techniques.

2.4.1 DC Tachogenerator

The DC Tachogenerator is an accurately calibrated miniature DC generator. To function, it requires a constant excitation and, for this reason, the construction usually involves a permanent magnet field system. The armature is wound with fine wire and, partly because of this, only small load current values (in the mA region) should be drawn from the machine. By so minimising the armature resistance voltage drop, the user ensures that, to a very good approximation, terminal voltage is directly proportional to shaft velocity. Typical sensitivities for permanent magnet types are in the $3V$ to $7V$ per 1000 r p m range. The output polarity reverses when the rotation is reversed.

The principal problems with this type of tachogenerator are:

- poor reliability and maintainability associated with commutators;
- brush contact voltage drop, which imposes a small offset on the static characteristic;
- commutator ripple, which manifests as an alternating (non-sinusoidal) parasitic noise component superimposed upon the DC output signal — to some extent, ripple may be attenuated with a low-pass filter (see Section 12.2) but this cannot be completely satisfactory, because the noise frequency varies in proportion to shaft speed and excessive filter time constant could harm the dynamic behaviour of the system for which the tachogenerator is providing the feedback signal;
- relatively high breakaway torque;
- relatively high polar moment of inertia.

2.4.2 AC Drag-Cup Tachogenerator

The principle of operation of this machine is indicated in Figure 22.

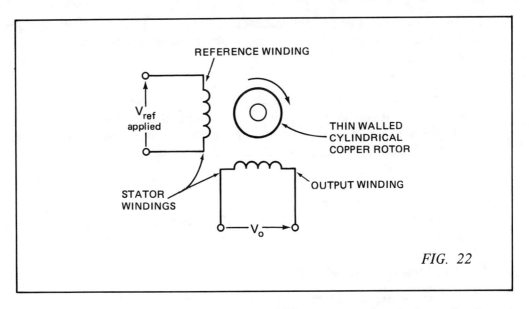

FIG. 22

The two windings are aligned axially at 90° to one another and are distributed in slots around one or two stators. In some versions, a single outer stator carries both windings; in others, the outer stator carries one winding and an inner stator carries the other. The rotor usually is a hollow cylindrical copper cup driven from one end by the input shaft. A constant AC reference voltage (usually a standard synchro reference) is applied to one winding and this establishes a pulsating magnetic flux, with a stationary axis, in which the cup is free to be turned. The alternating eddy currents, which circulate in the cup whenever the cup is in motion, establish a pulsating flux proportional in strength to the speed of rotation and axially aligned with the output winding. By transformer action, this flux induces in the output winding an alternating e m f proportional in magnitude to the shaft velocity. When the direction of rotation reverses, the phase of the output e m f reverses.

The principal advantages with this type of tachogenerator are:

- high reliability, maintainability, and life, due to complete absence of moving electrical contacts;
- very low breakaway torque;
- very low polar moment of inertia.

The principal disadvantage is that the output voltage is AC (albeit at the fixed reference supply frequency) and this is subject to a parasitic phase shift, the value of which can vary as a function of shaft speed. The output may be converted to DC, using a phase-sensitive demodulator as described in **Section 10.5**.

When excited with DC, this machine will generate a DC output voltage having a value proportional to the shaft angular acceleration.

2.4.3 AC Signal Alternator

This machine is a miniature single phase alternator with a rotating permanent magnet field system. The generator produces a sinusoidal AC output voltage having both amplitude and frequency proportional to the shaft speed. Because of the absence of a reference phase, this machine is unable to indicate the direction of rotation.

Since the frequency of the output is related precisely to the shaft speed, the alternator can be used in digital applications after the sinusoidal output wave has been converted to a suitable squarewave, using a zero-crossing detector: a digital frequency counter can then be used to generate a numerical indication of the shaft speed.

This machine will be characterised by high reliability, maintainability, and life, due to the complete absence of moving electrical contacts; breakaway torque will be low but the polar moment of inertia will be relatively high.

2.4.4   Digital Velocity Transducers

Any of the digital displacement transducers discussed in Section 2.2 can be used to generate velocity data, if a serial digital output is made available for input to a digital frequency counter. Thus, absolute shaft encoders (using the output from one channel only), incremental shaft encoders, and optical diffraction gratings can all be used as primary sensors for velocity measurement. Additional logic will be required in order to generate an indication of the direction of rotation: this could be complex in the case of absolute encoders.

Dedicated digital velocity transducers are available commercially, and most of these use a castellated disc which causes either a light beam to be interrupted or the reluctance of a magnetic circuit to be stepped. In both cases, the sensing circuit will generate either a squarewave or a pulse train, the frequency of which can be converted, using a digital frequency counter, to a digital word representing the speed of the disc shaft. An alternative technique is to cause the change in magnetic reluctance to modulate the frequency of an oscillator and to convert the modulation frequency to a DC voltage. The electronics may be packaged with the sensor, as a single unit. Some versions will also give an indication of the direction of rotation, by incorporating a duplicate, offset, disc.

With the exception of electromechanical shaft encoders, digital velocity transducers will be characterised by high reliability, maintainability, and life and by low breakaway torque; the polar moment of inertia will depend upon the principle of operation used. Refer to Section 10.14 for a description of digital frequency counters.

2.4.5   Bridges to Measure Back-E M F

In Section 5.6.2, the control of DC motors for use in servosystem applications is discussed. In those configurations in which the motor is operated with constant field excitation and the armature is controlled by means of a suitable servo-amplifier, an approximate measure of the shaft speed may be obtained by incorporating the armature circuit into a type of Wheatstone bridge arrangement, as shown in Figure 23.

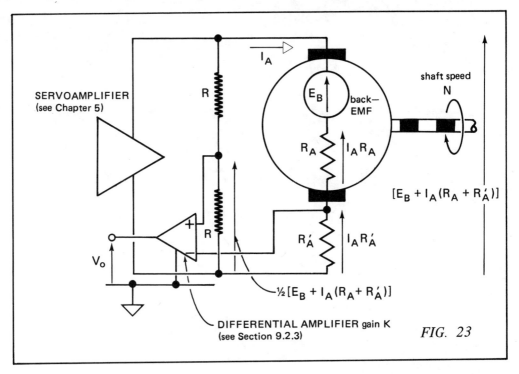

$$[E_B + I_A(R_A + R_A')]$$

$$\tfrac{1}{2}[E_B + I_A(R_A + R_A')]$$

DIFFERENTIAL AMPLIFIER gain K
(see Section 9.2.3)

FIG. 23

If the differential amplifier has a gain of K, then its output voltage V_o is given by

$$V_o = \frac{K}{2}\left[E_B + I_A(R_A + R_A')\right] - K\,I_A\,R_A', \quad \text{with } K \ll 1 \text{ normally.}$$

If the external resistor R_A' is matched in value to the armature resistance R_A of the motor, the expression reduces to $V_o = K\,E_B/2$, so that this voltage can be fed back to the signal combination network of the servosystem. Provided that it is justifiable to assume that the back-e m f E_B is proportional solely to the motor shaft speed then it will be valid to use V_o as a speed feedback signal.

The following factors are relevant to this technique:

- no velocity transducer is required;
- R_A' will have a very low resistance value but must have a current rating to match that of the motor armature;
- the values of R_A and R_A' will both be affected by self heating and it will be difficult to match them over a wide range of loading;
- armature reaction will tend to corrupt the linearity of the E_B vs N characteristic, but to some extent this effect can be compensated for by slightly increasing the value of R_A' ;
- the use of a differential amplifier assumes that it is impractical to connect either of its two inputs to signal common, which sometimes may not be the case;
- R can have a relatively high value, so that the R + R limb need not draw a significant level of current from the servoamplifier;
- the accuracy obtainable with this technique cannot approach that provided by a good velocity transducer.

3

TRANSDUCERS — STRAIN, FORCE, TORQUE, ACCELERATION, LOAD AND TENSION

3.1   STRAIN GAUGES AND MEASURING BRIDGES

3.1.1   Strain Gauges

A strain gauge consists of a wire or foil element mounted on paper or some other low-modulus backing material. When the strain gauge is attached, using adhesive, to the surface being instrumented, it will undergo the same strain variations as the material to which it is bonded. Except in the case where the gauge is attached to a thin foil, the gauge itself will have little influence on the strain variations in the base material.

When the gauge metal is subjected to strain, its electrical resistance changes and this change is detected and used to monitor the cause of the strain. Two factors will contribute to this change in resistance:

- the change in length and cross-sectional area of the element;
- the change in the resistivity, of the gauge material, resulting from the strained condition.

In metal gauges, these two factors are roughly equal in significance. The Gauge Factor k is defined by the formula

$$\frac{\Delta R}{R} = k\epsilon$$

where ΔR is the change, in the original resistance value R, due to the strain ϵ. The strain ϵ is defined by $\epsilon = \frac{\Delta x}{x}$, where Δx is the extension of the original effective length x of the gauge element, due to the external cause. A typical value for k is 2 and, since ϵ can have values typically in the range from 10^{-6} to 10^{-3}, it follows that relatively small values of $\Delta R/R$ have to be sensed.

The resistivity of metals is affected by temperature, in addition to strain. Strain gauges often use temperature compensated elements, in which the elements are constructed using two materials, so matched that the temperature-dependent resistance change of one just balances that of the other, over a specified temperature range. Where the gauge element is bonded to a base material, the compensation requirements will depend on the type of base material used.

Strain gauges are also made using semiconductor materials. These have a higher gauge factor, in the order of 50, and are more temperature-sensitive and more expensive.

3.1.2   Strain Gauge Bridges

The usual method of detecting the resistance change of a strain gauge is to incorporate it into a Wheatstone bridge, as shown in Figure 1.

When the bridge is balanced, $V_o = 0$ and $R_1/R_2 = R_3/R_4$. If R_1 changes, then the change in output voltage is given by $V_o = \frac{V}{4} \cdot \frac{\Delta R_1}{R_1} = \frac{V}{4} \cdot k\epsilon$, provided that

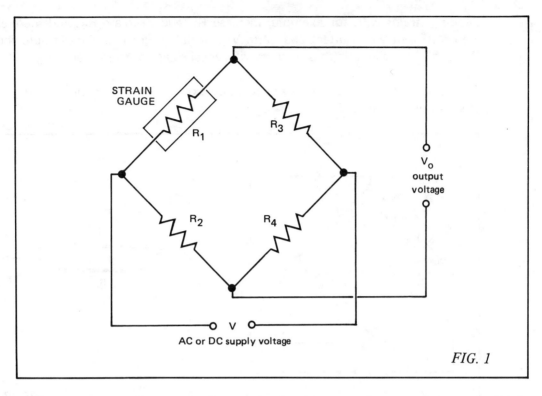

FIG. 1

all four resistances are nominally equal. In this example, only the element R_1 is active, whilst the other three resistors are passive and must be highly temperature stable.

When two or four of the bridge elements are active, the bridge can be made sensitive to specific strain conditions. Figure 2 is an example in which R_1 and R_2 are used to detect bending strain, in such a way that axial strain effects cancel electrically.

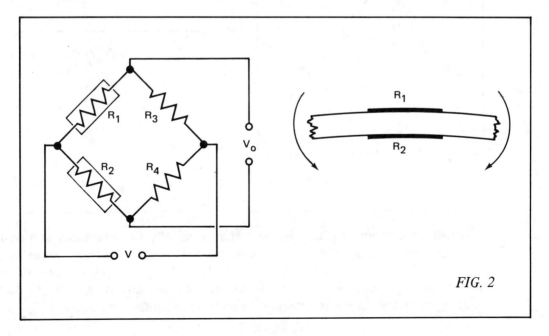

FIG. 2

Bending strains will, for example, increase R_1 and decrease R_2, and these effects are additive in the resultant change in V_o. Axial strains will, for example, increase R_1 and R_2 equally, and these effects will cancel so as not to influence V_o.

The bridge can be rearranged so as to sense axial strains and ignore bending strains, as shown in Figure 3.

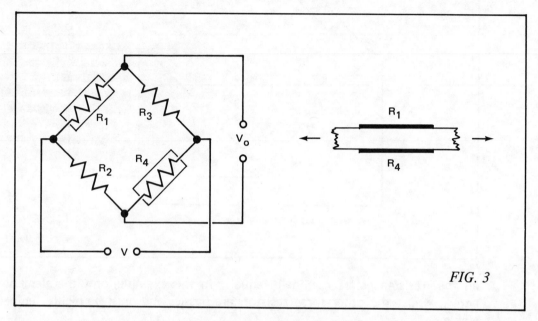

FIG. 3

To sense torsional strain, for which both axial and bending strains are ignored, all four elements are made active and mounted as shown in Figure 4.

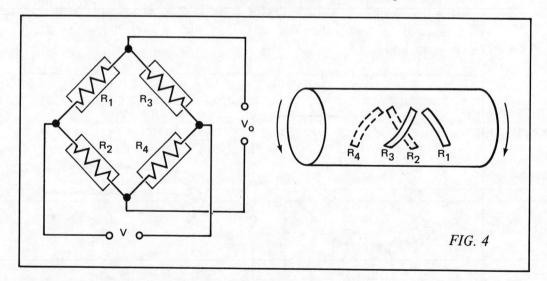

FIG. 4

The pair of elements R_1 and R_2 will change equally (in resistance) as a result of both bending and axial strains, so that their effects on V_o will cancel to zero. A similar situation will exist for the pair R_3 and R_4. However, torsional strain would typically cause R_1 and R_4 to increase equally and R_2 and R_3 to decrease equally, so that all four effects would be additive in influencing V_o.

Although strain gauges are designed to be sensitive only along one nominated axis, it is inevitable that they should be slightly sensitive to strains along the perpendicular axis. This results from the configuration of the elements, as shown by Figure 5.

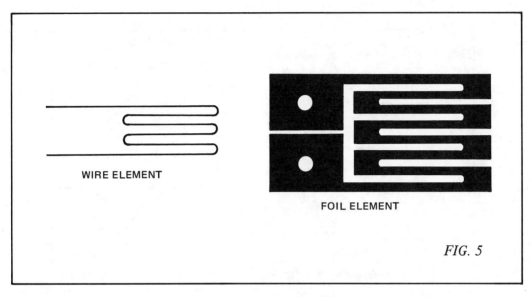

WIRE ELEMENT

FOIL ELEMENT

FIG. 5

The wire type gauge can be up to 5% cross-sensitive whereas the foil type can be well below 1%.

Some bridge configurations make use of a combination of active and "dummy" gauges. The dummy gauge is attached to the same base material as the active gauge and mounted in close proximity to it (but aligned along an unstrained axis), so that both gauges (which are electrically identical) will always experience the same temperature. With the active and dummy gauges connected in adjacent arms of the bridge, as shown in Figure 6, temperature effects will cancel out and therefore will not influence V_o.

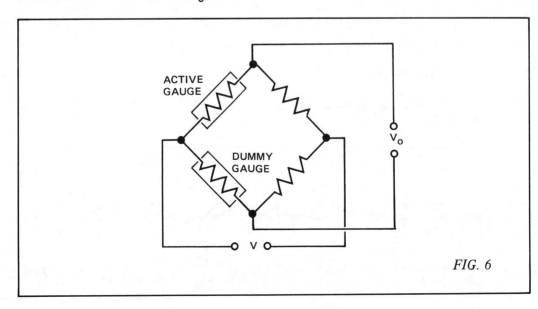

ACTIVE
GAUGE

DUMMY
GAUGE

V_o

V

FIG. 6

When gauges compensated for temperature on steel backing are attached to an aluminium body, for example, the use of a dummy gauge is important.

Strain gauge configurations may be of the single, two, or three element type, as illustrated symbolically in Figure 7.

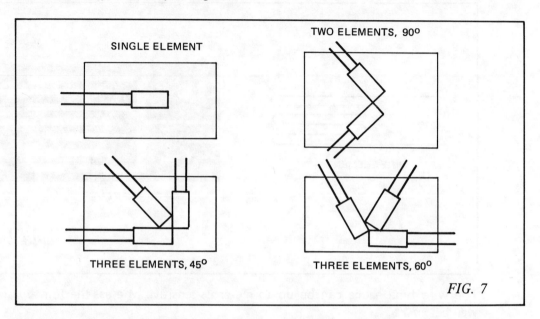

SINGLE ELEMENT

TWO ELEMENTS, 90°

THREE ELEMENTS, 45°

THREE ELEMENTS, 60°

FIG. 7

Multiple-element gauges of the foil type usually are referred to as "rosettes". Four-element rosettes, with elements aligned along one or two (perpendicular) axes, are also manufactured, for use in full bridge circuits. Multiple-axis rosettes often are used in applications where the direction of the strain is not known beforehand; in transducer applications, the direction usually is specific, so that rosettes would not then be used, as a rule.

3.2   USE OF STRAIN GAUGES IN TRANSDUCERS

Strain gauges are used in a number of transducers, and representative applications will be described.

3.2.1 Force Transducers

The simplest configuration is a bar or strip subjected to axial force, as shown in Figure 8.

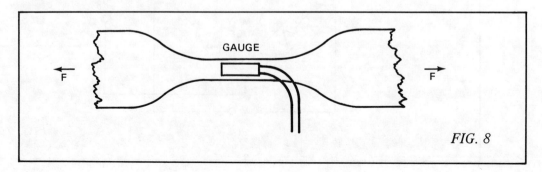

GAUGE

F

F

FIG. 8

This type of transducer is very rigid and ideal for tensile forces. When compressive forces are to be measured, it is more suitable for small forces, because of the tendency of the sensing member to buckle.

To instrument both tensile and compressive forces of comparable magnitude, the sensing member is designed to distort in shape. Figure 9, which shows a "load ring" sensor, is designed for this type of application.

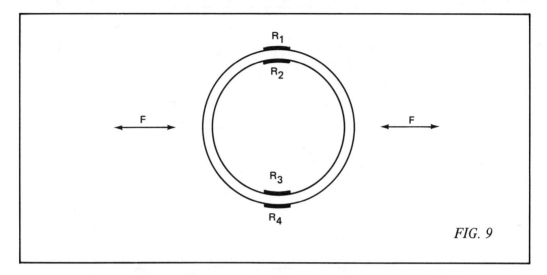

FIG. 9

The elements will be attached as shown and connected electrically to sense bending stresses, as shown in Figure 10.

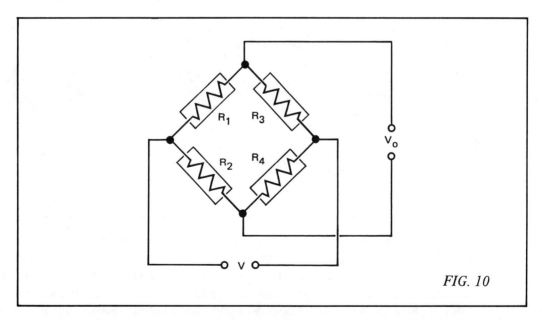

FIG. 10

3.2.2   Torque Transducers

Where torque is to be measured on a stationary body, there are three optional techniques, as illustrated in Figure 11. The choice is largely a matter of convenience and accessibility.

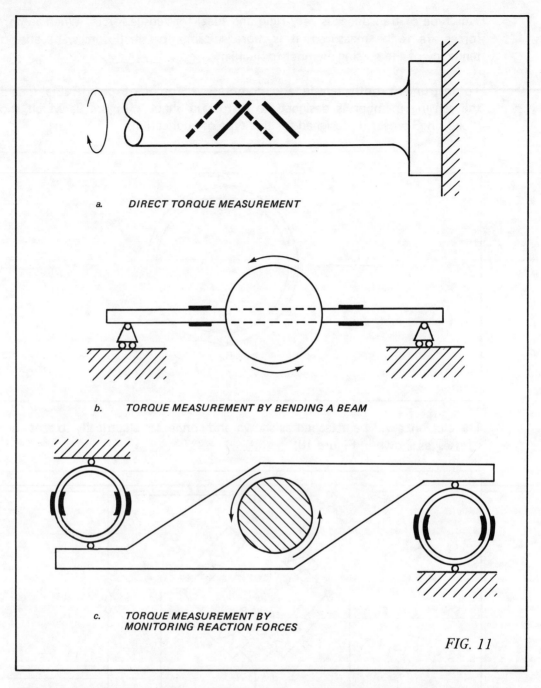

a.   DIRECT TORQUE MEASUREMENT

b.   TORQUE MEASUREMENT BY BENDING A BEAM

c.   TORQUE MEASUREMENT BY
     MONITORING REACTION FORCES

FIG. 11

When torque is measured in rotating shafts, the sensing configuration is almost always of the type shown in Figure 11 a. It frequently happens that shafts are greatly overdesigned and the strain values to be measured are too small to give good signal-to-noise separation. In such cases, the use of semiconductor strain gauges in half or full bridge configuration is indicated. Where the environment (mainly temperature) precludes this, the shear strain can be intensified as shown in Figure 12. A sleeve is pushed over the shaft and rigidly attached in planes A and B. In plane C, the section of the sleeve is greatly reduced. As a consequence, almost all of the twisting from A to B is concentrated in the reduced section of the sleeve. The strain gauges are located at that point.

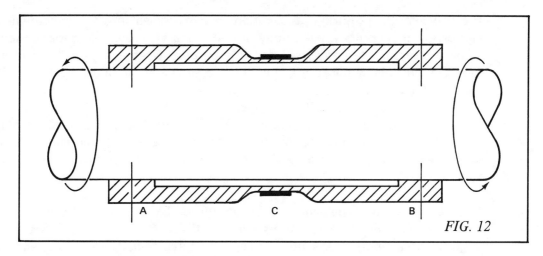

FIG. 12

Transferring the strain gauge signal from a rotating body to the "outside world" has been attempted in various ways and some in current use involve:

- using slip rings;
- using an RF carrier from a transmitter attachment to the shaft;
- using inductive or capacitive coupling and frequency-modulating a carrier.

Each of these methods contributes a certain amount of additional noise to the signal and requires that various pieces of apparatus be attached to the shaft.

By measuring reactions at prime mover or gearbox foundations, the need for "on the shaft" torque measurement can often be avoided and the additional difficulty of getting the signal from the shaft is then avoided.

3.2.3   Acceleration Transducers

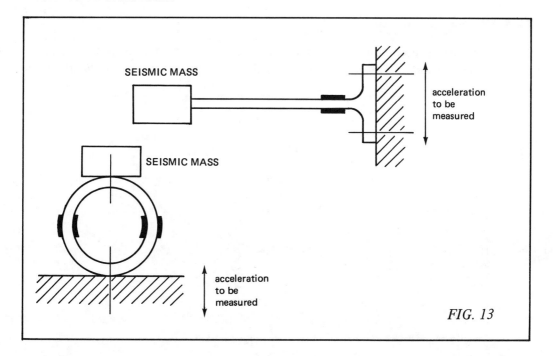

FIG. 13

The problem of measuring acceleration is transformed into the measurement of the force which results when a body of known mass is subjected to the acceleration to be measured.   A body used for this purpose is known as a "seismic mass" and two possible applications, for the measurement of linear acceleration, are shown in Figure 13.

To measure the angular acceleration of shafts, one may mount accelerometers such as those of Figure 13 on them and measure the tangential acceleration. When this is done, the problem of transmitting the signal to the outside world arises again.

A commonly used expedient that avoids the problem of signal transfer is illustrated in Figure 14. A roller is pressed against the shaft and rolls freely without slip. Angular acceleration shows up as tangential forces which are sensed and give a measure of this acceleration.

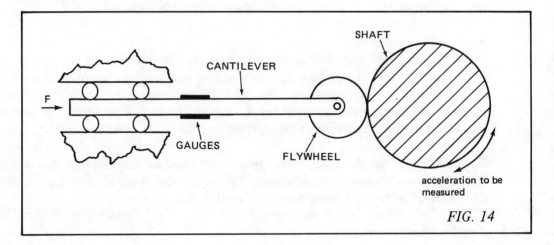

FIG. 14

3.2.4   Pressure Transducers

The most common type of pressure sensor using strain gauges is the "flexing plate sensor". This has a high speed of response and is illustrated in Figure 15.

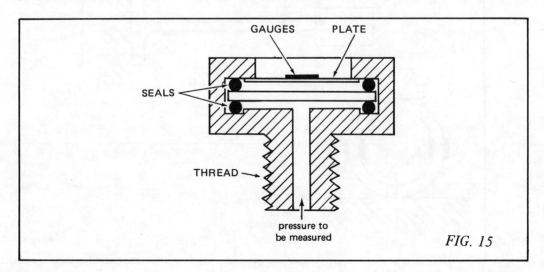

FIG. 15

3.2.5 Load Cells

When the weight of a body has to be sensed, the weight can be used to compress a member of the types illustrated in Figure 8 and Figure 9, by physically connecting the scale pan to the member. Alternatively, the weight on the scale pan may be used to pressurise hydraulic fluid, using a cylinder and piston, and the hydraulic pressure so established can then be sensed by a pressure transducer, possibly of the type shown in Figure 15.

3.3 OTHER TRANSDUCERS FOR MEASURING FORCE, TORQUE, ACCELERATION AND TENSION

3.3.1 Force, Torque, and Acceleration Transducers.

Force may be measured by firstly causing the force to extend or compress a linear spring of known spring rate, and then instrumenting the spring deflection with a rectilinear displacement transducer.

Torque on a stationary body may be measured by causing the torque to extend or compress a torsional spring of known spring rate, and then instrumenting the spring deflection using an angular displacement transducer.

An alternative arrangement is to sense the linear (angular) displacement of whatever body the force (torque) is applied to, using a suitable displacement transducer, to amplify the transducer output signal and to use the amplified signal to excite an electrical linear actuator (torque motor). The force (torque) thus developed is applied to oppose the force (torque) being measured, by means of a suitable mechanical connection. Closed loop action will tend to keep the transducer output signal close to zero, thus establishing a force (torque) balance. The signal supplied by the amplifier to the actuator (torque motor) will be a measure of the value of the force (torque) being fed back and hence will also be a measure of the force (torque) which it is desired to measure. Figure 16 is a block diagram illustrating the process for the rectilinear case. (Chapter 5 deals in part with electric torque motors; an electrical linear actuator can be constructed using a solenoid attracting a ferrous armature).

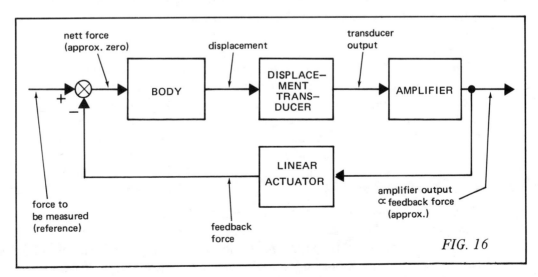

FIG. 16

Linear acceleration may be measured using the above techniques, if a seismic mass is subjected to that acceleration and the resulting force is measured. Angular acceleration may similarly be measured, if the resulting torque on the seismic mass is measured.

Angular acceleration may also be measured for a freely rotating body, by coupling to it an AC Drag-Cup Tachogenerator of the type described in Section 2.4.2. If such a machine is excited from a constant voltage DC supply, the output voltage generated will now be a DC voltage proportional in magnitude (and representative in polarity) to the shaft angular acceleration.

Torque in a freely rotating shaft may also be measured by incorporating a coupling of the type shown in Figure 17.

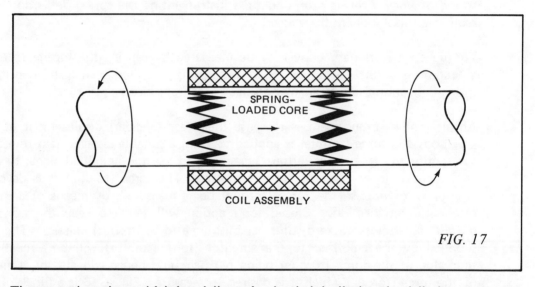

SPRING-LOADED CORE

COIL ASSEMBLY

FIG. 17

The central section, which is axially spring-loaded, is displaced axially by an amount proportional to the level of torque being transmitted. If this section is made the (ferrous) core of an LVDI or LVDT (see Section 2.2.2), by virtue of fitting the coil assembly around the coupling (with suitable clearance), then the signal generated will be a measure of the transmitted torque.

The torque transmitted by a shaft may also be measured by loading the shaft with a "Dynamometer", which is an electric generator or an hydraulic pump which must be suitably loaded to a controllable extent. If the frame of the generator (or case of the pump) is mounted in journal bearings and restrained by springs of known spring rate, then the extension (or compression) of the springs will be a measure of the torque transmitted, and can be instrumented with a displacement transducer. Such an arrangement often is used in test beds for motors, engines, and turbines.

3.3.2 Tension Transducers

Tension in wires, yarns, cable, tape, sheets, filaments, felts, paper webs, plastic webs, etc. may be instrumented by using the material to support a light roller. The roller is restrained by a spring and the motion is damped by means of a dashpot (which generates an opposing force proportional to velocity), as shown in Figure 18.

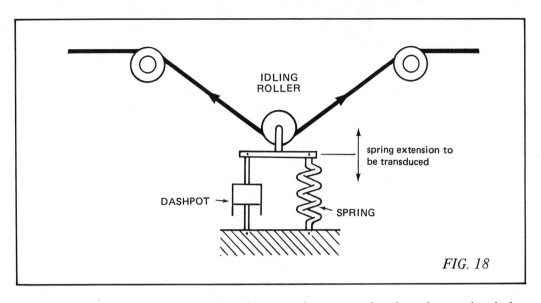

IDLING
ROLLER

spring extension to
be transduced

DASHPOT →

SPRING

FIG. 18

The extension of the spring can be shown to be proportional to the tension being measured, in the steady state. This extension may be instrumented with a linear displacement transducer.

Alternatively, if the material is being pulled by a driven pulley, then the tension may be inferred by measuring the torque in the drive shaft from the motor to the pulley.

4

TRANSDUCERS — TEMPERATURE, PRESSURE, FLOW, LEVEL, DENSITY, pH, HUMIDITY, MOISTURE AND THICKNESS

4.1   INTRODUCTION

In this chapter, we are concerned with transducers for the measurement of variables which occur typically in production processes. Thus, the process may be creating some continuous product, and the variable to be measured might well be a major influence upon, or a direct measure of, the quality of that product. A range of transducers known loosely as "On-Stream Analysers", and not covered in this chapter, tend to be more sophisticated in their nature and involve the application of complex measurements to the analysis of the process product: these are dealt with separately, in Chapter 17.

With many of the transducers under consideration here, one very often needs to make a distinction between the different stages of the transduction process. Thus, a particular measuring device may involve a "primary element" or "sensor", which is in direct physical contact with, or in close proximity to, the process medium, and a "secondary element", which causes a useful display or control signal to be generated, as a result of the stimulus applied to the sensor. Primary elements tend to be distinctive in their construction and principle of operation, whereas secondary elements are limited in their variety and tend to have many common features.

4.2   TRANSMITTERS

A Transmitter is a device for converting the response of a primary element into a useable signal, which then is transmitted either to an indicating instrument or to a controller. Thus, transmitters can be regarded as being forms of secondary element. The most common output signals generated by transmitters are either pneumatic pressure signals, in the 3 to 15 psi (20 to 100 kPa) gauge pressure range, or DC currents, in the 4 to 20 mA range. However, this latter, electrical, range is not exclusive, and alternative DC current, DC voltage, AC voltage, and digital transmissions sometimes are used.

The advantages arising from using a current as an electrical signal for transmission purposes are as follows:

• very often, the power source for the transmission circuit can be sited within the receiver, so that only a two-wire connection then need be used;

• several loads at varying locations can be connected in series, up to a specified limit on the total resistance, with the transmitter behaving as a current source;

• the length and resistance of the transmission circuit does not affect the signal sensitivity, provided that the upper limit on circuit resistance is not exceeded.

The use of an offset datum (typically 4 mA) enables a high signal/noise ratio to be preserved at all times and also enables the complete absence of a signal to be interpreted as an indication of equipment failure.

Where the signal from the primary element is a (process or instrument) pressure, the most common types of transmitter used as the secondary element are either pneumomechanical or electromechanical. The primary element may convert a single pressure into a force (for example, when the element is a Bourdon tube) or it may develop a differential pressure (for example, when the element is an orifice plate): in the latter case, the transmitter often would be referred to as a "D−P Cell" or a "ΔP Cell".

Mechanical transmitters may be of the position balance or force balance type. The former is operated by the displacement of the primary element from a null position; the latter operates on the "force balance" principle whereby an unknown force, the value of which is related (by the primary element) to that of the measured variable, is applied to a beam arm and is counterbalanced by a force of known magnitude.

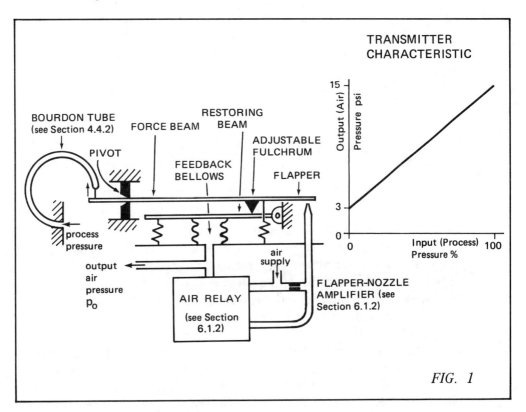

FIG. 1

A pneumatic force balance pressure transmitter is illustrated in Figure 1. The force beam will be in equilibrium when the force developed by the output air pressure, acting in the feedback bellows, cancels the force developed by the primary element (in this case, the Bourdon tube), together with the datum-offsetting spring forces.

An electronic force balance differential pressure transmitter is shown in Figure 2. The force beam will be in equilibrium when the force developed by the output current I_o, causing the feedback coil to be attracted to the magnet, cancels the force due to the differential pressure $\Delta p = p_2 - p_1$ acting upon the diaphragm capsule, together with the force due to the datum-offsetting spring.

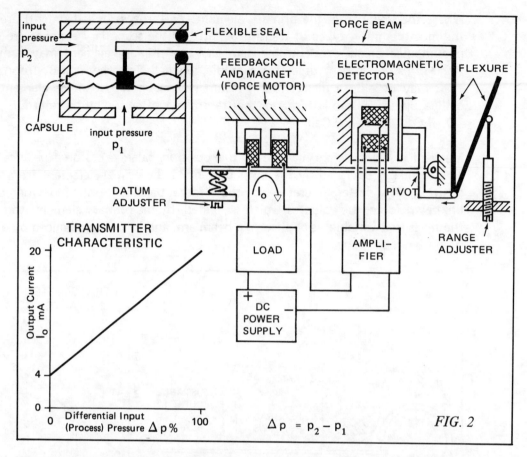

FIG. 2

With both transmitters, the instrument behaves as a closed loop control system. In the steady state, the output signal magnitude should follow a linear relationship with the transmitter input signal generated by the primary element. With the pneumatic transmitter, the flapper and nozzle form a displacement error sensor and error amplifier (refer to Section 6.2.2) whilst, with the electronic transmitter, the armature and electromagnetic detector act as a component in a displacement error sensing circuit.

Some non-mechanical transmitters also are manufactured and many of these involve integrated circuit technology. Many of the electronic converters described in Chapter 10 feature in these transmitters, together with some of the amplifier circuits of Section 9.2. The advantages arising from the use of solid state technology include:

- fast response
- high linearity
- low power requirement
- physical compactness.

In some of these transmitters, the circuit may include a Wheatstone bridge, with the primary element supplying one or more limbs of the bridge: this technique is used, for example, with some temperature and pressure measuring systems. In a few cases, the bridge is constructed from strain gauge elements diffused into a single silicon crystal chip.

4.3   TEMPERATURE TRANSDUCERS

There are many methods by which temperature may be measured. Thermometers may be classified as follows:

Expansion Thermometers

- solid expansion
- liquid expansion
- gas expansion

Change—of—State Thermometers

Electrical Transduction Thermometers

- variable resistance
- semiconductor
- thermoelectric
- radiant energy

The types most suited to indication and control applications are those most capable of remote electrical transmission without appreciable transmission loss, which would create inaccuracy. As a consequence, electrical transduction thermoments usually are used wherever high accuracy is required. Primary temperature sensors (in this case, pressure thermometers) which convert temperature changes into pressure changes, which then are detected by a pressure transducer, are popular for some applications because they are reliable and relatively inexpensive, if less accurate.

Various solid expansion thermometers are available, the most common being the bimetal strip type. This device utilises the different coefficients of expansion of different metals which have been bonded together, thereby causing deformation when the strips are heated. Bimetal strips may be in straight, spiral or helical configurations. Other solid expansion types are the solid rod thermostat and the hot wire vacuum switch.

The most common liquid expansion thermometer is the mercury—in—glass type. For higher temperature measurement, mercury—in—steel thermometers may be used. These devices are connected to a Bourdon tube (refer to Section 4.4.2), which measures the pressure developed by the mercury as a result of thermal expansion. Several alternative filling liquids may be used, depending upon the temperature range and cost considerations. These thermometers sometimes are referred to as "Filled Thermal Systems", and will be described in greater detail in Section 4.3.3.

Gas expansion thermometers utilise the expansion of gases which results from increasing temperature. There are two types: the "constant pressure" type, which develops an increasing volume, and the "constant volume" type, which develops an increasing pressure, as the sensed temperature increases.

Change-of-state thermometers basically are liquid expansion thermometers in which the liquid is allowed to partially vaporise in the thermometer. The temperature then is measured in terms of the vapour pressure developed. These thermometers often are used because they are cheaper than mercury-in-steel thermometers and because they are not affected so adversely by changes in ambient temperature away from the thermometer bulb. Their useful temperature ranges are considerably narrower than those for mercury-in-steel types, however.

In electrical transduction thermometers, temperature is converted into an electrical quantity: that is, resistance, current, or voltage. The most commonly used examples of this class of thermometer are the Thermocouple, Resistance Thermometer, Thermistor, and semiconductor temperature sensors, and these will be described in detail.

4.3.1   Thermocouples

The Thermocouple is classified as a thermoelectric temperature transducer, and Figure 3 demonstrates the construction of a simple version.

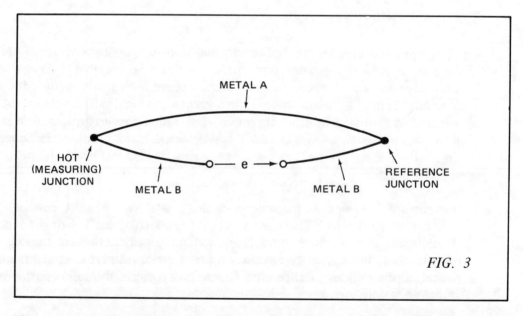

FIG. 3

The principle of operation is based upon the Seebeck effect, which states that, whenever two dissimilar metals are connected together as shown and the junctions are subjected to different temperatures, an emf e is generated. Moreover, this emf is approximately proportional to the difference between the temperatures of the two junctions.

The wires of a thermocouple may be connected together, to form a junction, by twisting, clamping, soldering, or (electric or gas) welding, with the last two methods being the preferred alternatives for good industrial practice. The choice of wire materials depends upon the temperature range to be sensed by the hot junction, amongst other considerations, and tends to be limited to the combinations listed in Table 1. Other selection factors include physical strength, corrosion resistance, electrical resistance and cost.

TABLE 1.

COMMONLY USED THERMOCOUPLE MATERIALS

Thermocouple Type	Wire Materials		Typical Useful Temperature Range °C.	
			minimum	maximum
B	platinum rhodium 6%	— platinum rhodium 30%	38	1800
C	tungsten rhenium 5%	— tungsten rhenium 26%	0	2300
E	Chromel	— Constantan	0	982
J	iron	— Constantan	−184	760
K	Chromel	— Alumel	−184	1260
R	platinum	— platinum rhodium 13%	0	1593
S	platinum	— platinum rhodium 10%	0	1538
T	copper	— Constantan	−184	400
—	platinum 30% rhodium	— platinum 6% rhodium	0	1780
—	iridium 40% rhodium	— iridium	0	2000
—	tungsten	— rhenium	0	2220
—	tungsten	— tungsten 26% rhenium	0	2330

NOTE: Alumel — nickel-alumium alloy
Constantan — copper-nickel alloy
Chromel — nickel-chromium alloy

It will be seen that the useful temperature range is very dependent upon the types of wire material used, with the lower range corresponding to base metals and base metal alloys. The wires are manufactured in a range of gauges, and usually are supplied as sleeved pairs, with the sleeving frequently colour coded for ready identification.

Figure 4 shows some typical calibration curves for the thermocouple types listed in Table 1. It will be seen that some of the curves depart significantly from straight line relationships, with the departure being most prominent in certain temperature ranges. EMF versus temperature tables are published by various standards institutions, and the data therein, together with the published calibration curves, assume that calibration has occurred with the reference junction held at 0°C. Typical tolerance figures on published data range from ±1/4% to ±2% of measured temperature.

Some temperature controllers include provision for analog or digital computation of correction laws to linearise the voltage vs temperature relationship, especially for the most common types of base metal thermocouple.

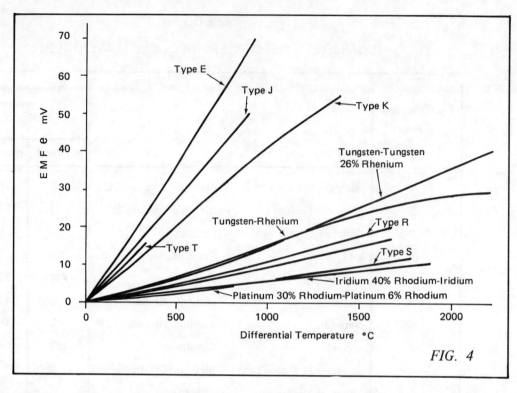

FIG. 4

Because of the small magnitude of the emf generated, care must be taken to preserve a good signal/noise ratio. Wherever feasible, it is preferable that the voltage should be suitably amplified at a point as close as possible to the reference junction, before the signal is transmitted to a temperature controller, indicator, or recorder. The amplifier often would be of the instrumentation amplifier variety, which is described in Section 16.2.1. It also is preferable that the reference junction should be as close as practicable to the measuring junction.

Because the thermoelectric emf is a function of the temperature differential between the two junctions, the temperature of the measuring junction can only be interpreted, from the emf, if the temperature of the reference junction is known and preferably is held constant.

Because of the various technical and cost factors, it often is impracticable to use extensive lengths of thermocouple wire. For this reason, specified types of extension wire (with alternative insulation materials), together with copper interconnections, may be interposed between the thermocouple and its load. Figure 5 shows some possible alternative connection configurations.

Typically, the composite reference "junction" would be in thermal contact with a metal heat sink, but electrically isolated from it. Often, this heat sink would be shared with a set of similar thermocouple circuits. The heat sink would have its temperature measured by, for example, a resistance thermometer (see Section 4.3.2) and the signal developed either would be used in a temperature feedback loop to control the temperature of the heat sink, using a small integral electrical heater, or would be used for compensation purposes to correct the thermocouple-generated data for sensed changes in reference junction temperature.

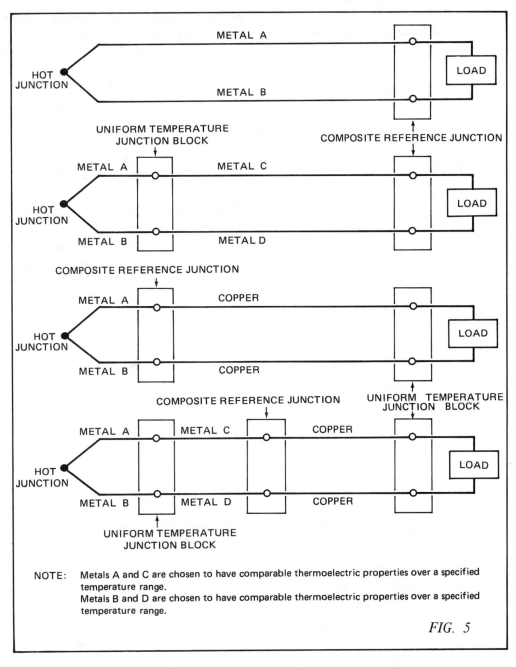

FIG. 5

Because its thermal mass usually is very small, the hot junction can have a very fast response, typically in the millisecond range, to changes in temperature. However, for physical and chemical protection, the hot junction often has to be enclosed in a rigid tube (sometimes called a "thermowell"), which usually is made either from metal (typically, stainless steel) or ceramic. This tube will add considerably to the thermal mass of this composite temperature sensor, so that the overall response time is likely to be in the range of many seconds.

Unprotected, the hot junction can be used to sense spot temperatures. When mounted within a tube, it will tend to sense the average temperature of the extremity of the tube.

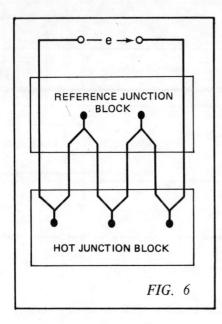

REFERENCE JUNCTION BLOCK

HOT JUNCTION BLOCK

FIG. 6

Figure 6 shows a "thermopile", which is a series-connected set of thermocouple junctions and which develops a voltage equal to the product of the emf generated by one junction pair multiplied by the number of such pairs. Typically, this would be used as the sensor in a Radiation Pyrometer: this instrument usually is used to measure the surface temperature of a physically inaccessible heat – radiating body (for example, a molten ingot inside a furnace). A proportion of the thermal radiation is arranged to be transmitted through a system of windows and lenses, and focussed onto the sensor. The Temperature of the sensor will settle to a steady value, which will be a measure of the temperature of the radiating body.

The advantages of thermocouples are:

- high temperature range, if appropriate metals are chosen;
- small size, if unprotected;
- fast response, if unprotected;
- relatively linear, especially over specific temperature ranges;
- low cost, especially if unprotected.

The disadvantages of thermocouples are:

- the need for compensation for changes in cold junction temperature or for control of this temperature;
- low output signal level;
- limited accuracy, even with precision cold junction temperature compensation or control;
- the need for special extension wires, in some circumstances;
- the difficulty experienced with distinguishing between an open circuit fault, in the thermocouple, and zero temperature differential.

4.3.2   Resistance Thermometers and Thermistors

A Resistance Thermometer is an element wound from metallic wire, and it senses temperature by virtue of the dependence of the metal resistivity upon the value of the temperature. Sometimes, it is known as a "Resistance Temperature Detector", or RTD. The most commonly used wire materials are listed in Table 2.

RTDs are manufactured in nominal values ranging from tens of ohms to several kilohms, with hundreds of ohms being commonplace. Typically, the element is

TABLE 2.
COMMONLY USED RTD MATERIALS

Material	Temperature Range, °C.	Temperature Coefficient at 25° C., /°C.
nickel	− 80 to +320	0.0067
copper	−200 to +260	0.0038
nickel-iron	−200 to +260	0.0046
platinum	−200 to +850	0.0039

encapsulated in a small solid glass rod, producing what sometimes is called a "resistance bulb"; in addition, the element may be installed within a metal or ceramic tube, similar to the thermowells in which thermocouples frequently are enclosed.

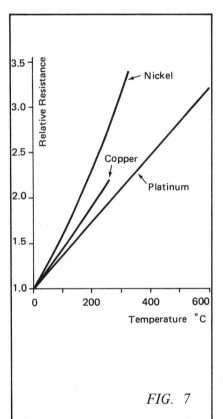

FIG. 7

Figure 7 shows calibration curves for three of the resistance materials: it will be seen that platinum yields by far the most linear characteristic, even over a wide temperature range, and this factor, together with the advantage of the wide useful temperature range, account for the popularity of this material, despite its high cost. In general, the element resistance r_θ will be related to its temperature θ by a law of the form

$$R_\theta = R_o[1+\alpha\theta+\beta\theta^2+\gamma\theta^3].$$ α, β, and γ are constants, and the values of β and γ may be very small. R_o is the resistance at 0° C.

Thermistors consist of small pieces of ceramic material made by sintering mixtures of oxides of chromium, cobalt, copper, iron, manganese, nickel, etc. They are moulded, in various sizes, into a number of different shapes, such as beads, discs, rods, etc. and finally are encapsulated, with copper leads, with a colour coded vitreous material, typically. The nominal resistance of a thermistor can vary from tens of ohms to several megohms, depending upon the type of material and the physical dimensions. The resistance versus temperature relationship is highly nonlinear, being defined by a power law of the form $R_T = ae^{b/T}$, where a and b are constants over a small range of temperature and T is absolute temperature. The majority of thermistors are of the negative temperature coefficient (NTC) type, for which R_T falls (nonlinearly) with increasing temperature; however, a few positive temperature coefficient (PTC) types also are made. Figure 8 shows typical resistance vs temperature curves for three different examples: although highly nonlinear, they can be much more sensitive to temperature change than comparable RTDs, within a specified temperature range. In addition they can be much cheaper.

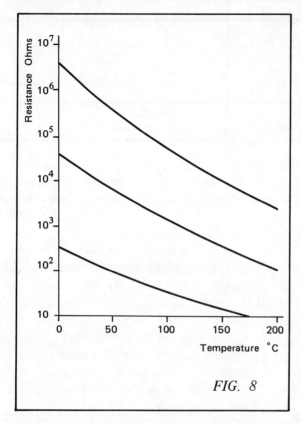

FIG. 8

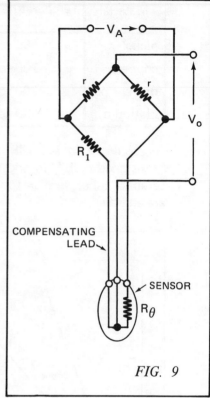

FIG. 9

RTDs and thermistors normally are connected as one element in a Wheatstone bridge, a typical arrangement being shown in Figure 9. The "three wire" method of connection between the temperature sensor and the bridge is used in order that the change in lead resistance with change in ambient temperature does not affect unduly the law of the bridge: this requires that the two outer leads be identical electrically.   A four wire method of connection also is used, as an alternative.   For the arrangement of Figure 9, V_o is related to the applied voltage V_A and the sensor resistance R_θ by the law

$$V_o = \frac{V_A}{2} - V_A \cdot \left[\frac{R_1 + r}{R_1 + 2r + R_\theta} \right]$$

where r is the lead resistance. Thus, V_o is a (nonlinear) measure of the difference between R_θ and R_1 so that, in a temperature controller, R_1 could be set manually to equal that value of R_θ corresponding to the desired value of temperature: at the null, when $V_o = 0$, R_θ would be equal to R_1.

The applied voltage V_A must be given a reasonably low value, so that the "self-heating" effect within the termperature sensor is minimised. This effect can result from internally generated heat, due to $I^2 R$ dissipation, so that the temperature rise detected by the sensor resistance change then would be due only partly to the heat transmitted from the surrounding medium.

4.3.4 The Filled-System Bourdon Tube

The Bourdon tube is a device for converting a pressure within the tube into a displacement at the end of the tube, and is described in Section 4.4.2. When used in a temperature transducer, the pressure is developed, by the temperature of the thermometer bulb, within the liquid, gas, vapour, or mercury which has been used to fill the system: that is, the bulb, connecting capillary, and Bourdon, as shown in Figure 10.

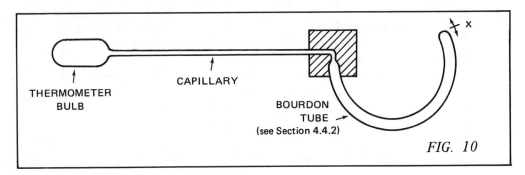

FIG. 10

A change in pressure causes a physical deformation of the Bourdon, resulting in a displacement x at its free end: this displacement can be made to be proportional approximately to the temperature change at the bulb. The device is robust and cheap but not particularly accurate, especially if means are not included for compensating for the effect of changes in ambient temperature upon that part of the fluid circuit within the capillary and the Bourdon.

Filling media include alcohol, xylene, mercury, nitrogen, and hydrogen, selectively covering a temperature range from $-120°$ C. to $+650°$ C.

4.3.5 Semiconductor Temperature Transducers

Over a specified temperature range (typically, $-55°$ C. to $+150°$ C.), silicon junction semiconductor devices are well suited to temperature measurement, being fast, highly linear, and cheap. The junction potential of silicon diodes and transistors, although varying between devices, changes at about 2.2mV/°C.

A typical 2—terminal sensor is made using a junction transistor, as shown in Figure 11 with a representative calibration graph.

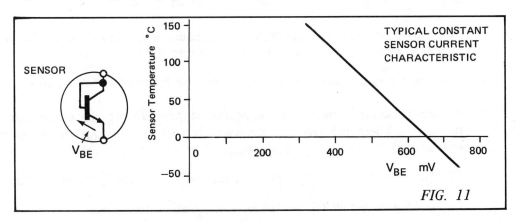

FIG. 11

In order that variation in device current should not be allowed to affect the calibration, this type of device should be supplied from a constant-current DC source and the voltage dropped across it should be sensed by a buffer amplifier, as shown in Figure 12.

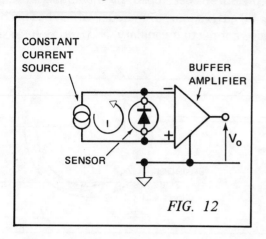

FIG. 12

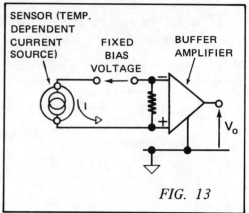

FIG. 13

Other, more sophisticated, semiconductor temperature sensors have been designed to function as current sources: a typical IC device develops a current in μA numerically equal to the temperature, in Kelvin, of the case. A typical application is shown in Figure 13. Yet another type behaves as a temperature-dependent zener diode, with the zener voltage related to the temperature with a sensitivity of 10 mV/K. Some commercially available devices incorporate the temperature sensor, buffer amplifier, and possibly the DC power source, into a single IC package, having a typical accuracy of 1°C.

4.4   PRESSURE TRANSDUCERS

Pressure is defined as force per unit area and the fundamental unit in the SI system is the Newton per square metre (N/m^2), also known as the Pascal (Pa). Because the N/m^2 is an inconveniently small unit, the kN/m^2 (kPa) and the Bar (100 kN/m^2) more commonly are used. Low pressures often are expressed in millimetres of water (mm H_2O) or millimetres of mercury (mm Hg). It is important to note that the liquid column is not a true pressure unit, since it does not have the dimensions of force/area. A liquid column is related to pressure by the expression $p = \gamma h$, where p is the pressure in N/m^2, h is the height of the column in metres, and γ is the specific weight of the liquid in N/m^3.

Pressure measured from the true zero pressure is termed "absolute", and that measured relative to the local atmosphere is termed "gauge", so that

absolute pressure = gauge pressure + atmospheric (barometric) pressure.

Pressures measured relative to atmospheric pressure may be either positive or negative. Where the latter is the case, the word "vacuum" often is used to indicate an amount of pressure below the atmospheric value : for example,

10 kN/m^2 vacuum = atmospheric pressure − 10 kN/m^2, on an absolute scale;

that is, approximately 100 − 10 = 90 kN/m^2 absolute.

In vacuum measurements, the Torr unit often is used, where 1 torr = 1 mm Hg.

Most pressure transducers generating an electrical output incorporate one of the following elements as the primary pressure sensor, which converts the pressure into a displacement or a force:

- manometer
- Bourdon tube
- bellows
- diaphragm.

Most of the devices used to convert the resulting displacement or force into an electrical signal have been discussed in Chapters 2 and 3, and may be either strain gauge, capacitive, inductive, variable reluctance, piezoelectric, or variable differential transformer types.

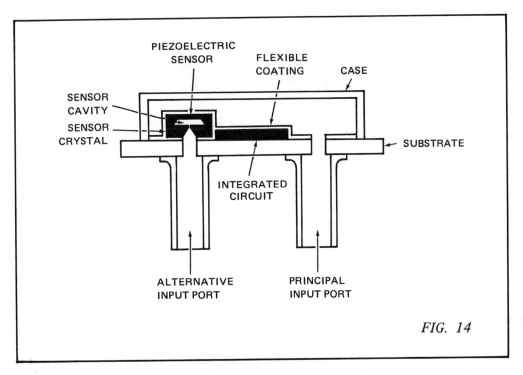

FIG. 14

A recently introduced type of pressure transducer, utilising a piezoelectric sensor in conjunction with an integrated circuit, is illustrated in Figure 14. The silicon sensor, which responds to either positive or negative pressure differentials, includes a reference pressure cavity which encloses a vacuum, in absolute transducers, or is open (via the alternative input port), in gauge and differential transducers. With minor circuit modifications for the differential and backward gauge versions and inclusion of appropriate input ports, the same basic transducing device can serve all three types of pressure measurement. The accuracy of this type of transducer is limited to about 1½% and it is unsuitable for measurement of very low pressure differentials, but it has an extremely fast response to pressure changes.

4.4.1 Manometers

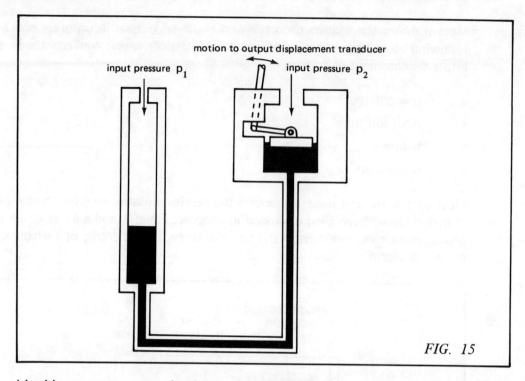

motion to output displacement transducer

input pressure p$_1$

input pressure p$_2$

FIG. 15

Liquid manometers are simple pressure pressure sensors which are economical, reliable, and accurate. There are two types: the visual (sometimes called a "sight glass" or "sight gauge") and the float. The latter type is necessary for high pressure service and/or where transduction is desired, and is illustrated in Figure 15: the float displacement will be converted into an electrical signal by one of the displacement transducers of Section 2.2. The use of this type of instrument is declining.

4.4.2 Bourdon Tubes

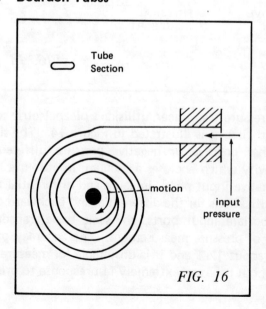

Tube
Section

motion

input
pressure

FIG. 16

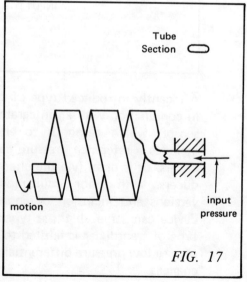

Tube
Section

motion

input
pressure

FIG. 17

Bourdon tubes are elastic deformation elements and, because of their simple design and low cost, they are used more widely than any other type of pressure sensor. There are three types of Bourdon element: the "C", the spiral, and the helical. These are illustrated in Figures 1, 16, and 17 respectively. Bourdon tubes are made from metals such as phosphor bronze, beryllium copper, stainless steel, Monel, and certain steel alloys. Pressure ranges up to 100 000 psi (680 MPa) are quoted. Typical accuracy is in the range of ±½% to ±1% of span.

The advantages of Bourdon tubes are:

- low cost
- simple construction
- high reliability
- high pressure ranges
- good accuracy versus cost, except at low pressure ranges
- suitability for transducers for generating electrical outputs.

The disadvantages of Bourdon tubes are:

- low spring rate and therefore limited measure precision, at pressures below about 350 kPa
- susceptibility to shock and vibration, due to the large overhang
- poor repeatability, due to mechanical hysteresis.

Bourdon tubes need to be operated in pairs, mechanically linked, when they are required to measure differential pressure.

4.4.3 Bellows

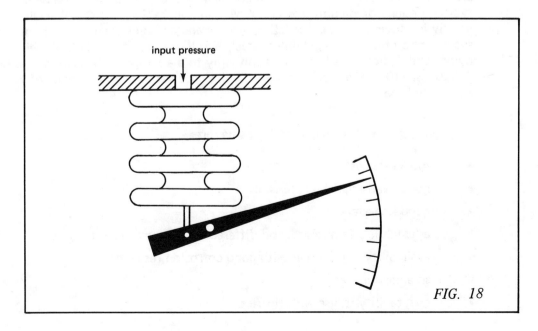

input pressure

FIG. 18

A bellows is an elastic deformation element usually formed from a thin seamless tube. A simplified representation of the element, used as an indicator, is shown in Figure 18. The greatest use for bellows units is as receiving elements for pneumatic recorders, indicators, and controllers. Bellows are made from metals such as brass, phosphor bronze, beryllium copper, stainless steel, and Monel. Often, they are supplemented with an integral helical spring, to modify their spring rate. Pressure ranges up to 400 psi (2.7 MPa) are common. Typical accuracy is ±½% of full span.

The advantages of bellows are:

- high delivered force
- moderate cost
- adaptability to absolute and differential pressure measurement
- good accuracy in the low-to-moderate pressure range.

The disadvantages of bellows are:

- ambient temperature compensation requirement
- unsuitability for high pressures
- limited range of materials.

Bellows need to be operated in pairs, mechanically linked, when they are required to measure differential pressure.

4.4.4   Diaphragms

The operating principle of the diaphragm is similar to that of the bellows. Pressure is applied to the element, causing it to deform elastically, in direct proportion to the applied pressure. Unlike the bellows element, calibrated springs are rarely required, because the diaphragm movement usually is small. Some typical designs of diaphragms are shown in Figure 19: the double-walled type usually is known as a "capsule". Diaphragms and capsules are made from materials such as phosphor bronze, stainless steel, beryllium copper, nickel, Monel, rubber, nylon, and Teflon: the last three apply only to diaphragms. Pressure ranges up to 15000 psi (100 MPa) are quoted. Typical accuracy is in the range of ±½% to ±1% of full span.

The advantages of diaphragms and capsules are:

- moderate cost
- good overrange characteristics
- good linearity
- adaptability to absolute and differential pressure measurement
- availability in materials with good corrosion resistance
- smallness in size
- adaptability to use with slurries.

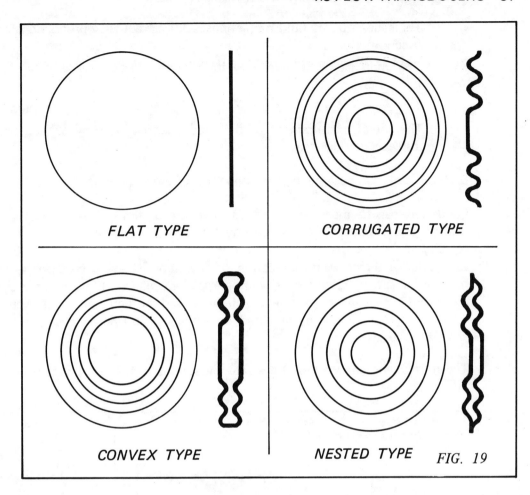

FLAT TYPE   CORRUGATED TYPE

CONVEX TYPE   NESTED TYPE   *FIG. 19*

The disadvantages of diaphragms and capsules are:

- poor shock and vibration resistance
- limitation to relatively low pressures, with many types.

Evacuated capsules need to be used for the measurement of absolute pressure.

4.5   FLOW TRANSDUCERS

There are at least eight different physical properties used for measuring the flow of fluids. These are as follows:

- The transformation of kinetic energy into pressure energy, which then is measured.
- The generation of an electrical voltage which is proportional to linear velocity.
- The transformation of the linear velocity of the fluid into a corresponding rotational velocity, which then can be measured.
- The inference of fluid velocity from its effect upon the cooling of a hot body in the fluid.

- The generation of fluid oscillations, with a frequency proportional to the fluid velocity.

- The inference of fluid velocity from its effect upon the velocity of sound in the moving fluid.

- The use of some form of tracer, to detect linear velocity of the fluid.

- The direct measurement of the total quantity flowing, using a positive displacement device.

Each principle can be applied to a number of different methods.

Fluid flow can be measured either as flow rate or flow volume. Flow rate is the integrated velocity of the individual streamlines, which make up the total velocity profile across the pipe. Flow rate measurement devices can be used to provide a direct visual indication or the transmitted output can be fed to remote indicators, recorders, or automatic controllers. Flow volume devices measure the total volume of fluid which has passed through a pipe in a given interval of time: typically, they are used for fiscal monitoring purposes, but rarely as feedback transducers.

The most common types of flow rate measurement device are shown in Figure 20.

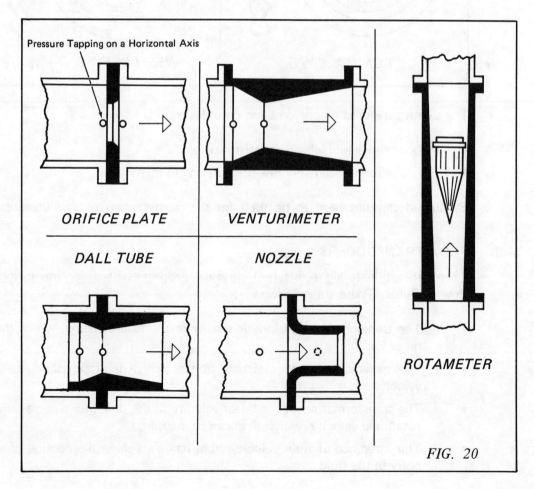

FIG. 20

4.5.1 Orifice, Venturi, Dall Tube, and Nozzle

The most commonly used types of flowmeter for process control applications are the orifice plate and the venturi (meter). The orifice plate owes its popularity to its simplicity and the fact that it is inexpensive. It can be manufactured cheaply from metal plate and inserted between the flanges of a pipe union, and across it the pressure drop may be measured using tapping lines, with flowrate being inferred from the differential pressure measurement. The orifice plate can be mass produced to such high standards that its calibration coefficient is predictable to within limits of about ±1%; if greater accuracy is required, it can be calibrated individually. The orifice plate has several disadvantages, of which the most important are the high irrecoverable pressure loss and a tendency to become blocked if the fluids being metered contain solids in suspension. A number of national standards have been published, covering orifice plate design, with the data being presented in tabular or graphical forms.

The venturimeter costs more than an orifice plate but has only a fraction of the irrecoverable pressure loss of the latter. It is suited to applications where the low pressure loss will result in such a large saving in energy costs throughout its life that the extra initial cost is justified; for this reason, venturimeters often are used in large water mains. They also are used where the flow contains solids in suspension, since build up of particles is not possible. Both the orifice plate and the venturi have the advantages of freedom from moving parts and the ability to maintain calibration over long periods. Again, venturi design normally is undertaken using data available in standards publications.

The nozzle is a compromise between the venturi and the orifice plate, and shares to some extent the advantages and disadvantages of each.

Devices such as the Dall tube combine the lower pressure loss and smoother flow path advantages of the venturi with a shorter, simpler, construction. The Dall tube resembles a miniature venturi and it is inserted within the pipeline.

These four types of flowmeter, which all feature the insertion of an obstruction in the pipeline, all suffer from the disadvantage that the measured differential pressure is proportional to the square of the inferred flowrate, so that, when the flow is (say) at 1/3rd of maximum, the differential pressure is only 1/9th of maximum. With the flowmeter connected to a differential pressure transmitter, the output signal can be processed by means of a "Square-Root Extractor" (refer to Section 11.4.3), in order to restore the relationship between the generated signal and the flowrate to a linear law.

4.5.2 Rotameters

Rotameters are variable area flowmeters which must be inserted in vertical pipelines in which the flow is directed upward. The rotameter consists of a glass or metal tube which is tapered on the inside, with the narrower end at the bottom, and in this sits a heavy plummet, which typically is tapered to a point at the bottom. The flow lifts the plummet to a stable position whereby the upthrust just cancels the weight of the plummet. The displacement will be proportional approximately to the flowrate, so that the rotameter can be regarded as a linear transducer. For adaptation to signal transmission applications, the plummet may become the moving member within an LVDI or LVDT surrounding the tapered tube, if ferrous material is embedded within the plummet; alternatively, the plummet may contain a permanent magnet, with the displaced magnetic field being tracked by a moving ferrous member outside the tube. In some designs, the plummet is fluted, so that it spins with an angular velocity proportional to the flowrate, with this velocity being sensed by a suitable angular velocity transducer. The main disadvantage with the rotameter is that the calibration is dependent upon the density of the flow medium and this may not be constant; in addition, the plummet tends not to be stable for flowrates much below 10% of full range. Ranges up to 1300 gal/min (5850 l/min) are possible, with accuracy varying from ±½% to as poor as ±10%.

4.5.3   Magnetic Flowmeters

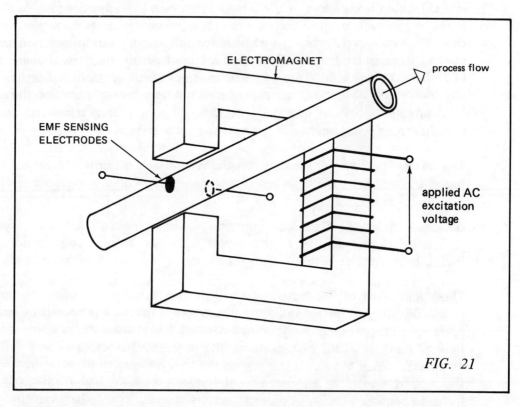

FIG. 21

The principle of these devices is indicated by Figure 21. The liquid must have at least a minimal conductivity and acts as a (liquid) conductor moving through an electromagnetic field, so that an emf, proportional in magnitude to the velocity of the fluid, is developed between the orthogonal electrodes. Usually, the excitation is AC, to prevent build up of corrosive deposits on the electrodes. This flowmeter has the advantages of good linearity, of presenting zero obstruction to the liquid flow, of being bidirectional, of generating an electrical signal directly, and of having a calibration almost independent of the type of flow medium; however, it is affected by entrained bubbles.

4.5.4 Turbine Meters

With turbine meters, a small impeller is mounted coaxially with the centreline of a straight length of tube. The flow stream causes the impeller to spin with an angular velocity which is proportional to the flowrate, with a good linearity in the range between about 10% and 100% of rated flow, which may have a value as high as 200 000 l/min. The angular velocity of the turbine needs to be sensed, and typically this is achieved by making the impeller the rotor of a digital tachogenerator, as described in Section 2.4.4. The impeller would be made from metallic material and the pickup coils would be placed against the outside of the (non-metallic) tube. Typical accuracy is in the ±¼% to ±½% range. The turbine meter will cause a small pressure loss to be developed, proportional to the square of the flowrate, and the impeller and its bearings may be susceptible to corrosion and entrained solids.

4.5.5 Pitot Tubes

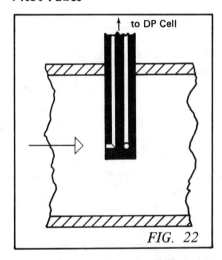

FIG. 22

Figure 22 shows a cross section through a Pitot tube, which measures linear velocity of the flow at one point in the cross section through the flow stream. The forward facing tap senses dynamic pressure, whilst the sideways facing tap senses static pressure: the pressure difference is proportional to the square of the linear velocity. Pitot tubes are suitable mostly for gas, vapour, and clean liquid streams, and can be accurate to within from ±½% to ±5%. They must be calibrated to relate volumetric flowrate to the linear velocity at the point of impact. Pressure loss is small.

4.5.6 Target Meters

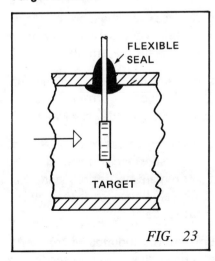

FIG. 23

With target meters, a small disc target is inserted into a flow stream, mounted on a bar which passes through a flexible seal in the wall of the pipeline, as shown in Figure 23. The velocity of the flow at the point of impact causes a force to be developed in the bar, and this force is proportional to the square of the velocity. The constant of proportionality will depend upon the properties of the flow medium. The force exerted upon the bar can be sensed, outside the pipeline, either by using bonded strain gauges or by nulling the force with a force-balance type of transmitter. These meters are suitable particularly for viscous, dirty, and corrosive fluids. They must be calibrated to relate volumetric flowrate to the linear velocity at the point of impact, and can be accurate within from ±½% to ±3%.

4.5.7   Vortex Meters

Vortex meters are constructed typically by inserting a fixed, fluted, obstruction into a pipeline, to create a swirling flow which oscillates at a frequency proportional to the volumetric flowrate. Thermistors are mounted in this swirling flow and are energised so that the temperature developed by self-heating oscillates at the frequency of the vortex: refer to Section 4.3.2. The frequency of the pulsating voltage developed by the thermistor network is used as a measure of the flowrate, and can be converted into an equivalent voltage magnitude using a frequency-voltage converter, as described in Section 10.16. Excellent linearity can be achieved, within specified operating limits, and the accuracy can be better than ±1%.

4.6   LEVEL TRANSDUCERS

Level measurement may be classified broadly into two general groups: direct and inferential. Direct level measurements are simple and economical. Usually, they are visual as, for example, sight glasses, dip sticks, and calibrated tapes, and are not adapted easily to signal generation.

Inferred methods depend upon the medium having a property which is related to level and is measurable. For this purpose, use has been made of the many physical and electrical properties which are well suited to the generation of proportional output signals for remote transmission. Included in these properties are the following:

- Hydrostatic head – the force or weight produced by the height of the liquid, which would be sensed by a pressure transducer placed at the bottom of the vessel.

- Buoyancy – the upward force of a submerged body, which is equal to the weight of the fluid which it displaces, or the upward displacement of a float on the surface. Here, strain gauges or displacement transducers would be used, in order to establish a suitable output signal.

- Conductance – at desired points of level detection, the medium to be measured conducts (or ceases to conduct) electricity between two fixed probe locations or between one probe and the vessel wall.

- Capacitance – the medium to be measured serves as a variable dielectric between two capacitor plates. Two substances form the composite dielectric: the medium whose measurement is desired and the vapour space above it. The total capacitance value changes as the volume of one material increases whilst that of the other decreases.

- Radiation – the measured medium absorbs radiated energy. As in the capacitance method, vapour space above the measured medium also has

an effect upon the measurement, due to its own absorption characteristic, but the difference in absorption between the two is great enough
for the measurement to be made.

● Sonar or ultrasonic — the medium to be measured reflects, or affects in
some other detectable manner, high frequency sound signals generated at
appropriate locations near the test medium.

Caution must be applied, when utilising inferred level measurement, to ensure
that the measured property has a well defined relationship to level.

Normally, little difficulty is experienced with measuring the level of clean, low
viscosity fluids. Slurries, viscous substances, and solids present much greater
problems. For evaluation of the method to be used for a particular application,
certain operating conditions, such as level range, fluid characteristics, temperature, pressure, and the state of the fluid around the operating area, must be
known. Figures 24, 25 and 26 show examples of hydrostatic head, capacitance,
and buoyancy types, respectively.

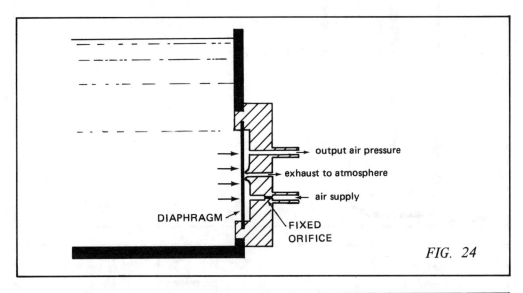

output air pressure

exhaust to atmosphere

air supply

DIAPHRAGM

FIXED
ORIFICE

FIG. 24

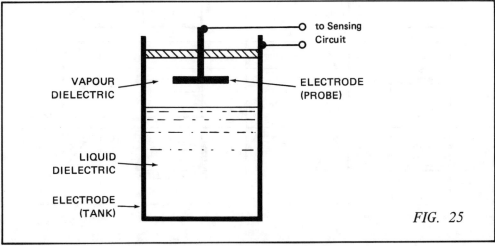

to Sensing
Circuit

VAPOUR
DIELECTRIC

ELECTRODE
(PROBE)

LIQUID
DIELECTRIC

ELECTRODE
(TANK)

FIG. 25

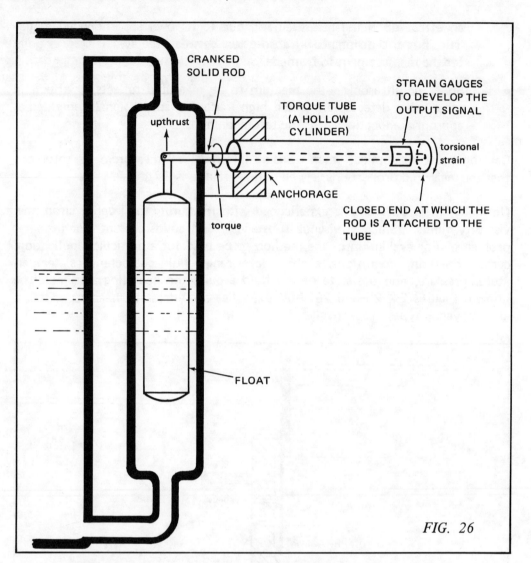

CRANKED
SOLID ROD

upthrust

TORQUE TUBE
(A HOLLOW
CYLINDER)

STRAIN GAUGES
TO DEVELOP THE
OUTPUT SIGNAL

torsional
strain

ANCHORAGE

torque

CLOSED END AT WHICH THE
ROD IS ATTACHED TO THE
TUBE

FLOAT

FIG. 26

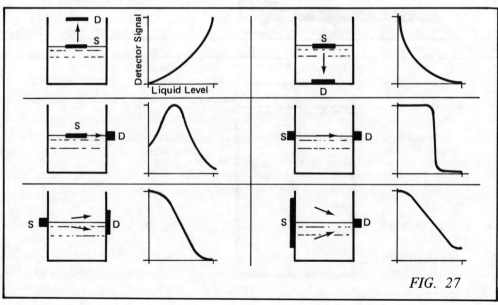

Detector Signal

Liquid Level

FIG. 27

Figure 27 shows alternative arrangements for mounting a radiation source (S) and a radiation detector (D) for the measurement of liquid level. (Section 17.9 discusses types of radiation, radiation sources,and radiation detectors). Because the absorption varies in inverse proportion with the thickness of the absorbing material, the relationship between detector signal and liquid level will depend heavily upon the orientation of the source and detector. These techniques may be modified to suit the measurement of levels of solids and slurries.

4.7 DENSITY TRANSDUCERS

Density may be defined as mass per unit volume, and is expressed in kg/m^3 in the SI system of units. Specific gravity (which is not recommended in the SI system) often is used synonymously with density, and is defined as the ratio of the density of the fluid in question to the density of water, at a specific temperature.

Common density measurement methods involve air bubble, displacement, displacement U-tube, vibrating U-tube, and radiation techniques.

4.7.1 Air Bubble Type

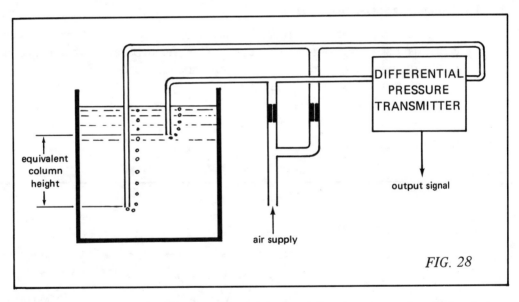

FIG. 28

The simplest and possibly the most widely used density measuring device is two bubbler tubes set at different levels in a vessel containing liquid, as shown in Figure 28. The two tubes act as back-pressure generators, and the difference between the two pressures is measured by a differential pressure transmitter and is equal to a constant height column of the liquid. Change in differential pressure is proportional to density change.

4.7.2 Displacement Type

Displacement density instruments operate using the buoyancy of a completely submerged body, as shown in Figure 29. The force acting on the balance (or torque) arm is related directly to the density of the liquid displaced by the float.

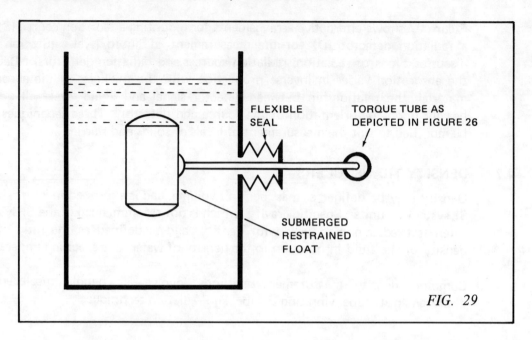

FLEXIBLE SEAL

TORQUE TUBE AS DEPICTED IN FIGURE 26

SUBMERGED RESTRAINED FLOAT

FIG. 29

4.7.3   Displacement U-Tube Type

In this arrangement, the process liquid flows through a U-tube, the weight of which is balanced on a weigh beam. The weigh beam is linked mechanically to the flapper-nozzle assembly of a force balance transmitter. Change in density modifies the flapper-nozzle separation, changing the back-pressure within the nozzle and hence the transmitter output signal: refer to Section 6.2.2.

4.7.4   Vibrating U-Tube Type

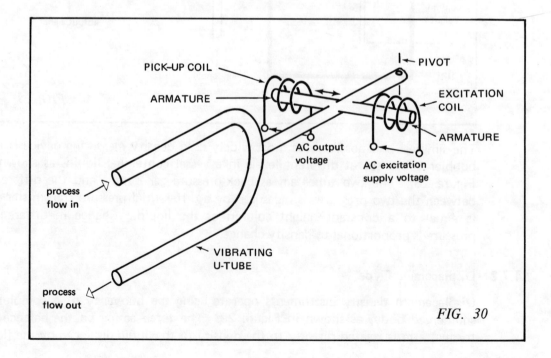

PICK-UP COIL

PIVOT

ARMATURE

EXCITATION COIL

ARMATURE

AC output voltage

AC excitation supply voltage

process flow in

VIBRATING U-TUBE

process flow out

FIG. 30

The vibrating U-type operates on the principle that the amplitude of vibration, of a vibrating body, is proportional to its mass. In Figure 30, the total mass of the U-tube includes the mass of the flowing liquid and, therefore, changes with a change in density. An armature and coil assembly form a "pick-up" in which an AC voltage is induced by the vibration of the armature. This voltage is proportional to the amplitude of vibration and hence to the density of the liquid.

4.7.5 Radiation Type

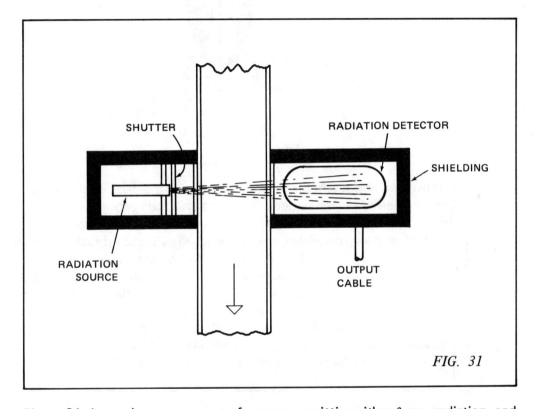

FIG. 31

Figure 31 shows the arrangement of a source, emitting either β or γ radiation, and a radiation detector, for the measurement of the density of a material flow. The absorption of the radiation by the flow medium will increase as the density of the medium increases, so that the detector will sense a corresponding reduction in received radiation. (Section 17.9 discusses types of radiation, radiation sources, and radiation detectors.) This technique is particularly useful for density measurements on slurries.

4.8 pH TRANSDUCERS

The effective acidity or alkalinity of a liquid normally is expressed in pH. A pH of 7 corresponds to a neutral solution. The pH increases towards 14 when the alkalinity increases and the pH approaches 0 as the acidity increases. The electrochemical reaction which takes place in a liquid, when acid is added, consists of an increase in hydrogen ions and a decrease in hydroxyl ions. Since the hydrogen ions are positive and the hydroxyl ions are negative, it is possible to measure the change by electrical means.

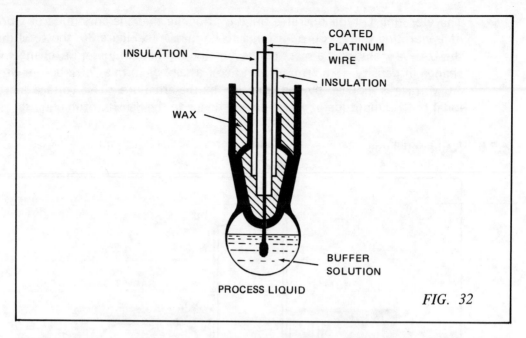

FIG. 32

The most common method of measurement uses the glass electrode and calomel reference electrode combination. The glass electrode contains a buffer solution, which is a solution which maintains a certain pH level even when a limited amount of acid or base substance is added. The standard Beckman glass electrode, which is shown in Figure 32, has a spherical end with a diameter of about 12mm filled with the buffer solution. The wall is of very thin glass and constitutes a membrane between the buffer solution and the liquid under measurement. A platinum wire, coated with silver chloride, connects the buffer solution to the electrode head. The potential difference between the buffer solution and the process liquid, across the glass membrane, is of measurable size, despite the high membrane resistance which may be as high as 100 MΩ.

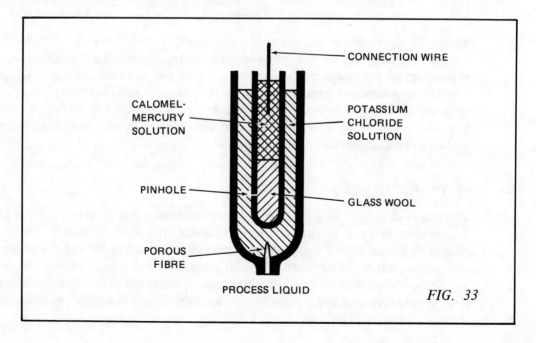

FIG. 33

The circuit is completed through a calomel electrode, shown in Figure 33, which serves as a reference electrode with a constant output emf. A liquid junction between the process liquid and the calomel is established by means of an outer chamber, which is filled with a saturated solution of potassium chloride. A minute flow of this solution diffuses, through a porous fibre, into the process liquid. The inner chamber of the reference electrode is filled with glass wool in its lower part, and on top of this is placed a layer of paste made from a mixture of calomel and mercury. A pinhole provides a liquid junction between the two chambers and completes an electrolytic cell of constant emf.

The two electrodes are mounted in close proximity and exposed to the process liquid, although they are likely to be partly enclosed by a protective envelope. Figure 34 shows the connection of the electrodes to an instrumentation amplifier, which must draw a current not exceeding 1 pA, if polarisation of the cells is to be avoided.

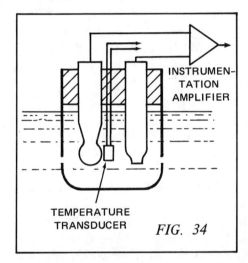

FIG. 34

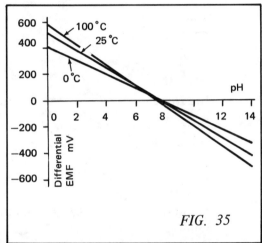

FIG. 35

Figure 35 shows calibration curves for the electrode system and indicates that the calibration is strongly temperature dependent. For this reason, some form of temperature transducer would be mounted close to the glass electrode, and the temperature data generated would be used in computation to compensate, for temperature effects, the amplifier output voltage.

Because the definition of pH is given by pH = −log (hydrogen ion concentration) any control system designed to manipulate acid or alkali flow, in order to maintain a set pH level, may be highly nonlinear because of this logarithmic relationship.

4.9 HUMIDITY TRANSDUCERS

The term "humidity" means the concentration of water vapour in a gas, with this gas usually being air. The maximum concentration of water vapour which can exist in a gas depends upon the temperature of the gas. "Relative humidity" is the ratio of actual concentration to maximum possible concentration at the prevailing temperature, and normally is expressed as a percentage.

4.9.1 The Hygrometer

Certain threads, such as human air or nylon thread, are hygroscopic and therefore tend to absorb an amount, of water, which is dependent upon the prevailing relative humidity. The thread will contract or extend, depending upon whether water is released (by evaporation) or absorbed, respectively. One common type of mechanical hygrometer uses a suspended thread, and the contraction and extension of this thread is measured by a suitable displacement transducer. An alternative form uses a pneumatic force balance arrangement similar to that of Figure 1, except that the source of input force now becomes the tension in the suspended thread.

Electrical hygrometers generally use two precious metal wires or grids which are precisely spaced a small distance from each other. The intervening space is filled with a layer of hygroscopic compound,such as lithium chloride, the electrical conductivity of which changes in proportion to the amount of water absorbed or released. The two wires normally would be connected to form one limb of a Wheatstone bridge, so that the output from the bridge would be a measure of the change in conductance of the path through the hygroscopic coating.

4.9.2 The Wet and Dry Bulb Thermometer

This instrument uses two thermometer bulbs, with the dry bulb measuring the ambient temperature. The wet bulb is surrounded by a porous material which is kept moist and across which a stream of the test medium is arranged to flow, using a fan if necessary. The wet bulb temperature falls in value as a result, because of evaporation, and this fall in temperature is dependent upon a combination of the ambient temperature, as sensed by the dry bulb, and the relative humidity of the gas flow. Resistance thermometers or filled system thermometers usually are used, with the output data provided by the two thermometers being employed in the computation of the relative humidity.

4.9.3 The Dew Point Thermometer

The dew point is that temperature to which a sample atmosphere can be cooled before water condensation occurs, and therefore is a measure of the relative humidity, of the sample, existing before cooling is commenced.

One type of dew point instrument causes the sample gas to be drawn past a mirror, which is mounted on a refrigerated chamber. This mirror is used to reflect a light beam, and the intensity of the reflected light is reduced when condensation occurs on the mirror. The reflected light is sensed by a photosensitive detector, the output of which is amplified and used to energise a heater, which is mounted against the back of the mirror. Because condensation diminishes when the mirror is heated, the feedback action ensures that the condensation does not grow, so that the mirror temperature is held at the dew point. A temperature transducer, mounted on the mirror, is used to measure the dew point temperature.

4.10 MOISTURE TRANSDUCERS

The term "moisture" means the concentration of liquid water in a solid material, and its measurement is particularly important in the manufacture of paper and textile webs.

One of the most commonplace moisture transducers uses a Wheatstone bridge arrangement to measure the conductance of a path through the web: this conductance is a measure of the moisture content. The web is passed through two metal pinch rollers which establish the electrical path through the web, and the resistor created by this path is connected as one limb of the bridge.

The other most commonplace moisture transducer uses an AC circuit arrangement to measure the web permittivity, which also is an indication of the moisture content. The web is passed over the faces of two separated metal electrodes, which cause the segment of web between these two faces to behave as the dielectric of a capacitor, the value of which is converted, by the circuit, into a corresponding signal level.

4.11 THICKNESS TRANSDUCERS

Thickness transducers are used for measuring the thickness of a body which, in most instances, is in motion.

Where the variation in thickness is large and physical contact with the body is permissible, it may be possible to measure the position of a probe touching the surface or the separation of two pinch rollers enclosing the body, using one of the displacement transducers described in Section 2.2.

In the many instances where physical contact with the body is not permitted and/or the variation in thickness is small, displacement transducers cease to be appropriate. In these cases, more sophisticated means are necessary and typical of these are techniques employing radiation sources and sensors.

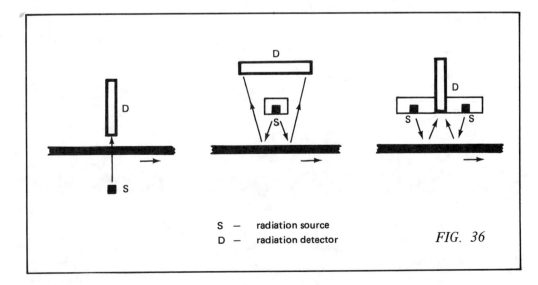

S — radiation source
D — radiation detector

FIG. 36

Figure 36 shows alternative arrangements of radiation sources and detectors for the measurement of thickness, either by direct transmission or by reflection (which is known as "back-scattering", in this context). Radioactive sources may be chosen for the emission of α, β, γ, or X rays, depending upon the type of material being measured. α, β, γ, and X ray detectors may be used, the last named being required for "X-ray fluorescence" detection in which X-rays at specific frequencies are reflected from the test body when it is irradiated with γ or X rays. (Refer to Section 17.9 for a description of radiation, radiation sources, and radiation detectors). These techniques are suitable for measuring the thickness of sheets of cardboard, paper, rubber, plastics, metal, cloth, mica, etc., of coatings of paint, of metal plating and film, and of moving beds of slurries and solid particles.

5

ELECTRIC AMPLIFIERS AND FINAL CONTROL ELEMENTS

5.1   INTRODUCTION

With the exception of solenoid actuators ("force motors") and linear induction motors, all electrical drives generate rotary motion which, if rectilinear motion is desired, must be converted using screw-nut or rack-pinion arrangements. In the majority of cases, the drive will need to be reversible, but, in those cases where reversibility is not desired, the specifications for the drive amplifiers can be relaxed.

The general arrangement of amplifiers and motor is shown in Figure 1.

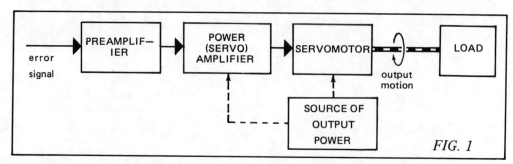

FIG. 1

In terms of power requirements, the motor power rating must be matched to the requirements of the load. The power amplifier is required to "gate" the amount of power delivered by the motor to the load: the power rating of the power amplifier must match the power rating of the motor in those applications where the amplifier directly controls the full power delivered by the motor, whereas in other configurations the power requirements of the power amplifier may be only a small fraction of the power delivered by the motor. The power rating of the preamplifier normally would be low, since its principal function usually is signal amplification and not power amplification.

5.2   PREAMPLIFIERS

The various stages of preamplification can be called upon to implement some or all of the following tasks:

- Signal combination — that is, summation or subtraction. Refer to Section 9.2.

- Signal (usually voltage) amplification.

- Signal conditioning — for example, noise filtering, level shifting, shaping with nonlinear static characteristics, etc. Refer to Chapters 11 and 12.

- Signal conversion — for example, current to voltage conversion. Refer to Chapter 10.

- System compensation, by the incorporation of active or passive R-L-C circuits to implement a specific transfer function. Refer to Chapter 12 and Section 15.3.

- Impedance level changing — for example, to provide a high impedance load for a transducer signal source.

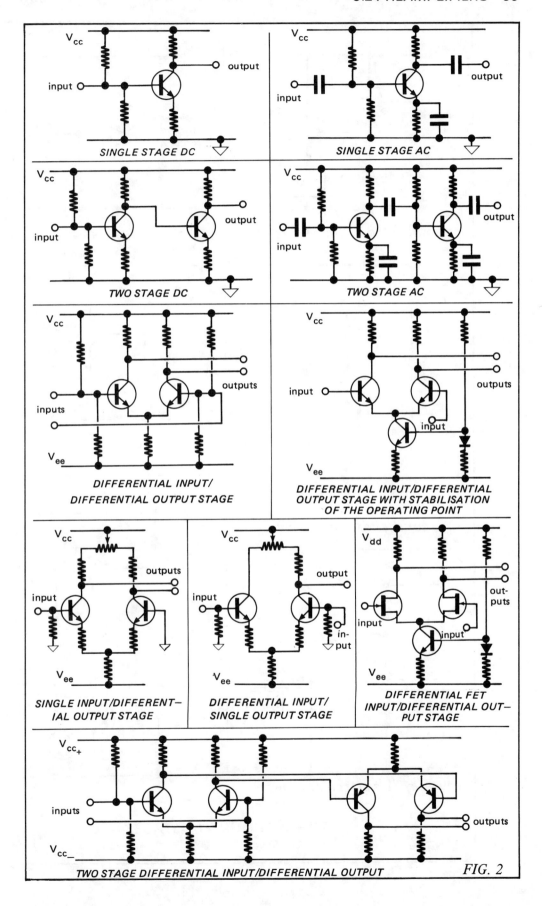

FIG. 2

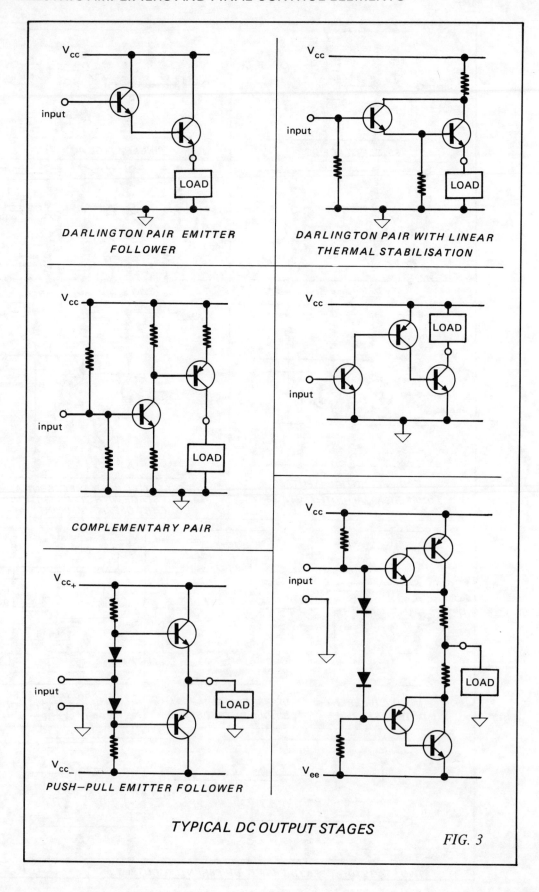

TYPICAL DC OUTPUT STAGES

FIG. 3

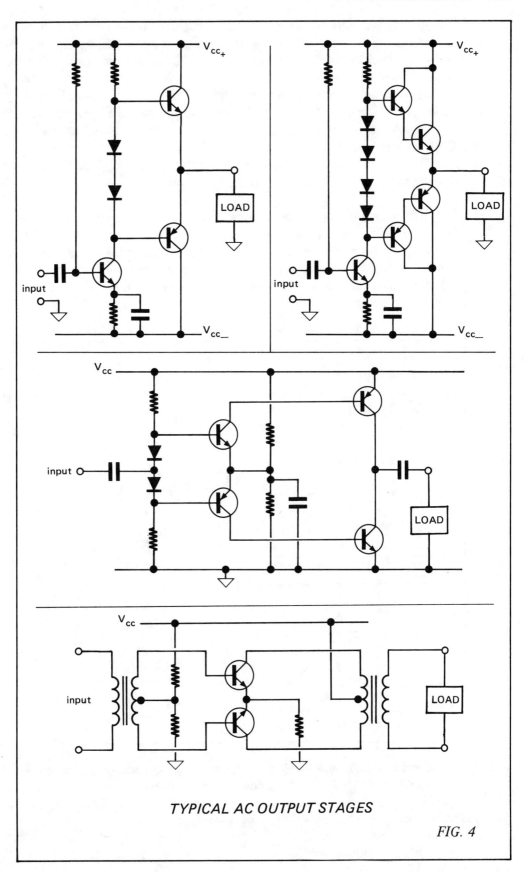

TYPICAL AC OUTPUT STAGES

FIG. 4

Normally, the signals to be processed, using analog computing techniques, are DC voltages. In some applications, the voltages may be AC, operating at a carrier frequency which typically is either 50, 60, 400 Hz or several kHz. Preamplifiers may be designed using discrete components, in which cases the stages in the amplifier normally would be direct-coupled when DC signals are being amplified. In the case of the amplification of AC signals, the stages in the amplifier normally would be AC coupled, using either capacitors or signal transformers to transmit AC components and to block the transmission of DC components. Figures 2, 3 and 4 show a number of representative transistor stages, but this by no means represents the full range of alternatives.

The performance of the various stages shown can be enhanced by the application of negative feedback, for reasons similar to those discussed in Section 5.5. Figure 5 shows four types of network arrangement for the implementation of negative feedback, which can take the form of either a current or a voltage being fed back and having a magnitude proportional to either the voltage or the current being developed at the output of the stage.

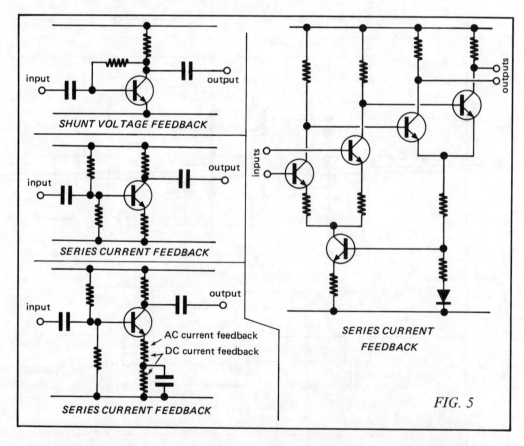

SHUNT VOLTAGE FEEDBACK

SERIES CURRENT FEEDBACK

SERIES CURRENT FEEDBACK

AC current feedback
DC current feedback

SERIES CURRENT FEEDBACK

FIG. 5

In modern practice, nearly all preamplifier configurations are integrated circuit operational amplifiers (IC Op. Amps), which employ stages of amplification and negative feedback arrangements of the types shown in Figures 2, 3, 4 and 5. These amplifiers exhibit the following advantages:

- high open loop voltage gain;

- high frequency bandwidth;
- high input impedance, especially with those having a FET input stage;
- low output impedance;
- low input voltage offset;
- low input bias current, especially with those having a FET input stage;
- high common mode rejection ratio — that is, a low susceptibility to a common component of voltage applied to both input terminals simultaneously;
- low cost;
- small physical size.

The applications of IC operational amplifiers are discussed in many places throughout this volume. Almost without exception, they are used within local negative feedback configurations, which may be either sign inverting or non-inverting, which may process signals either from single-ended or double-ended signal sources, and which may generate outputs behaving either as voltage sources or as current sources. Dual (positive and negative) voltage supply rails normally are required, although some configurations may operate satisfactorily from a single supply rail. Figure 6 shows the usual symbol used to depict an operational amplifier; note, however, that in this volume this same symbol also has been used to depict a closed loop differential-input amplifier, as described in Section 9.2.3. To prevent confusion, the legend *Differential Amplifier* has been placed against the symbol, where this is relevant.

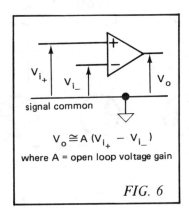

$$V_o \cong A (V_{i_+} - V_{i_-})$$

where A = open loop voltage gain

FIG. 6

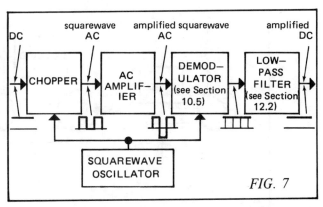

FIG. 7

Figure 7 represents one version of a "Chopper Amplifier", which uses an AC amplifier in order to amplify a DC voltage. With this, the DC input voltage is converted to a squarewave of comparable amplitude, using a solid state switching "chopper" circuit, which acts as half wave squarewave modulator: see Section 10.4. The alternating component of this squarewave is amplified by the AC amplifier and subsequently demodulated by a phase–sensitive demodulator (see Section 10.5) and smoothed, to eliminate switching spikes. The DC output voltage is an amplified version of the DC input voltage, and the chopper amplifier exhibits very high voltage gain stability and very low input voltage and current offsets; however, its bandwidth is limited by the frequency of the oscillator output.

5.3   TRANSISTOR POWER AMPLIFIERS

Transistor power amplifiers normally use direct-coupled transistor stages and are biassed to operate in the Class AB mode. Their principal function is to amplify power levels, so that the voltage amplification may be small or even unity. Negative feedback often is incorporated into the amplifier. Typically, the amplifier output would drive a winding, or windings, on a servomotor.

Typical considerations to be made when developing a power amplifier would be:

- the voltage, current and power requirements of the load;

- the availability of suitable DC power supplies;

- the requirement (or otherwise) for reversibility of the output voltage;

- the nature of the load — whether single-ended, double-ended, centre-tapped or split;

- the probable requirement for a push-pull output stage, which can be used to minimise crossover distortion.

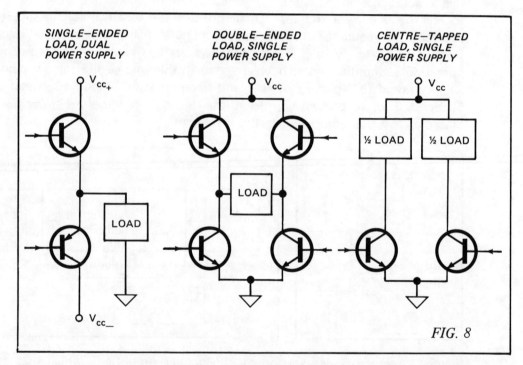

FIG. 8

Figure 8 gives examples, simplified, of some alternative configurations for output stages and loads: all can develop a reversible output voltage.   For non-reversing output requirements, simpler output stages may be used.

Some monolithic power amplifiers are manufactured and these can develop several tens of watts of output power. They can be cascaded with an IC operational amplifier, and then negative feedback typically would be applied around the combination.   Figure 9 shows two examples, both of which can drive only a single-ended load. Alternatively, the output stages of Figure 3 could be used as the power amplifiers in the Figure 9 configurations.

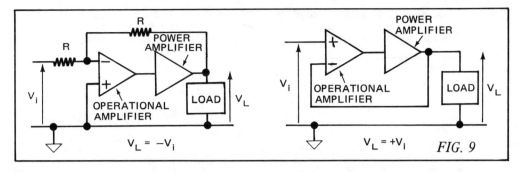

FIG. 9

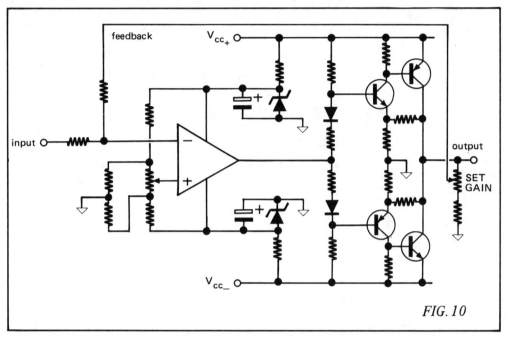

FIG. 10

Figure 10 shows a typical discrete component servoamplifier, which uses an IC operational amplifier as an integral preamplifier and which is suitable for amplifying either DC or AC voltages. It incorporates negative feedback (in fact, a feedback current proportional to a fraction of the output voltage) which has been applied around the complete amplifier.

The power amplifier designed for Class AB operation can generate an output waveform which is a faithful (amplified) reproduction of the input waveform up to signal frequencies in the region of 10 kHz. Although the output from a Class AB amplifier essentially is ideal, the method of amplification results in substantial internal power dissipation.

Switching transistor amplifiers employ high speed switching transistors to provide a proportional output. This type of amplifier has at least two transistors connected to a positive and negative voltage generated by a high power internal power supply. In contrast to the Class AB amplifier, the output transistors in a switching amplifier are in either a totally conducting or a non-conducting state. Power control is obtained by modulating the pulse width duty cycle in accordance with the magnitude of the input control signal, so that the average value of the output voltage is proportional to the input signal. Figure **11** shows an example of a switching amplifier, using field effect transistors.

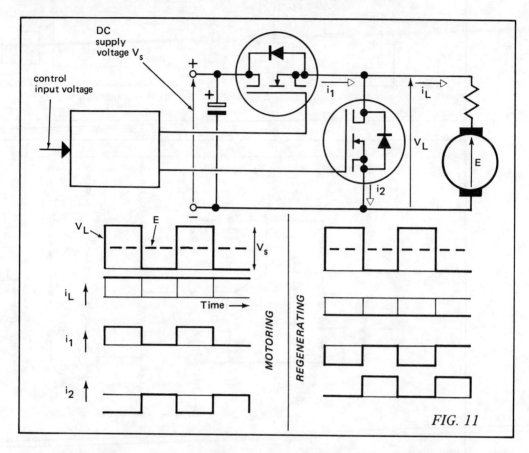

FIG. 11

The switching frequency is typically between 1 and 25 kHz. The relatively high switching frequency provides excellent reproduction, up to about 1/3 of the switching frequency. The switching transistor amplifier offers excellent power efficiency because the output transistors are either totally on or off.

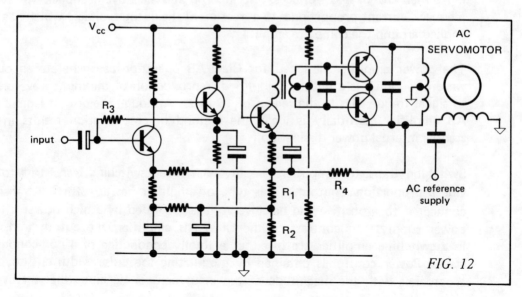

FIG. 12

Figure 12 shows a typical AC servoamplifier, capable of controlling a small two phase servomotor of the type described in Section 5.6.1: it incorporates several feedback paths, involving voltages developed across resistors R_1 and R_2 and currents flowing through resistors R_3 and R_4.

5.4   HIGH—POWER POWER OUTPUT STAGES

Where a power transistor output stage cannot meet the power requirements of the load, it normally becomes necessary to employ either a DC generator, a Triac network, or an SCR network. Note, however, that power MOSFETs are being manufactured with increasingly high power ratings and that eventually networks using these devices may take over many of the roles for which Triac and SCR networks currently are used. The MOSFET exhibits the advantages of very fast switching, low ON resistance, and the capability of being switched off as easily as it is switched on; moreover, it can be used in both proportional and on-off configurations.

5.4.1   DC Generators

When used as a power amplifier, a DC generator would have a power rating to match that of the load, and would be driven at nominally constant speed, usually by a three phase induction motor of comparable power rating, as shown in Figure 13.

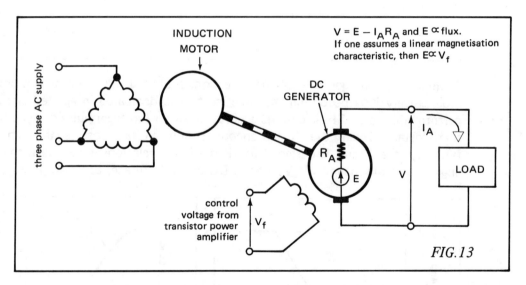

FIG.13

Typically, the power gain might be in the order of 100, whereas the voltage gain would be in the range of 1 to 10. The advantage of drawing a good current waveform from the AC mains must be offset against the capital cost of two machines to match the load, in terms of power rating, together with the reliability and maintainability limitations of commutator machines.

Where the generator output drives the armature of a comparably rated DC drive motor, the system becomes a "Ward-Leonard Set". The generator field sometimes may be centre-tapped or split, to suit the requirements of the transistor power amplifier. Regenerative braking is inherent, whereby the motor can be decelerated by returning energy, via the other two machines, back into the AC mains.

5.4.2 Triac Networks

A Triac network would be used where the load is a heating or lighting element. In many arrangements, the load voltage waveform would be alternating but not sinusoidal, as demonstrated in the simple single phase example of Figure 14.

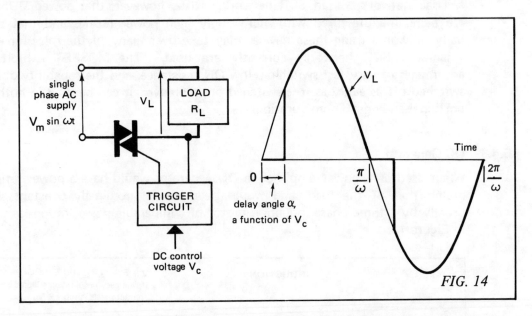

FIG. 14

Although the trigger circuit may be constructed using discrete components, progressively it is becoming the practice to use dedicated integrated circuits to perform this role. These circuits generate a trigger (voltage) pulse delayed behind that instant when the instantaneous supply voltage passes through zero: typically, the circuit is designed to yield a linear relationship between the delay angle α and the magnitude V_c of the DC control voltage, as shown in Figure 15.

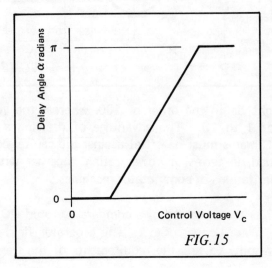

FIG. 15

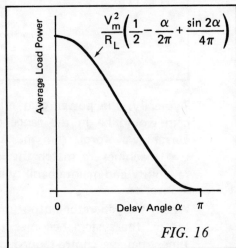

$$\frac{V_m^2}{R_L}\left(\frac{1}{2} - \frac{\alpha}{2\pi} + \frac{\sin 2\alpha}{4\pi}\right)$$

FIG. 16

The RMS value of the load voltage is given by $V_m \left(\dfrac{1}{2} - \dfrac{\alpha}{2\pi} + \dfrac{\sin 2\alpha}{4\pi} \right)^{\frac{1}{2}}$ and, for a resistive load, the average value of the load power is given by $\dfrac{V_m^2}{R_L} \left(\dfrac{1}{2} - \dfrac{\alpha}{2\pi} + \dfrac{\sin 2\alpha}{4\pi} \right)$.

In Figure 16 this latter function has been plotted to a base of α, and it will be seen that the relationship between power and delay angle is far from linear. With a trigger circuit having the type of characteristic shown in Figure 15, the relationship between load power and control voltage V_c will be equally nonlinear.

Another type of IC trigger circuit fires the Triac in bursts of complete cycles of the AC supply, always generating the trigger pulse coincidentally with the positive going zero crossing of the AC supply voltage. Typically, the circuit is arranged to yield a characteristic of the form

$$\frac{\text{number of conducting cycles in a given time period}}{\text{total number of (conducting and non-conducting) cycles in the same period}} = KV_c,$$

where K is a constant and V_c is the DC control voltage.

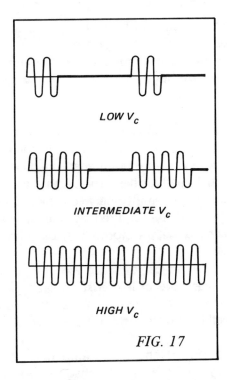

LOW V_c

INTERMEDIATE V_c

HIGH V_c

FIG. 17

Figure 17 shows typical load voltage waveforms, and the average value of the load RMS voltage will be proportional to the magnitude V_c of the DC control voltage.

This type of arrangement is unsuitable for loads required to react rapidly to changes in V_c, but this does not apply in most of those applications which utilise Triacs. Firing the Triac always at the instant of zero voltage crossing prevents radio frequency interference from being generated by the triggering action.

Where necessary, the trigger circuit may be isolated electrically from the gate of the Triac, using either a pulse transformer or an opto-isolator, which is a light emitting diode and a photosensitive transistor packaged together.

The trigger circuits which have been described also are used extensively for triggering SCRs, the applications of which are covered in Sections 5.4.3, 5.4.4 and 5.4.5.

5.4.3 Converters

A suitable SCR network may be used to replace the DC generator and induction motor of the system in Figure 13, and such a network, which is converting AC power into DC power, is known as a "Converter". The results from using solid state converters are an improvement in power efficiency and a distortion of the waveform of the current drawn from the AC supply.

Many alternative networks are possible, and these may be classified as follows:

- half wave, full wave (push-pull), or bridge;

- single phase or polyphase (including three phase);

- fully SCR or part SCR and part power diode;

- reversing or non-reversing;

- regenerating (bidirectional) and non-regenerating (unidirectional).

Examples of several different configurations are shown in Figures 18, 19 and 20. Note that the examples shown do not represent the full range of alternatives. All of the networks shown in Figures 18 and 19 may be operated in a "bidirectional" mode: this means that, if the DC load includes a source of emf, energy may be returned from the load to the AC supply, if the SCRs are triggered at appropriate instants in the AC voltage cycle.

All of the networks shown in Figure 20 are being operated in a "unidirectional" mode: the presence of the power diodes prevents an energy transfer from the DC load to the AC supply. Diodes D_c are known as "commutating diodes", and they provide a short circuit discharge path for any residual current flow through the load.

Each of the SCRs in all of the networks shown requires a suitable trigger network, and the trigger networks will require to be carefully synchronised with each other. In some cases, the gates of pairs of SCRs may require simultaneously dual trigger pulses, when the network is switched on initially: these ensure that two SCRs are switched on, in order to effect a circuit continuity between the AC supply and the load. Usually, electrical isolation will be required between the set of trigger circuits and the set of SCRs, using pulse transformers or opto-isolators.

The circuit defined by Figure 15 would be typical of those used for triggering the SCRs in these networks, in which case the characteristic relating average load power to delay angle would be nonlinear and similar to that of Figure 16, although the range of delay angle may well be different from that shown.

All of the networks shown in Figures 18, 19 and 20 assume that the load requires a unipolar average voltage. This voltage may be made reversible, by duplicating the SCR network and its set of trigger circuits, and connecting the two networks back-to-back across the load. Figure 21 shows one example, using a pair of three phase six pulse bridges.

The waveform of the current drawn from the AC supply depends upon the "pulse number" of the network and, as a general rule, the waveform will get closer to the ideal sinusoidal shape as this number is increased. Thus, with very high power installations, it would not be uncommon to find being used twenty-four pulse networks, for example.

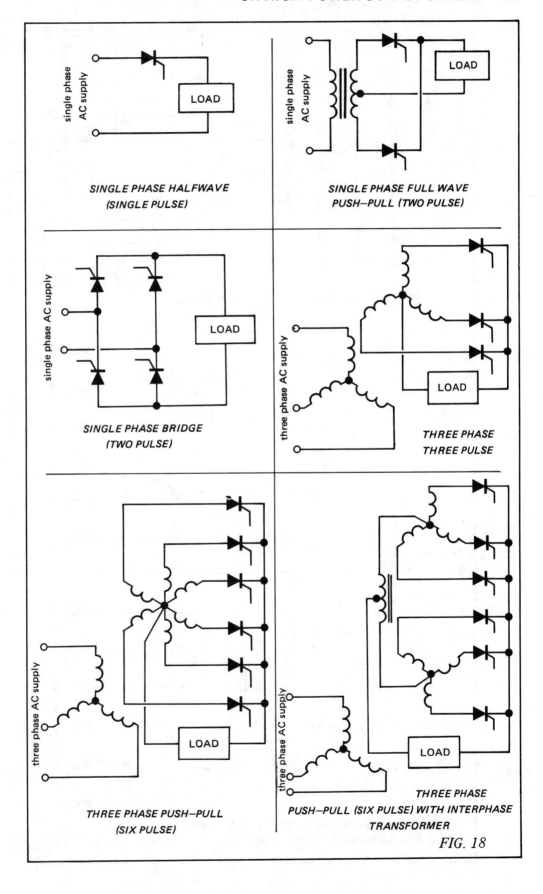

FIG. 18

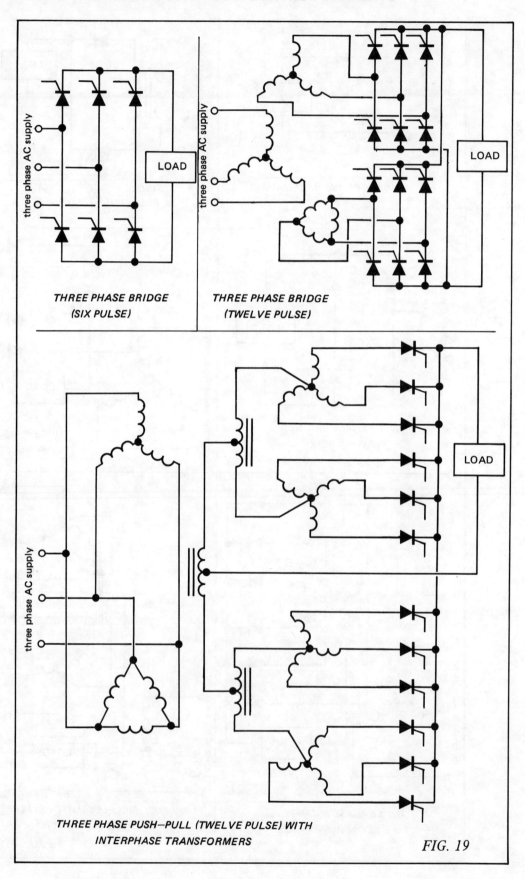

THREE PHASE BRIDGE
(SIX PULSE)

THREE PHASE BRIDGE
(TWELVE PULSE)

LOAD

three phase AC supply

three phase AC supply

LOAD

LOAD

three phase AC supply

THREE PHASE PUSH–PULL (TWELVE PULSE) WITH
INTERPHASE TRANSFORMERS

FIG. 19

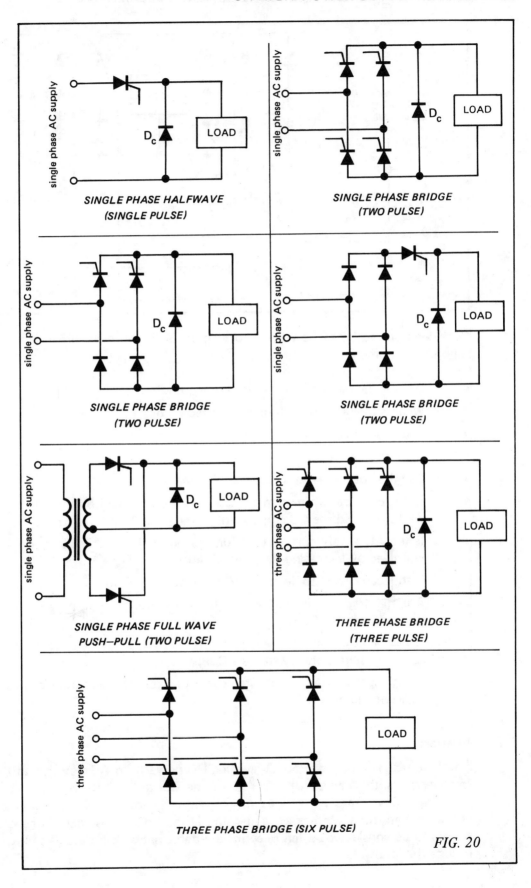

FIG. 20

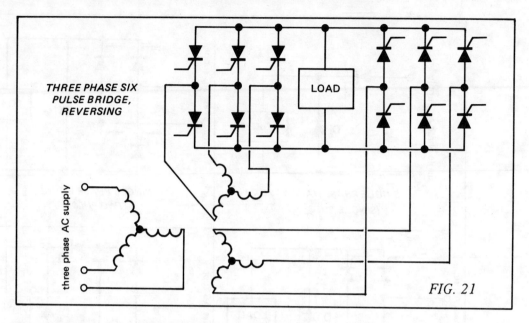

FIG. 21

Considerations to be made when choosing an SCR converter drive include the following factors:

- What is the range of output voltage required?

- What is the range of output current required?

- Is the load centre-tapped or split?

- Does the load require a reversible signal?

- Can the output waveform be half wave?

- Is a supply transformer to be used? If so, what will be the effect of the waveshape and the DC component of the secondary current?

- Is the AC supply current waveform critical? If so, this distortion can be improved by increasing the pulse number.

- Is the load circuit to be earthed? If so, at what point?

- Are the trigger control circuits to be earthed? They may need to be isolated from the SCRs.

- Is regenerative action required? This involves arranging the triggering so as to return load energy to the AC supply.

- Is high speed switching of large currents likely to cause interference with adjacent equipment?

5.4.4   Inverters

An "Inverter" is a network for converting DC power into AC power, and therefore performs the reverse of the role of the Converter. Inverters function by chopping DC voltages by various means, with the result that the alternating output waveform is synthesised and often is far from sinusoidal. Some of the factors to be considered, when selecting a suitable network for use as an Inverter, include the following:

- What output voltage range is required?

- What output current range is required?

- What output frequency range is required?

- What harmonic content can be tolerated in the output voltage waveform?

- Is the load centre tapped, with magnetic coupling between the two halves?

Most Inverters use SCRs as the switching devices, in which cases special trigger circuits are required in order to switch the SCRs both off as well as on. (Note that, in Converters, each SCR normally is switched off by virtue of the anode-cathode voltage eventually falling to a zero value). However, some types of "Gate Turn-Off" (GTO) Devices are manufactured: these are four layer semi-conductor devices which can be switched off, as well as on, by the application of suitable triggering pulses. In addition, power MOSFETs are most suitable as power switches, because they can be switched off and on with equal ease, so that these will be used increasingly in Inverters.

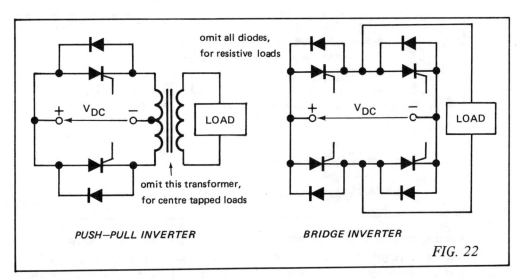

PUSH–PULL INVERTER   BRIDGE INVERTER

FIG. 22

Figure 22 shows two alternative, and basic, Inverter configurations using SCRs. The triggering ("commutating") circuits have not been included in the diagrams.

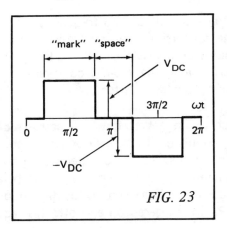

FIG. 23

The SCRs are switched on and off so that full current flows through the load in one direction, in the reverse direction, or not at all, alternately: thus, the load voltage waveform will resemble Figure 23, for the bridge inverter.

The RMS value of the load voltage may be controlled either by manipulating the value of V_{DC} (by, for example, generating it using a controlled Converter) or by varying the triggering of the SCRs, so as to manipulate the mark-space ratio. Similarly, the frequency of the load voltage may be varied by manipulating the frequency at which the trigger circuits generate the pulses required by the SCRs.

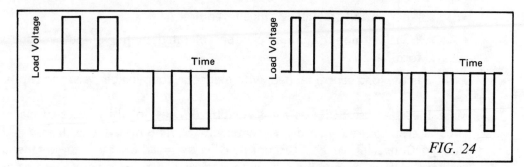

FIG. 24

The SCRs may be triggered in a more complex sequence, to yield different load voltage waveforms. Two representative examples are shown in Figure 24, but many alternatives are possible. A significant reduction in the harmonic content of the output (which may be filtered subsequently, in any case) can result, but at the cost of increased complexity for the trigger circuits.

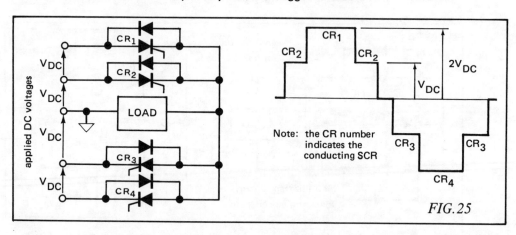

FIG. 25

Figure 25 shows one alternative arrangement for reducing the harmonic content, and this requires the establishment of stacked multiple DC supplies. Other arrangements to achieve the same type of load voltage waveform are possible.

5.4.5   Frequency Converters

A "Frequency Converter" converts AC at one voltage and frequency into AC at a different voltage and frequency. The conversion may involve an intermediate DC stage, so that the frequency converter consists of an AC-DC Converter followed by a DC-AC Inverter. Alternatively, the AC-AC conversion may be direct, and the network then is known as a "Cycloconverter".

Figure 26 shows a simple single phase Cycloconverter, which consists of two single phase bridge converter networks, connected in opposition across the load. Figure 26 also shows a typical load voltage waveform together with its fundamental component. The output fundamental frequency can be seen to be a submultiple of the supply frequency, with the relationship depending upon the sequence and instants at which the SCRs are triggered on and off; this sequence

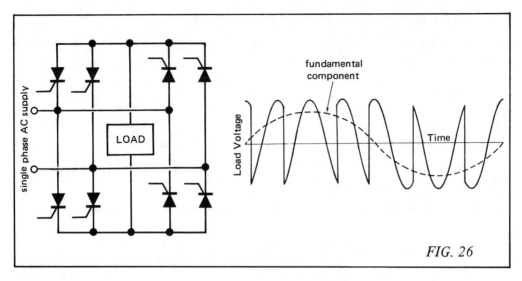

FIG. 26

also will affect the RMS value of the fundamental component. The sequence of triggering the SCRs may be organised to transfer energy in either direction.

The harmonic content of the load voltage waveform is reduced progressively as the pulse number of the Cycloconverter network is increased, so that most practical networks have high pulse numbers and generally convert from three phase to three phase. Figure 27 shows a typical twelve pulse network.

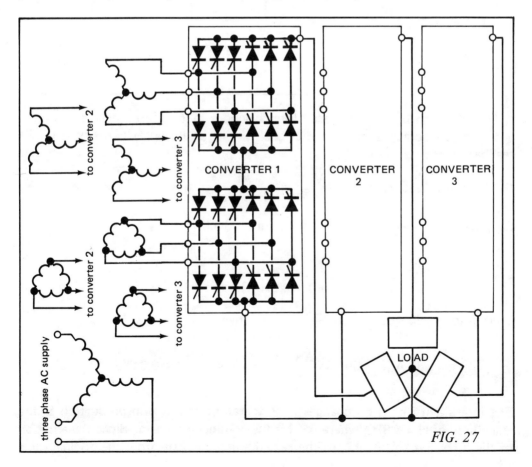

FIG. 27

5.5   THE USE OF MINOR NEGATIVE FEEDBACK LOOPS

Often, it is found that (minor) negative feedback loops have been incorporated around one or more elements in the forward path of a control system. There are several possible reasons why this should be the case, and these will be explained.

5.5.1   Negative Feedback to Linearise a Nonlinear Static Characteristic

Referring to Figure 28, suppose that the element with a gain B has significant nonlinearities in its static characteristic.

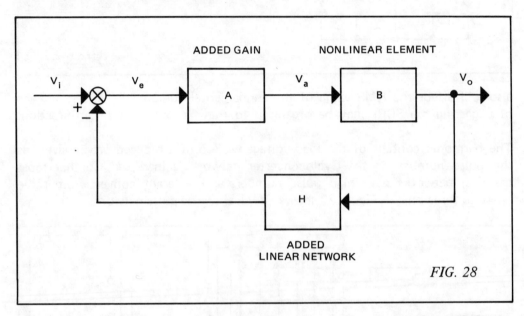

FIG. 28

It is possible to produce a closed loop having a much more linear static characteristic, by adding gain A to the forward path and a linear network H to the feedback path.

Overall steady state gain, $G \overset{\Delta}{=} \dfrac{V_o}{V_i} = \dfrac{AB}{1 + ABH}$

Suppose B changes by ΔB and, as a result, G changes by ΔG. It can then be

shown that $\dfrac{\Delta G}{G} = \dfrac{\Delta B}{B} \cdot \left(\dfrac{1}{1 + ABH} \right)$

Thus, if loop gain ABH = 9 and $\dfrac{\Delta B}{B}$ = 1%, then $\dfrac{\Delta G}{G}$ = 0.1%;

if loop gain ABH = 99 and $\dfrac{\Delta B}{B}$ = 1%, then $\dfrac{\Delta G}{G}$ = 0.01%.

The insensitivity of G to changes in B therefore improves in proportion to the magnitude of (1 + ABH), where ABH is the nominal loop gain. Since the addition of the other loop elements has changed the nominal gain from the original value of B to the new value of $\left(\dfrac{AB}{1 + ABH}\right)$, then, if the original level of gain is still required, it may be restored by adding, outside the loop, amplification of value $\left(\dfrac{1 + ABH}{A}\right) = \left(\dfrac{1}{A} + BH\right)$. If $A \gg 1$, the additional gain is approximately BH.

Negative feedback will have a linearising effect on all nonlinear properties except saturation. If physical considerations limit the excursion of the output V_o of element B, then no amount of feedback will change this limit: $\Delta G = 0$ whenever $\Delta B = 0$, irrespective of the magnitude ABH of the loop gain. However, the amount of feedback *will* determine the value of input signal V_i needed to drive the output V_o to its limit.

The shape of the closed loop static characteristic can be predicted as follows. Suppose that Figure 29 represents the static characteristic of element B.

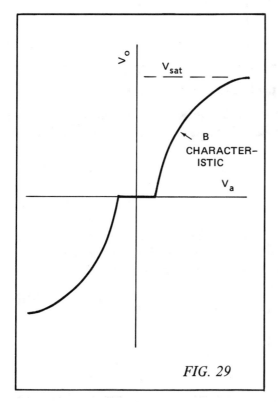

FIG. 29

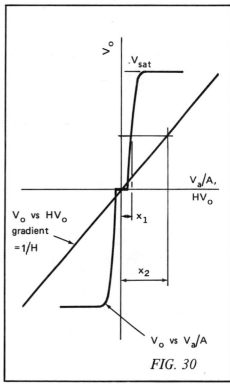

FIG. 30

This can be plotted to a base of $\dfrac{V_a}{A}$, for the chosen value of A, as shown in Figure 30. Superimposed on this is a plot of V_o vs HV_o, for the chosen value of H. Now $V_i = (HV_o + V_e) = \left(HV_o + \dfrac{V_a}{A}\right)$ so that, for any arbitrary value of V_o, the corresponding value of V_i may be determined by adding the two horizontal ordinates x_1 and x_2, as shown in Figure 30. For the given example, the final closed loop static characteristic would resemble Figure 31. Note that the output V_o still saturates at the original level V_{sat}.

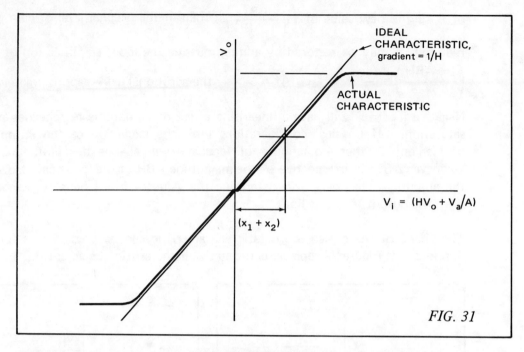

FIG. 31

5.5.2   Negative Feedback to Enhance the Speed of Response of an Element

Suppose that a linear element has a DC gain K and a simple lag time constant of T seconds, as shown in Figure 32. Then its unit step response will be given by

$$V_o(t) = K\left(1 - e^{-t/T}\right).$$

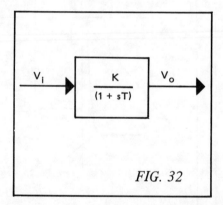

FIG. 32

If gain A and linear feedback H (both assumed to be frequency independent) are added, as shown in Figure 33, this closed loop configuration then will have a unit step response given by

$$V_o(t) = \frac{AK}{(1 + AHK)}\left(1 - e^{-t(1 + AHK)/T}\right).$$

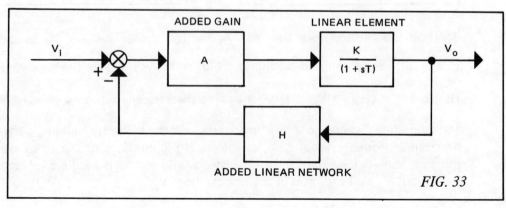

FIG. 33

Thus, the DC gain and the lag time constant have effectively been reduced by the factor $\left(\dfrac{A}{1+AHK}\right)$ and $\left(\dfrac{1}{1+AHK}\right)$ respectively, so that, if $AKH \gg 1$, a considerable reduction in time constant will result. The level of DC gain may be restored by adding amplification of value $\left(\dfrac{1+AHK}{A}\right)$ externally to the loop: if $A \gg 1$, the added gain will need to have a value of HK, approximately.

5.5.3 Negative Feedback to Change a Voltage Source into a Current Source

Consider the configuration of Figure 34, in which the output of amplifier A behaves as a voltage source and dropping resistor R has been added in series with the load.

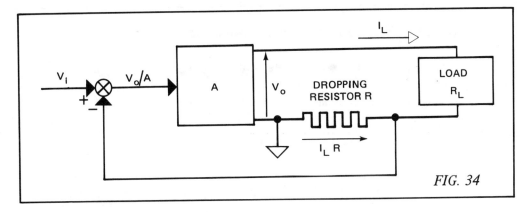

FIG. 34

Now $\quad V_o = A(V_i - I_L R) = I_L(R + R_L)$

$\qquad AV_i = I_L(R + R_L + AR)$

$\qquad \dfrac{I_L}{V_i} = \dfrac{A}{(1+A)R + R_L}$

If $A \gg 1$ and $AR \gg R_L$ then $\dfrac{I_L}{V_i} \cong \dfrac{1}{R}$.

The relationship between load current and loop input voltage therefore is a linear one, since $I_L \cong V_i/R$, and is virtually independent of possible variations in R_L and A. The loop therefore behaves as a voltage-controlled current source, as far as the load is concerned.

5.5.4 Negative Feedback to Improve Signal-to-Noise Ratio

Where parasitic noise occurs within a control element, its effect within the system often can be reduced by adding a high gain negative feedback loop around that element. Frequently, one or more of the added elements would be frequency dependent, so that it introduces filtering action at the noise frequencies: refer to Chapter 12 for details on filters.

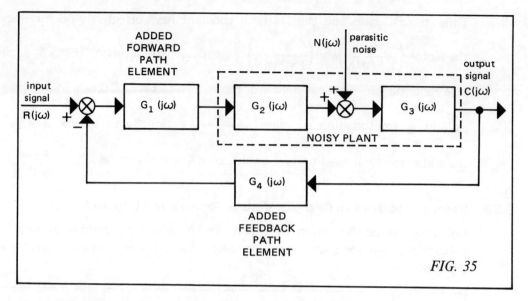

FIG. 35

Analysis of Figure 35 yields the following relationships:

Signal gain without the added elements, $\dfrac{C}{R}(j\omega) = G_2 G_3(j\omega)$

Noise gain without the added elements, $\dfrac{C}{N}(j\omega) = G_3(j\omega)$

Signal gain with the added elements, $\dfrac{C}{R}(j\omega) = \dfrac{G_1 G_2 G_3(j\omega)}{[1+G_1 G_2 G_3 G_4(j\omega)]}$

Noise gain with the added elements, $\dfrac{C}{N}(j\omega) = \dfrac{G_3(j\omega)}{[1+G_1 G_2 G_3 G_4(j\omega)]}$

The effect of the added elements has been to reduce the spectrum of the noise component of the output by the factor $[1 + G_1 G_2 G_3 G_4(j\omega)]$, whereas the spectrum of the signal component of the output has only been modified by the factor $G_1(j\omega)/[1 + G_1 G_2 G_3 G_4(j\omega)]$. The relationship between the two spectra will depend largely upon the choice of the $G_1(j\omega)$ frequency response.

5.6   SERVOMOTORS

Motors which are called specifically "servomotors" have been especially developed for use in position servosystems. Because of the nature of the market, they have been manufactured only in small power ratings so that, where higher power levels are required, it then is necessary to use conventional motors. The most common servomotors are the cage AC Servomotor, the DC Servomotor and the Stepper Motor; however, there are some less common alternative types of small motor used in servosystems.

5.6.1   AC Servomotor

This usually is a two phase cage rotor type of induction motor and it is operated as indicated in Figure 36.

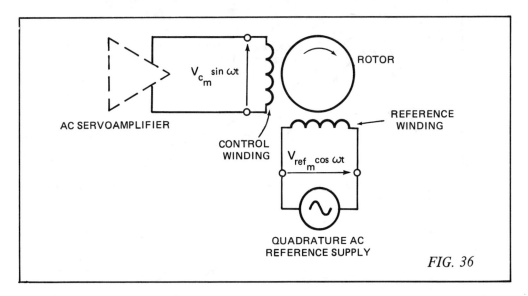

FIG. 36

The control winding is supplied with an AC voltage of varying magnitude V_c, delivered by an AC servoamplifier. The reference winding is supplied with a quadrature AC voltage of fixed magnitude V_{ref}, delivered by an AC power source. Typically, the frequency is 50, 60 or 400 Hz and synchronous speed will be proportional to the frequency chosen. The voltage levels will be such that $V_c \leqslant V_{ref}$.

Figure 37 is a phasor diagram of the voltages, on which V_{ref} has been resolved into two components: one equal in value to $|V_c|$ and which, when taken in combination with V_c, will result in polyphase action; the other is equal to $(V_{ref} - |V_c|)$ and will result in single phase action.

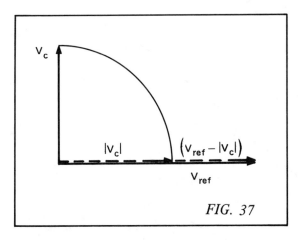

FIG. 37

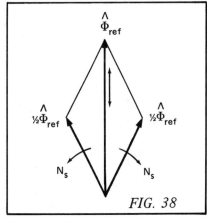

FIG. 38

When single phasing ($V_c = 0$), the motor flux Φ_{ref} is a pulsating one, aligned along an axis stationary in space. Such a flux may be resolved into two components, constant in magnitude and equal to half the peak value of Φ_{ref} rotating in opposite directions at synchronous speed, as indicated in Figure 38. Each component of flux is responsible for a polyphase type of action and these two actions, which will act in opposition to one another, can be combined graphically, as shown in Figure 39 for a conventional type of induction motor.

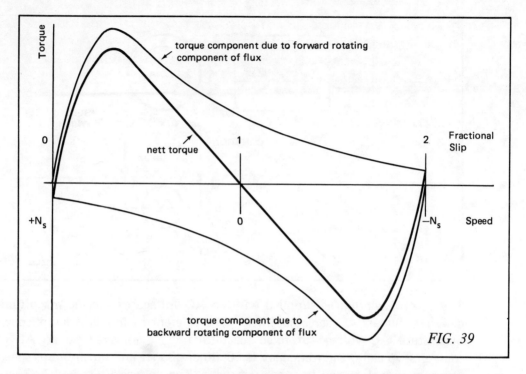

FIG. 39

In the AC servomotor, the rotor circuit is designed to have an abnormally high resistance, by using high resistivity material for the cage bars and/or end rings. The effect of this is to "stretch" each component torque curve horizontally, as shown in Figure 40.

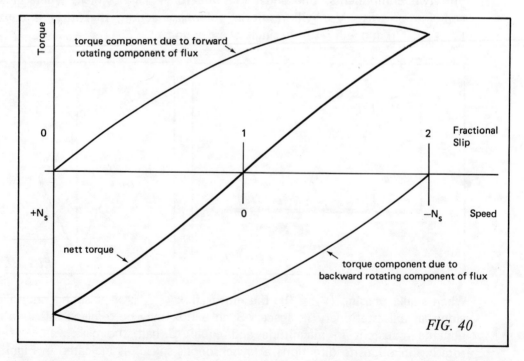

FIG. 40

The single phasing torque now is a braking torque, because the direction (sign) of the torque always is in opposition to the direction of the motion (sign of the velocity).

When $V_c > 0$, single phase and polyphase action occur simultaneously, in proportions depending upon the value of V_c: when V_c is small, single phase action predominates; when V_c is large, polyphase action predominates. This can be summarised graphically by the family of characteristics shown in Figure 41.

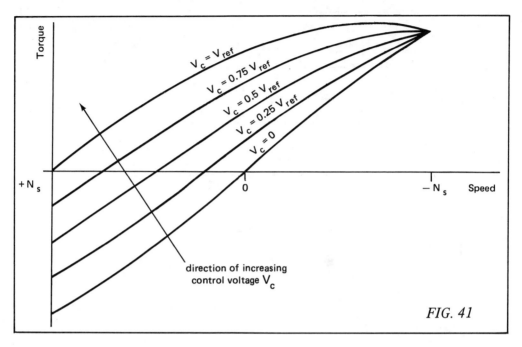

FIG. 41

Manufacturers normally publish one quadrant of this graph, for torque and speed both positive. The set of characteristics which results may be idealised by a set of parallel straight lines, equally spaced for equal increments in V_c, as shown in Figure 42.

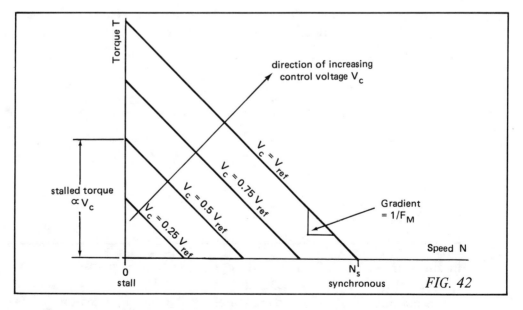

FIG. 42

Such a set of characteristics may be decomposed graphically as shown in Figure 43.

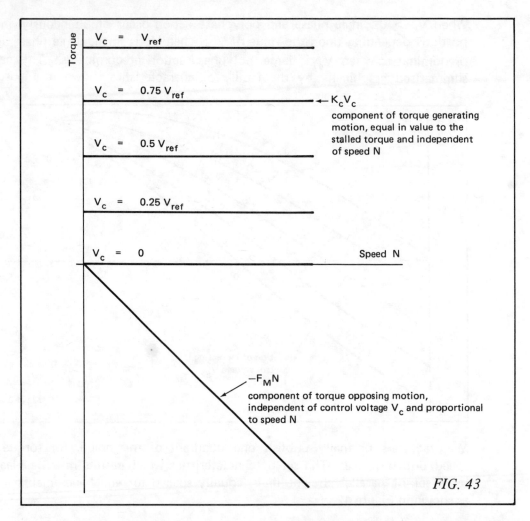

FIG. 43

This linearised representation enables the (idealised) steady state characteristic of the motor to be modelled by the block diagram representation of Figure 44.

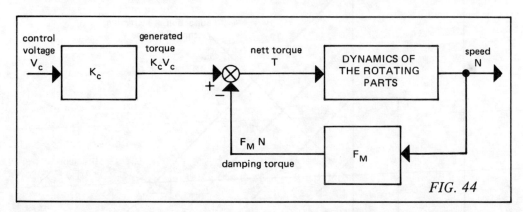

FIG. 44

In the context of the use of the motor in position servosystems, the torque component $\left(F_M N\right)$ often is called a "damping torque". If it is valid to regard F_M as constant in value, the damping effect inherent in the motor characteristic then also is constant. A more precise (small signal) equivalent block diagram may be created by replacing K_c by $\partial T / \partial V_c$ and F_M by $\partial T / \partial N$, in Figure 44.

The advantage of the AC servomotor is the ruggedness which results from the absence of electrical contacts in motion, which implies high reliability and maintainability. The disadvantages are:

- low efficiency;

- high heat dissipation, which means that heat sinking often is necessary in order to keep the case temperature down;

- the need for an AC quadrature power supply

These motors are made in sizes up to approximately 1kW and are used mainly in instrument servosystems.

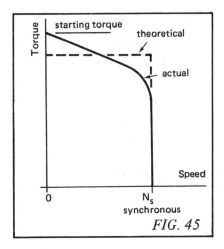

FIG. 45

Another type of small AC motor which sometimes is used in control systems is the "Hysteresis Motor", which typically is used as a constant speed source, when energised from a constant frequency supply. This is a small synchronous motor with good starting characteristics. The stator has a two phase winding which is excited conventionally. The rotor is a cylinder of magnetic material of the type normally used for permanent magnets. The stator field rotates at synchronous speed, due to pure polyphase action, and this induces a similar field in the rotor, when it is stationary. However, because of hysteresis effects, the rotor field lags behind the stator field and this lag causes a torque to be generated: this torque accelerates the rotor and load in the same direction as the field rotation. Theoretically, this situation is sustained at all speeds up to synchronous speed, which is the steady state speed of the motor. In practice, the starting torque is somewhat enhanced by induction motor action. Figure 45 shows a typical torque vs speed characteristic.

5.6.2 DC Servomotors

These motors are constructed like a conventional DC motor, but in miniature and with a high length/diameter ratio for the armature, in order to minimise the polar moment of inertia. The field may be wound, in which case it may be split or centre-tapped. Alternatively, the field system may be established by permanent magnets (often ferrites), in which case the motor often is called a "PM Motor" and only armature control of such a motor is possible. The armature and commutator may be a heavy-duty double-sided printed circuit, and such a motor often is called a "PC Motor": the low armature mass offsets the low length/diameter ratio, to keep the polar moment of inertia low in value.

When operated in a servosystem, the motor may be either field controlled or armature controlled, and the armature may be fed from either a voltage source or a current source. Each combination yields a different family of torque vs speed characteristics.

Field control of the motor gives rise to the following comments:

• it is only possible with wound field motors;

• the power rating of the field control amplifier need only match the (low) power requirements of the field;

• the field time constant will be relevant to the dynamic response of the motor;

• the magnetisation characteristic will be relevant to the linearity of the behaviour.

Armature control gives rise to the following comments:

• the field system can be wound or permanent magnet;

• the power rating of the armature control amplifier must match the (relatively high) power requirements of the armature;

• the field time constant and magnetisation characteristic are not relevant to the system dynamic performance.

When the armature is supplied from a voltage source, it often is necessary to incorporate a current limit facility within this source. This is often because damagingly high armature currents may otherwise circulate whenever the back-emf is significantly different in value from the terminal voltage. The current limit circuit may incorporate a time delay, enabling high transient armature currents to circulate for short time durations.

In the analysis which follows, Φ represents magnetic flux, T represents torque and N represents shaft speed; the Ks are constants of proportionality and a linear magnetisation characteristic is assumed.

Field Control, Constant Armature Voltage Supply

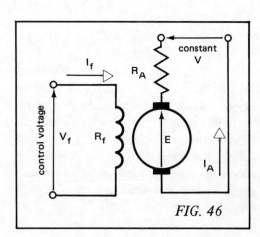

FIG. 46

Figure 46 represents this type of configuration.

$$\Phi = K_\Phi I_f = K_\Phi \frac{V_f}{R_f}$$

$$T = K_T \, \Phi \, I_A$$

$$= K_T K_\Phi \frac{V_f}{R_f} \cdot \frac{(V - E)}{R_A}$$

$$E = \frac{N\Phi}{K_N} = \frac{N K_\Phi V_f}{K_N R_f}$$

$$T = \frac{K_T K_\Phi V_f}{R_f R_A} \left(V - N \frac{K_\Phi V_f}{K_N R_f} \right) = K_1 V_f - K_2 N V_f^2$$

Thus, the stalled torque is proportional to V_f and the damping torque is proportional to V_f^2 (so that the damping effect is variable with control signal level), as well as speed N. The characteristic is represented in Figure 47.

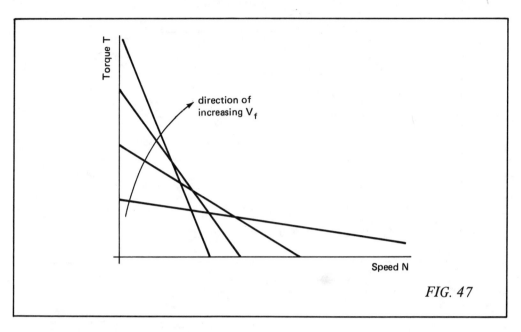

FIG. 47

Field Control, Constant Armature Current Supply

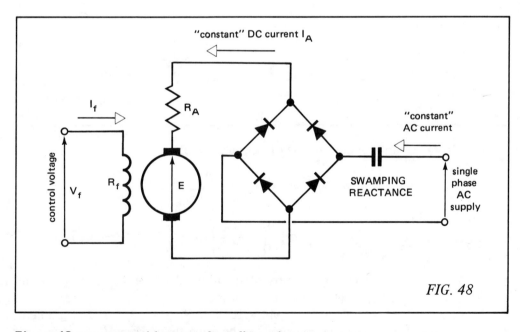

FIG. 48

Figure 48 represents this type of configuration.

$$\Phi = K_\Phi I_f = K_\Phi \frac{V_f}{R_f} \qquad T = K_T \Phi I_A = K_T K_\Phi \frac{V_f}{R_f} I_A = K_3 V_f$$

Thus, the torque is proportional to V_f and always is independent of speed N. The damping effect is zero. The resulting characteristic is shown in Figure 49.

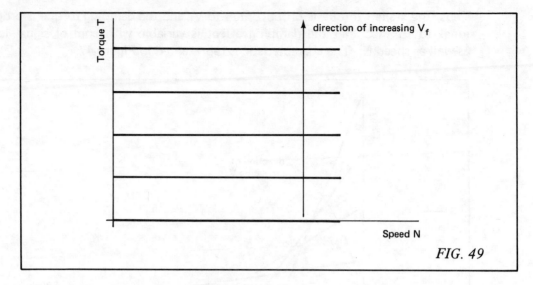

FIG. 49

Armature Voltage Control, Constant Excitation

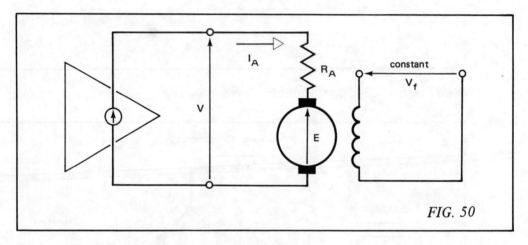

FIG. 50

Figure 50 represents this type of configuration.

$$E = \frac{N\Phi}{K_N} \qquad T = K_T \, \Phi \, I_A = K_T \, \Phi \, \frac{(V - E)}{R_A}$$

$$= K_T \, \Phi \left(\frac{V}{R_A} - \frac{N\Phi}{K_N R_A} \right) = K_4 \, V - K_5 \, N$$

The stalled torque now is proportional to V and the damping torque is proportional to speed N alone, so that the damping effect is constant. The torque vs speed characteristic now will resemble Figure 42, but the gradient will be $- K_5$ and the control voltage will be the armature voltage V.

Armature Current Control, Constant Excitation

Figure 51 represents this type of configuration.

$$T = K_T \, \Phi \, I_A = K_6 I_A$$

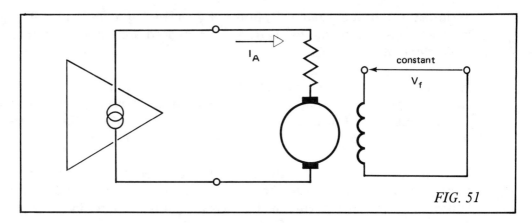

FIG. 51

The torque is proportional to I_A and always is independent of speed N. The torque vs speed characteristic will resemble Figure 49, except that the control signal now will be I_A. The damping effect is zero.

Further Comments on DC Servomotors

The advantages with DC servomotors are that they employ DC control signals and that a range of alternative torque vs speed characteristics is available, depending upon the mode of control. The disadvantages accrue from the use of a commutator: reliability and maintainability will be low and there may be problems arising from radio frequency interference generated by brush arcing.

In high power servosystems, the servomotors (AC or DC) may be used as input drives to hydraulic servovalves. In many cases, the angular travel may be extremely small (the motor may be driving against restraining springs), so that the primary function of the motor is to develop torque rather than achieve significant motion: the motor in this context generally is called a "Torque Motor". Simpler types of torque motor also are constructed, using DC excited coils and ferrous magnetic circuits incorporating permanent magnets: in those versions in which the coil moves, electrical connection to the coil can be by means of flying lead, because of the limited angular travel involved.

5.6.3 Stepper Motors

Stepper motors have been used principally for drives in computer peripherals: floppy disc head positioners, paper tape drives, incremental magnetic tape drives, printer drives, card reader drives, etc. Mostly, they have been small in physical size but developing a high torque/inertia ratio and a fast response. They also have been used as torque motors for hydraulic servovalves in high power servosystems.

More recently, higher power stepper motors have been developed for industrial applications, such as machine tools, industrial robots, automatic draughting machines, robot cameras, etc.

A stepper motor has a stator containing a number of poles carrying field windings, together with a rotor which, in most cases, is a permanent magnet or which is slotted and made from soft iron.   By energising the stator windings in sequence, the axis of the magnetic field is stepped around and the rotor axis tracks this motion.

The drive circuits normally accept a train of pulses, each pulse representing one quantum step in shaft angle, together with a signal indicating the direction of motion required.   The circuits use this information to establish a pattern of voltages, which then is applied appropriately to the stator windings.

These motors are unique in the sense that the control signals determine the rotor position, as opposed to the rotor speed, so that the motors can be used in position servosystems without the necessity for position feedback transducers. The motors are relatively inefficient and often require extensive heat sinking to remove heat.

The advantages of stepper motors, when contrasted with DC servomotors, are as follows:

- steppers do not require linear power amplifiers;

- feedback transducers are optional;

- steppers can respond directly to digital control data;

- steppers exhibit extremely short starting and stopping times;

- steppers have a very wide speed range.

The disadvantages of the stepper motor are as follows:

- it is the most difficult of all motor types to analyse and specify;

- it has low power efficiency, associated with high internal heat generation;

- it displays a tendency to oscillate about the equilibrium point.

Figure 52 shows the principles of construction of three different types of stepper motor.

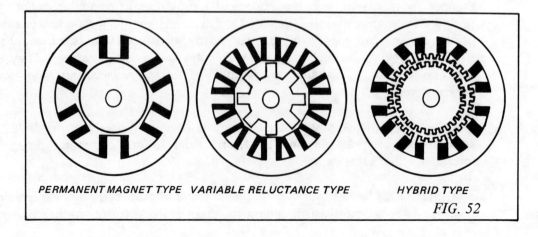

PERMANENT MAGNET TYPE   VARIABLE RELUCTANCE TYPE   HYBRID TYPE

FIG. 52

With the Permanent Magnet type of stepper motor, the rotor is a permanent magnet. The rotor aligns its magnetic axis with the axis of the magnetic field generated by the DC current being passed through the coils on the stator poles. When the coils are energised in sequence, the rotor steps around to track the motion of the stator field. The rotor is rather large, in order that an adequate field can be developed: this gives rise to a relatively high polar moment of inertia and a low maximum stepping rate (typically 300 to 400 steps/second). Because of the stator construction, the angular step size will be large: typically 30° or 60°. Damping is inherent, due to generator action which induces emfs in the stator coils whenever the rotor tends to oscillate. This type of stepper exhibits a high holding torque even without sustained stator energisation, and the stepping torque is proportional to the stator current.

With the Variable Reluctance type of stepper motor, the rotor is made from unmagnetised soft iron and is cylindrical but with slots. Changes in rotor position vary the reluctance of the flux path between stator poles having opposite polarities. The rotor always moves to a radial alignment of minimum reluctance, which depends upon which particular stator windings happen to be energised. The rotor can be small and light, and the resulting low polar moment of inertia yields a high maximum stepping rate (typically 700 to 800 steps/second) and fast starting and stopping. Because of the rotor construction, the angular step size will be smaller than with the permanent magnet type: typically 15°. The damping effect is negligible, due to the absence of any generator action. The variable reluctance type exhibits no holding torque when the stator is de-energised, so that a minimum stator energisation normally would be required at standstill. The stepping torque is proportional to the square of the stator current.

The Hybrid type of stepper motor has a slotted soft iron rotor but includes a permanent magnet in its magnetic circuit: usually the magnet forms part of the rotor construction. Hybrid stepper motors generally have a high stepping torque, small step size (typically 0.5° to 15°), high polar moment of inertia, and a relatively low maximum stepping rate (typically 150 to 250 steps/second).

Some speed controllers for stepper motors are described in Section 8.4.3, whilst further discussion on the use of steppers for position control and speed control is contained in Sections 13.4.3 and 13.5.3, respectively.

5.7   CONVENTIONAL MOTORS

Where an electrical drive having a power rating in excess of (say) 1 kW is required, it will be necessary to use conventional electric motors. It may be necessary to incorporate clutches and/or brakes in order to obtain the correct type of drive: for example, when a drive must develop high holding forces/torques when stationary. Before deciding upon an electric drive, it is advisable to consider the relative merits of alternative hydraulic or pneumatic drives, and a guide to this is presented in Section 6.6.1.

In the case of an AC motor, a conventional polyphase induction motor normally would be used. In order that it can be controlled over a very wide speed range, special control hardware is necessary.

In the past, DC speed control systems have been preferred to AC speed control systems, because of the higher initial costs of the latter (although AC motors are cheaper than corresponding DC motors). However, the costs of the AC control electronics have dropped to such an extent that both types of system now may be comparable, especially when the improved reliability and maintainability of induction motors, in contrast to commutator-type motors, are taken into consideration.

5.7.1   DC Drives

DC motors can match closely the requirements of the application, because the speed vs torque relationship can be manipulated to almost any useful form, for both motoring and regeneration in either direction of rotation. AC motors stall at torque loads above about twice their rating and cannot start loads requiring above about 150% of rated torque; on the other hand, DC motors often are used to deliver momentarily three or more times their rated torque. In emergency situations, DC motors can deliver over five times rated torque without stalling, assuming that the power supply can cope.

Dynamic braking (with which the motor-load energy is fed to a high dissipation resistor) or regenerative braking (with which the motor-load energy is fed back into the power supply) can be obtained easily with DC motors in applications requiring rapid stopping, thus eliminating the need for, or reducing the size of, a mechanical brake.

DC motor speed can be controlled down to zero, immediately followed by acceleration in the opposite direction, often without switching the power circuit. Because of their high ratio of torque to inertia, DC motors respond relatively quickly to changes in control signal. Refer to Section 8.4.1 for a discussion on general purpose speed controllers for DC motors.

DC motors may be classified according to the method of connection of the field windings: separately excited, shunt excited, series excited, and compound excited, the last three types being shown in Figure 53.

Usually, separately excited motors are operated in the same types of configuration as are used with DC servomotors, except that the power rating of the control hardware must be appropriate to the motor size: generally, the field windings will be neither split nor centre-tapped, so that the amplifier power output stage must be chosen accordingly, in the case of field control configurations.

Shunt Motors

Shunt excited DC motors are suitable for applications where approximately constant speed is required at all values of load torque. Most shunt motors are operated from controlled voltage sources and, therefore, do not require special starting equipment. To reverse the direction of rotation, either the armature supply or the field supply must be reversed, so that the equivalent separately excited mode of operation is preferable for this situation.

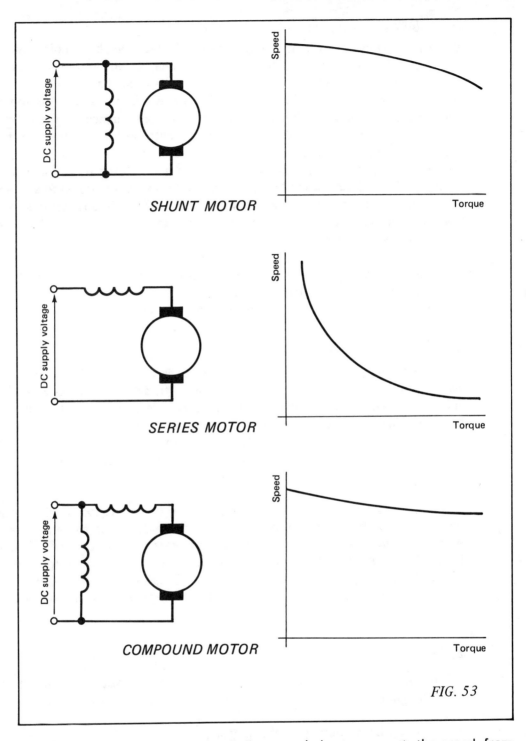

FIG. 53

A series connected stabilising winding can help to prevent the speed from increasing as the torque is increased, at low supply voltage levels, when armature reaction has a pronounced effect. This winding is disadvantageous in reversing applications, because its sense relative to that of the shunt winding must be reversed when the armature voltage is reversed. Where rapid reversing is required, the stabilising winding is omitted and the motor must be designed for satisfactory operation without it.

Series Motors

With series excited motors, the magnetic flux is established by windings which are electrically in series with, and thus carry the same current as, the armature. The current is a maximum at standstill, because then the back-emf is zero: the excitation therefore is a maximum and generates a large torque. As the motor speed builds up and the current reduces as a consequence of the increase in back-emf, the magnetic flux also diminishes. With no load on the motor shaft, the motor theoretically can run away, because of the nature of the speed vs torque characteristic. In small motors, brush and bearing friction and windage torque provide sufficient load to hold the steady state speed down to a safe value. However, high power series motors should not be used in applications in which the load torque can drop to very low levels: series motors find their greatest use in traction applications.

Split series motors are similar to straight series motors, except that they have two field systems operating in an opposing sense. These motors can be reversed readily, by switching the supply voltage from one field to the other.

Compound Motors

The disadvantage of the overspeeding of series motors at light loads can be avoided by using a compound excited motor: these motors possess both shunt and series fields. At low load levels, there is little current flowing through the series winding, so that the speed is determined largely by the shunt winding. At higher load levels, the speed depends upon the combined effects of the two windings, so that the speed reduction with increasing torque is similar to that for a series motor.

Like series motors, compound motors exhibit high starting torque. However, the polarisation of both the shunt and the series fields, or of the armature, must be switched in order to reverse the direction of rotation. Because of the complexity of the circuits needed to control the reversal of compound motors, only large bidirectional motors of this type are built. Occasionally, large blower and fan motors are slightly compounded, in order to improve their starting characteristics.

5.7.2   AC Drives

AC drives provide accurate speed control, synchronisation of multiple loads, and low maintenance costs. The factors favouring AC drives are:

- rugged, low inertia, reliable motors;
- very low maintenance requirement;
- insensitivity to severe environments;
- safe, convenient, high speed operation;
- 0.5 to 0.25% speed control accuracy with modest cost;
- digital speed control accuracy to 0.001%, with increased cost;

- ability to phaselock several motors to the same AC supply;

- multi motor systems with regeneration are possible.

Most modern variable speed AC motor drive systems employ a variable frequency AC supply, using one of the types of frequency converter described in Section 5.4.5. For motors in the power range from (say) 5 to 150 kW, pulse-width modulated inverters are used: these take DC power, generated from the AC mains by a converter, and invert it to adjustable-frequency AC power for a cage induction motor. Drives may be reversible and may incorporate regenerative braking.

For motors in the power range from (say) 500 kW to 10MW, cycloconverters often are used. Drives may be reversible and may incorporate regenerative braking. Typically, a dual cycloconverter is used for each of the three stator phases, with the frequency for continuous operation limited to the range from 0 to 20 Hz.

Refer to Section 8.4.2 for a discussion on general purpose speed controllers for AC motors.

6

HYDRAULIC AND PNEUMATIC AMPLIFIERS AND FINAL CONTROL ELEMENTS

6.1   SINGLE—STAGE FLUID AMPLIFIERS

Fluid pressure or fluid flowrate are the output signal from a fluid amplifier. However, the input signal may be a mechanical displacement, voltage, current or fluid pressure. Fluid amplifiers may be classified as follows:

Liquid amplifiers (usually using hydraulic oil)

- jet pipe
- flapper-nozzle
- spool valve
- Coanda (rarely used).

Gas amplifiers (usually pneumatic)

- flapper-nozzle
- Coanda.

6.1.1   Liquid Amplifiers

Jet Pipe Amplifier

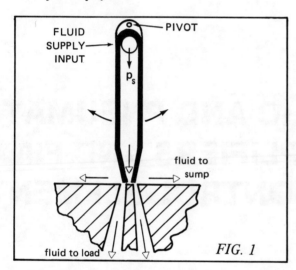

FLUID SUPPLY INPUT — PIVOT

p_s

fluid to sump

fluid to load

FIG. 1

The Jet Pipe amplifier employs a displaceable jet pipe from which high pressure oil is projected at two orifices, to achieve a push-pull type of output. When the pipe is central, the two output pressures will be the same; when the pipe is displaced, one output pressure increases whilst the other diminishes. The magnitudes of the pressures will depend upon the fluid resistance of the load. The internal arrangement of the amplifier is indicated symbolically in Figure 1.

The principal application of the jet pipe amplifier is as a preamplifier stage in a two-stage hydraulic servoamplifier.

Flapper-Nozzle Amplifier

The internal arrangement of a Flapper-Nozzle amplifier is shown in Figure 2. The nozzle chamber includes a fixed restriction R and a variable orifice O, the variation being effected by the displacement of the flapper plate by the input signals. When the orifice is fully closed by the flapper, the internal back-pressure (and hence the output pressure p_o) will be equal to the supply pressure p_s; when the orifice is fully open (maximum flapper displacement), the back-pressure will have collapsed to a value approaching sump pressure. The range of flapper displacement, as measured at the nozzle, to achieve the full excursion of output pressure is very small: typically, a displacement of less than 0.01 mm will produce a 5% change in output pressure.

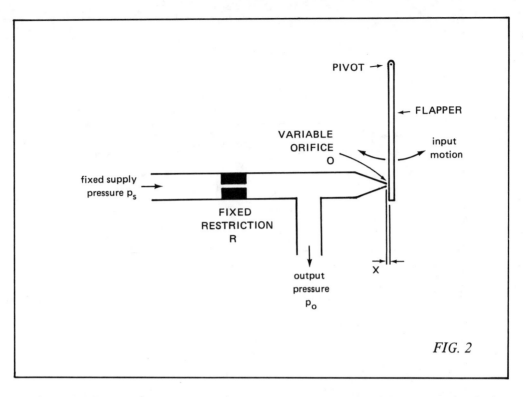

PIVOT

FLAPPER

input motion

VARIABLE ORIFICE O

fixed supply pressure p_s

FIXED RESTRICTION R

output pressure p_o

X

FIG. 2

For flapper displacements intermediate between the ends of the range, the device may be visualised as a fluid potential-divider, with an electrical equivalent circuit as shown in Figure 3.

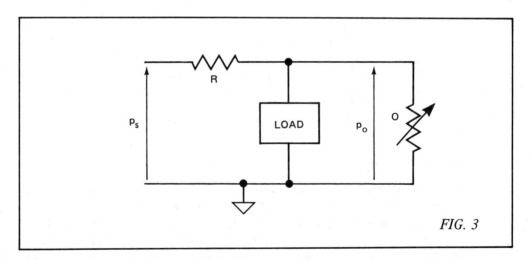

R

p_s

LOAD

p_o

O

FIG. 3

In this analog, the fluid resistances are nonlinear, because of the square law relating pressure to flow. A plot of output pressure p_o versus flapper displacement x will be highly nonlinear but this characteristic can be linearised by the appropriate application of linear negative feedback. The principal application of the flapper-nozzle amplifier is as a preamplifier stage in a two-stage hydraulic servoamplifier.

Where a push-pull type of output is required using flapper-nozzle amplifiers, these may be operated in pairs, arranged as indicated by Figure 4.

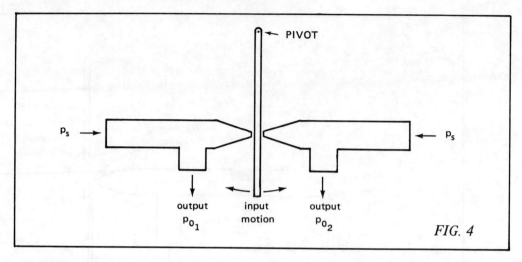

FIG. 4

Spool Valve

Figure 5 shows symbolically the principle of the spool valve, driving a typical load.

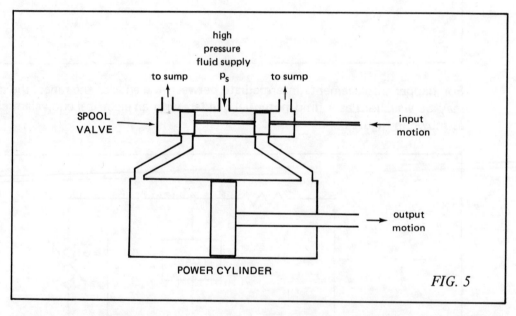

FIG. 5

Axial displacement of the spool results in a variation in the areas through which oil flows through the output ports, so that the output ports behave as variable orifices. In the example shown, displacement of the spool to the left of its central (null) position will cause supply oil to flow into the left hand side of the power cylinder: this will drive the power piston to the right and oil from the right hand side of the power cylinder will be exhausted to the sump via the right hand output port of the spool valve. Displacement of the spool to the right will similarly cause the piston to be driven to the left.

Typically, the excursion range of the spool will be very small, in the order of 1 – 2 mm overall. Because of the square law relationship for orifices, the load flow versus load pressure characteristic for the spool valve is highly nonlinear, as exemplified by Figure 6.

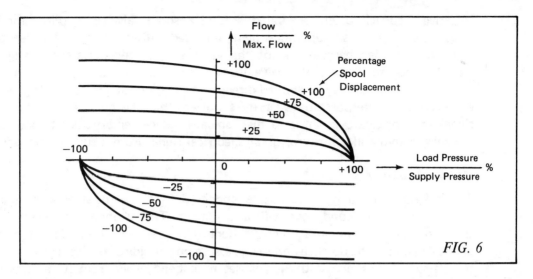

FIG. 6

The number of spool "lands" and the corresponding number of input and output ports will vary, depending upon the user's requirements. Where the width of the land is greater than that of the output port, this is known as "overlap" and is equivalent to class C operation of an electronic push-pull amplifier: this results in a deadspace in the output characteristic and enables the load to be locked. Where the width of the land is less than that of the output port, this is known as "underlap" and is equivalent to class AB operation: this gives continuity to the characteristic but prevents locking from being achieved. Zero lap, equivalent to class B operation, cannot be achieved precisely because of the fine machining tolerances which would be required. The different flow characteristics, for a constant load pressure differential, are shown in Figure 7.

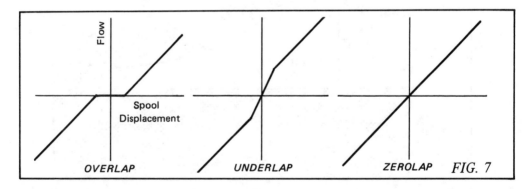

FIG. 7

Spool valves may be actuated by hydraulic pressure, controlled by a preamplifier stage, which is applied to the end of the spool: the end becomes a piston within an input cylinder. Alternatively, the spool may be displaced either mechanically, through a suitable linkage arrangement, or electrically: in the latter case, a servomotor (called a "torque motor" in this application, where motion is miniscule) would be suitably geared to the spool, so as to have its rotary motion converted to rectilinear motion. Another electrical alternative is the "force motor", which is a solenoid and ferrous armature combination which develops a force to establish linear displacement. Occasionally, the spool is "loaded" with compression springs, in order to provide it with the required displacement versus force characteristic.

Negative feedback often is applied around a spool valve, with pilot amplifier stages and/or the load sometimes being included within the loop. The feedback will linearise the characteristic of the valve and, if appropriately configured, may be used to convert the valve from a flow source into a pressure source. The feedback signal may be applied directly to the spool or sometimes to a ported sleeve which is interposed between the spool and the valve cylinder. The feedback signal may originate as either a mechanical displacement, transmitted through linkages, a hydraulic pressure, or an electrical signal from a suitable transducer.

Coanda Amplifier

A jet of fluid emerging from a nozzle tends to deflect towards an adjacent surface and, under certain conditions, will attach to it. This phenomenon is known as the "Coanda" or "wall attachment" effect. The presence of an adjacent surface creates an area of turbulence and low pressure on one side of the jet. The imbalance of pressure forces across the jet causes it to bend away from its free flowing direction.

Although the Coanda effect is well known in pneumatic devices, rarely is it used when the working substance is a liquid. However, Figure 8 shows a novel use of the Coanda effect for liquid level control.

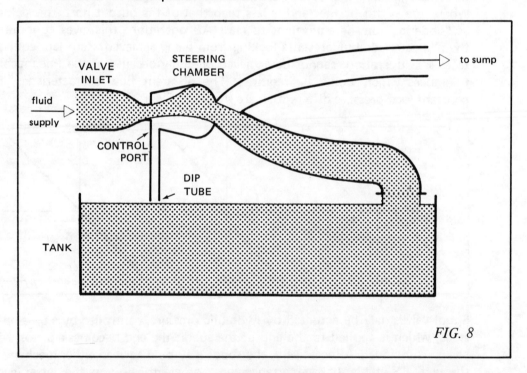

FIG. 8

Liquid entering the valve is formed into a jet by a nozzle at the valve inlet. This jet passes by the control port and through a steering chamber, at the end of which are two outlets. The pressure developed in the control port acts on one side of the jet. When the level falls below the end of the dip tube, the valve diverts liquid to the tank. When the level reaches the dip tube, liquid is diverted to a tank by-pass line. The entire flow can be diverted to one outlet, although the outlet may be at a higher pressure than that of the other.

6.1.2 Gas Amplifiers

Flapper-Nozzle Amplifier

Most pneumatic amplifiers employ the flapper-nozzle principle. This is because compressed air is not lubricating (unless oil mist is injected), it does not have the same heat-removing capability as oil, and it tends to include small particles of foreign matter, all of which render spool valves unsuitable for pneumatic service: the flapper-nozzle has a high tolerance to these disadvantages.

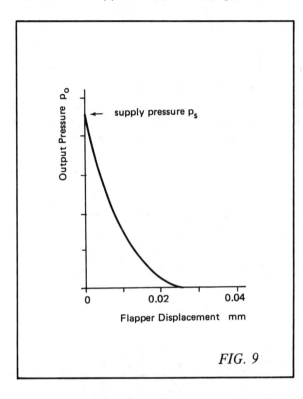

FIG. 9

Figure 1 and the description in Section 6.1.1 also apply when compressed air is the operating medium, except that the air now exhausts to atmosphere (creating a characteristic hissing noise) and that the flapper excursion is now typically in the order of less than 0.1 mm. Figure 9 shows a typical pressure vs displacement characteristic for a pneumatic flapper-nozzle amplifier.

Because of its high sensitivity, this type of amplifier may be regarded as the pneumatic equivalent of the electronic operational amplifier and, as a result, it is used in a number of analog computing types of application.

Coanda Amplifier

The "Coanda effect" has been described in Section 6.1.1, and this description also applies in pneumatic applications. Figure 10 represents a cross-section through a typical fluidic coanda amplifier.

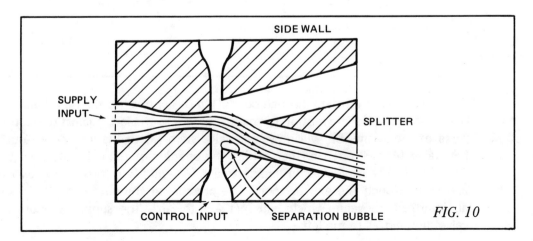

FIG. 10

The amplifier consists essentially of a number of carefully designed passages through which fluid may flow. If the velocity of the fluid emerging from the nozzle is such that a critical value of Reynolds number is exceeded, the stream will attach to one wall, due to the Coanda effect, and exit via one output port. If a jet of fluid now is injected into the appropriate control port, the pressure in the separation bubble will rise and the main jet will flip over and attach to the other wall. It is found that the energy required to be injected in the control port is considerably less than the main jet energy, and hence amplification has been achieved.

Air Relay

The Air Relay is the pneumatic equivalent to the electronic unity follower power amplifier. Normally, it has a pressure gain of approximately unity but the output flowrate may be many times the input flowrate which the amplifier draws. The relay is particularly suitable as the output stage of a multistage pneumatic amplifier. Figure 11 shows a cross-section through one type of air relay.

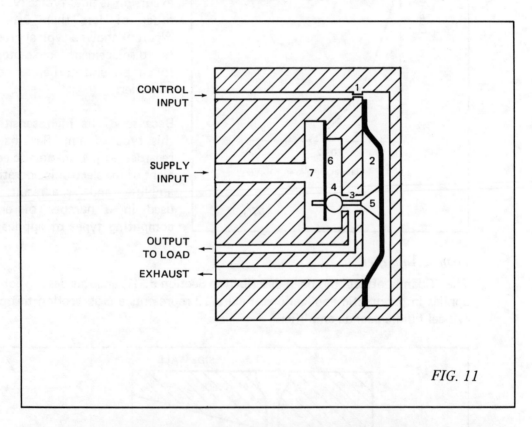

FIG. 11

The input pressure enters through port (1) and is applied to the right hand face of the diaphragm (2). The motion of the diaphragm to the left, against the restraining force of the spring (6), will move the valve stem (3) to the left. As a result, the ball valve (4) will open further, whilst the opening of the exhaust valve (5) will be reduced. The supply air in compartment (7) will bleed through the two valves and exit through the exhaust port. The pressure at the output port will assume an intermediate value which will increase towards the supply pressure as the valve stem moves to the left.

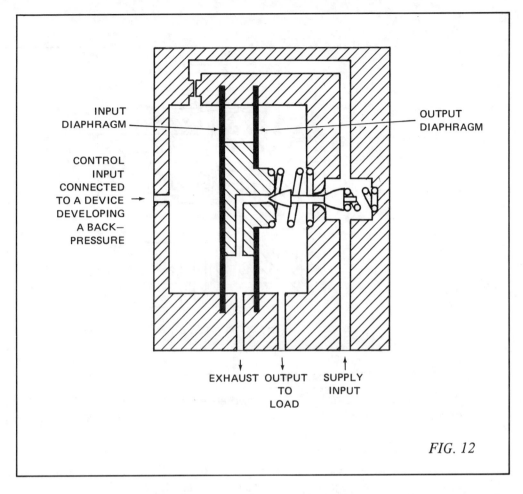

INPUT
DIAPHRAGM

OUTPUT
DIAPHRAGM

CONTROL
INPUT
CONNECTED
TO A DEVICE →
DEVELOPING
A BACK—
PRESSURE

EXHAUST OUTPUT SUPPLY
TO INPUT
LOAD

FIG. 12

A more complex version, which achieves a more precise equality between the input and output pressures, is shown in Figure 12. With this type, the output pressure is applied to a second diaphragm so that, in the steady state, the forces developed on the two diaphragms will balance. If these two diaphragms present the same value of effective surface area, the output pressure will match accurately the input pressure.

6.2 MULTI—STAGE FLUID AMPLIFIERS WITH FEEDBACK

In general, the disadvantages with single-stage fluid amplifiers will be as follows:

- the characteristics are highly nonlinear;
- although the output pressure range may be adequate, the flowrate limit may be far too small for the load;
- the dynamic behaviour may be too slow;
- the accuracy may be inadequate.

A considerable improvement can be effected using multistage amplifiers with linear negative feedback. Some techniques were discussed in Section 6.1.1. By multistaging hydraulic valves, a power gain in excess of 10^5 typically can be achieved, with excellent steady state and dynamic performance.

6.2.1 Servovalves

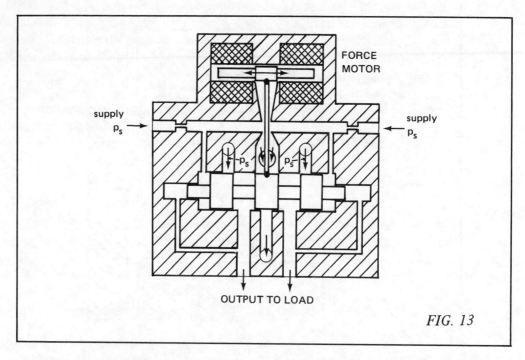

FIG. 13

Figure 13 is an example of a solenoid-armature force motor actuating the flapper of a push-pull pair of flapper-nozzle amplifiers which in turn drive, by means of their output pressures, the spool of a spool valve. Feedback from the spool displacement to the flapper plate is provided by the feedback leaf spring and hydraulic pressure feedback from the spool valve output is applied to the spool, so that this three-stage amplifier has two feedback paths.

6.2.2 Pneumatic Amplifiers

Figure 14 is an example of a two-stage pneumatic amplifier.

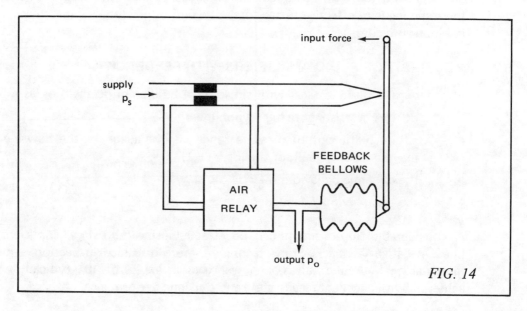

FIG. 14

The flapper plate will assume a quiescent position such that the input force is balanced by the feedback force arising from the output pressure within the feedback bellows. Thus, the output pressure will be proportional to the input force, irrespective of nonlinearities within the amplifier stages. The outflow which can be delivered to the load is much greater than that which the flapper-nozzle amplifier could supply.

The system of Figure 14 also may be used as a pneumatic displacement transducer since, taking into account the spring rate of the feedback bellows, a displacement balance also will exist at the flapper plate, in the steady state.

6.3   HYDRAULIC PUMPS

Hydraulic Pumps usually are employed to provide the flow in high pressure hydraulic power supplies, when normally they would be driven at constant speed, typically by an induction motor. However, gear and vane pumps also may be used as variable flowrate sources in process pipelines and, in this type of application, they typically would be driven by variable-speed electric motors: there would be an almost linear relationship between flowrate and shaft speed. Such pumps often are referred to as "positive displacement pumps".

There also is a range of axial and rotary piston pumps which typically would be used to drive piston motors: such a pump-motor combination can be regarded as the hydraulic equivalent to the electrical Ward-Leonard system. With these pumps, there is an almost linear relationship between outflow rate and the input signal, with the pump shaft being driven at constant speed typically by an induction motor. The input signal is in the form of a displacement, and this may be derived from a mechanical linkage, an electrical torque motor, or a pneumatic or hydraulic actuator.

6.3.1   Gear Pumps

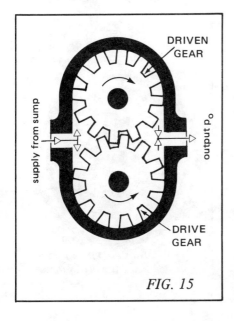

FIG. 15

Figure 15 shows a cross-section through a simple two-pinion gear pump. One gear is driven by the prime mover and, in turn, drives the other gear. The two gears draw oil in through the inlet port, propel it around the walls of the case, and expel it through the outlet port. The volumetric flow rate will be proportional to the gear shaft speed.

These pumps are used for pressures up to about 2000 psi (13.8 MPa). They are low cost items, mechanically simple, and reliable but they exhibit relatively low power efficiency.

6.3.2   Vane Pumps

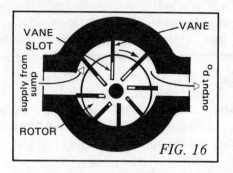

FIG. 16

Figure 16 shows a cross-section through a simple unbalanced sliding vane pump. The vanes are spring loaded and are free to slide radially in and out of slots in the eccentrically-mounted rotor. In the drawing shown, cavities passing the inlet port are expanding in volume, until they pass the uppermost point on the case, after which they progressively contract in volume as the outlet port is approached and passed. Thus, a suction action will be created on the inlet side, drawing oil in, and a compression action will be created on the outlet side, propelling oil out. The volumetric flow rate will be proportional to the rotor shaft speed.

These pumps are used for pressures up to 1500 psi (10.3 MPa). They are more costly, mechanically less simple, and less reliable than gear pumps but they exhibit medium levels of power efficiency.

6.3.3   Piston Pumps

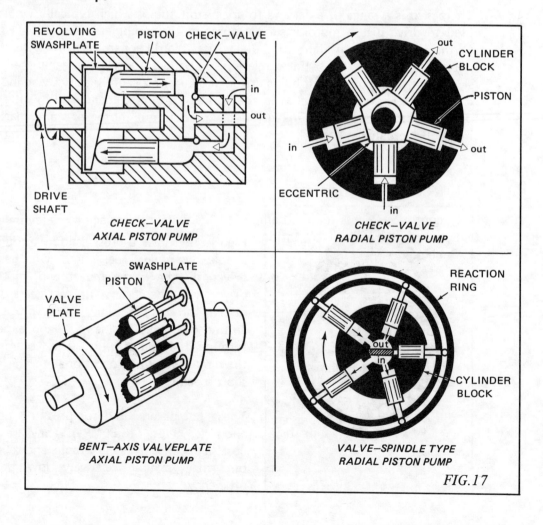

FIG.17

Piston pumps consist of a symmetrical set of cylinders with their pistons inter-connected, together with an appropriate rotating set of valve gear. The pistons may radiate with radially aligned axes, in the case of Radial Piston Pumps, or they may be aligned with their axes parallel and distributed around a circle concentric with the pump centre line, in the case of Axial Piston Pumps.

Figure 17 shows two types of Radial Piston Pump and two types of Axial Piston Pump. In most cases, the cylinder block and the associated valve gear are rotating, driven through the input drive shaft by a prime mover. At all instants in time, half the pistons are being withdrawn from their cylinders, whilst the other half of the pistons are being driven into their cylinders. The valve gear is organised so that those cylinders in which the enclosed volume is expanding are connected to the inlet port, whilst those cylinders in which the enclosed volume is contracting are connected to the outlet port. Thus, suction will be established at the inlet and compression will be established at the outlet.

In many of these pumps, the length of the piston stroke may be varied. In the case of the radial pumps, this is effected by varying the eccentricity of the rotor axis relative to the axis of the case. In the case of the axial pumps, the angle of inclination of the swashplate face, relative to the axis of the cylinder block, can be varied appropriately. The direction of inflow and outflow can be reversed, if the eccentricity or tilt-angle can be reversed, relative to the null position (at which the stroke is zero).

The volumetric flow rate will be proportional to the product of the drive shaft speed (usually constant) and the piston stroke (often variable). These pumps are used for pressures in the approximate range of 1500 to 5000 psi (10.3 to 34.5 MPa). They are expensive, mechanically complex, and have lower reliability than other pumps but they exhibit high levels of power efficiency.

6.4   FINAL CONTROL ELEMENTS

Final control elements for fluid amplifiers are mainly linear actuators (cylinders, rams, jacks), for rectilinear motion, and rotary actuators and motors, for rotary movement.

6.4.1   Linear Actuators

The construction of hydraulic cylinders differs from that for pneumatic cylinders, but the principles of operation are the same. Hydraulic cylinders are much more bulky, because of the much higher pressures involved. Hydraulic systems may operate up to 5000 psi (34.5 MPa) whereas pneumatic systems rarely operate much above 100 psi (690 kPa), at the final control element. Hydraulic cylinders often include "cushioning", to minimise the impact of the piston on the end of the cylinder: this requires a small chamber, at the end of the cylinder, in which oil becomes trapped by the end of the piston and compressed as the piston approaches the limit of travel. Table 1 lists some alternative styles of cylinder construction.

TABLE 1.   ALTERNATIVE STYLES OF CYLINDER CONSTRUCTION

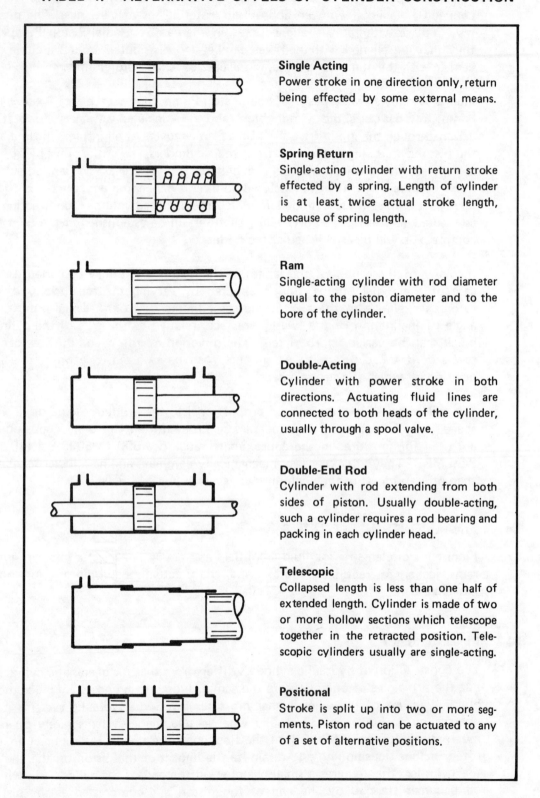

Single Acting
Power stroke in one direction only, return being effected by some external means.

Spring Return
Single-acting cylinder with return stroke effected by a spring. Length of cylinder is at least. twice actual stroke length, because of spring length.

Ram
Single-acting cylinder with rod diameter equal to the piston diameter and to the bore of the cylinder.

Double-Acting
Cylinder with power stroke in both directions. Actuating fluid lines are connected to both heads of the cylinder, usually through a spool valve.

Double-End Rod
Cylinder with rod extending from both sides of piston. Usually double-acting, such a cylinder requires a rod bearing and packing in each cylinder head.

Telescopic
Collapsed length is less than one half of extended length. Cylinder is made of two or more hollow sections which telescope together in the retracted position. Telescopic cylinders usually are single-acting.

Positional
Stroke is split up into two or more segments. Piston rod can be actuated to any of a set of alternative positions.

A "jack" is a self-contained unit, consisting of a cylinder, control valve, and piping.

Pressure applied to a piston produces a piston velocity proportional to the volumetric inflow rate, if compressibility and leakage effects are ignored. The force required will depend upon the characteristics of the mechanical load, and the internal pressure developed will be equal to this force divided by the effective area of the piston face. In the case of pneumatic and high performance hydraulic systems, compressibility effects must be taken into account.

6.4.2 Rotary Actuators

Where rotary motion with limited angular travel is required, a rotary actuator may be used. Alternatively, it would be possible to use a linear actuator in combination with a rack and pinion. Figure 18 illustrates three alternative styles of rotary actuator.

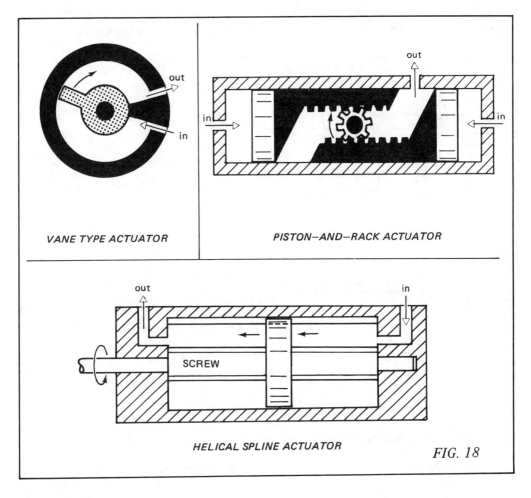

VANE TYPE ACTUATOR

PISTON—AND—RACK ACTUATOR

HELICAL SPLINE ACTUATOR

FIG. 18

6.4.3 Hydraulic Motors

The gear pumps of Section 6.3.1 and the vane pumps of Section 6.3.2 may be operated in reverse, with hydraulic fluid now the input and shaft rotation as the output. These devices now become Gear Motors and Vane Motors. However, because of their relatively low efficiencies and poor low-speed characteristics, it is much more common to use piston types of hydraulic motor, where continuous rotary motion is required.

The pumps illustrated in Figure 17 may be operated in reverse, thus becoming Radial Piston Motors and Axial Piston Motors. The eccentricity or the tilt angle between the face of the swashplate and the axis of the cylinder block (as the case may be) are fixed permanently at one value. At any one time, half the pistons are being forced outwards by pressurised oil flowing into the motor, whilst the other half of the pistons are being drawn inwards due to the suction action of oil flowing out of the motor. The combination of the translational forces in the set of piston rods will react to produce angular motion of the cylinder block. The direction of angular motion will reverse when the direction of oil flow is reversed, and the speed of rotation will be proportional to the volumetric flowrate, if compressibility and leakage effects are neglected.

Hydraulic motors may be controlled either by servovalves or by hydraulic pumps arranged to deliver variable flowrate. Figure 19 shows a typical installation of a spool-type servovalve being used to drive a swashplate axial piston motor.

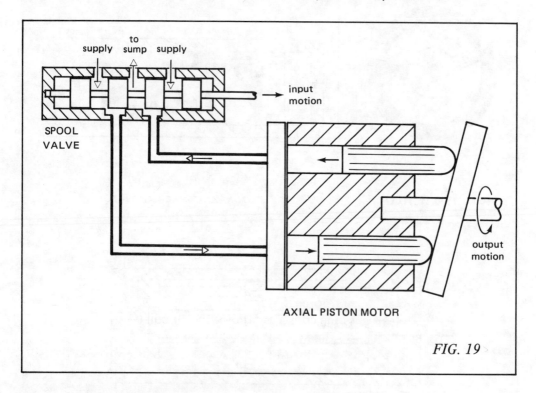

FIG. 19

6.5   BLOCK DIAGRAMS FOR HYDRAULIC DRIVES

Figure 20 shows a small signal block diagram of the drive represented by Figure 19. In this:

V	=	voltage applied to the force motor (V)
I	=	current in force motor coil (A)
Q	=	oil flowrate between valve and motor (l)
Q_l	=	leakage flowrate, past pistons (l/s)
Q_c	=	equivalent compressibility flowrate (l/s)
Q_m	=	useful flowrate to motor (l/s)
p	=	differential pressure across the motor (Pa)

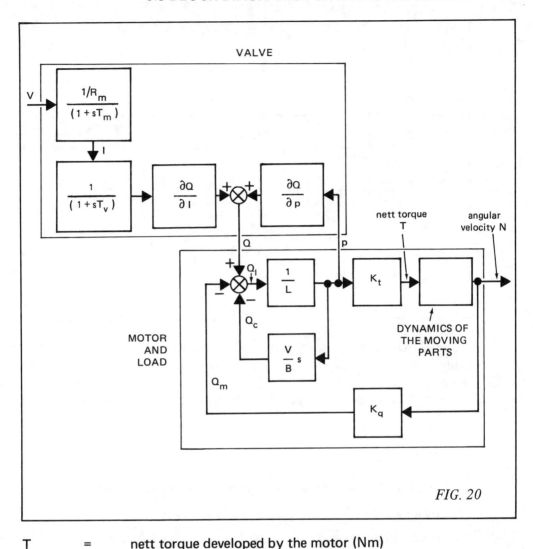

FIG. 20

T	=	nett torque developed by the motor (Nm)
N	=	angular velocity of the motor (rad/s)
R_m	=	resistance of force motor coil (Ω)
T_m	=	electrical time constant of force motor coil (s)
T_v	=	mechanical time constant of valve (s)
$\partial Q / \partial I$	=	sensitivity of flowrate to changes in force motor current (l/s per A)
$\partial Q / \partial p$	=	sensitivity of flowrate to changes in differential pressure across the motor (l/s per Pa)
K_t	=	motor torque sensitivity (Nm/Pa)
K_q	=	motor flow sensitivity (l/rad)
V	=	volume of oil in motor and pipes (l)
B	=	bulk modulus of oil (Pa)
L	=	leakage coefficient (l/s per Pa)

The bulk modulus is defined in order to accommodate any compression and expansion of the fluid, entrained vapour or air, and the pipe walls which may occur under pressure. The diagram does not include any minor negative feedback paths, which may be incorporated for linearisation and other purposes.

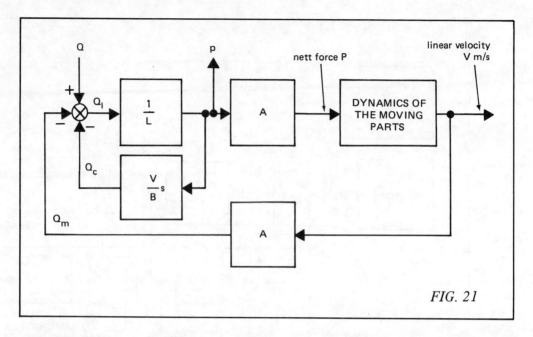

FIG. 21

Figure 21 shows a block diagram for a power cylinder and load: typically, the cylinder would be controlled by a servovalve. This diagram is similar to the representation, in Figure 20, of the motor and load, except that the constant A has been introduced to represent the effective surface area of the piston face (in m^2).

6.6   SELECTION OF EQUIPMENT

6.6.1   Advantages and Disadvantages of Hydraulic and Pneumatic Systems

The advantages of hydraulic systems are as follows:

- very high power to weight ratio
- very high peak torques (or forces)
- very short time lags enabling fast response

A direct result of operating at high pressures (up to 5000 psi, 34.5 MPa).

- smooth operation even at low speeds
- large holding forces, when stationary
- high power efficiency
- rugged
- self lubricating and cooling
- linear and rotary motions available.

The disadvantages of hydraulic systems are as follows:

- clumsiness of connections
- mess from oil leaks
- danger from large oil leaks (high pressure, toxicity, and flammability)
- oil properties change with temperature
- inertia of oil can degrade system performance
- expensive when power supply is included in cost
- fluid must be kept clean and gas free
- severe nonlinearities may necessitate special treatment.

The advantages of pneumatic systems are as follows:

- relatively cheap
- pressurised air often is available, so that no special supply then is required
- safe in potentially explosive atmospheres
- no mess or danger from leakage
- can exhaust to atmosphere.

The disadvantages of pneumatic systems are as follows:

- power to weight ratio is lower than with hydraulics (due to the lower operating pressures)
- relatively inefficient
- undesirable behaviour due to compressibility of air—for this reason, pneumatic drives tend to be used mainly in on-off (bang-bang) applications.

6.6.2 Selection of Hydraulic Servovalves and Final Control Elements

In selecting a servovalve, several questions must be considered.

- Is it flow or pressure that is to be controlled?
- Is the intention to control the velocity, position, or force developed by the actuator?
- Is gain compensation required?
- What frequency response is needed?
- How large must the valve be?
- Is 3-way or 4-way porting needed?

In addition to this, the size of the final control element must be determined. The usual procedure is to plot a pressure versus flow curve for a given final control element and load. Over this plot is superimposed the servovalve performance capability, which must be slightly outside the load curve for satisfactory overall performance.

6.7 POWER SUPPLIES

When hydraulic or pneumatic components are used, it will be necessary to provide a source of pressurised oil or air for them. Many plants have high volume compressed air mains, typically at a pressure in the region of 100 psi (690 kPa): this may be suitable for the final control elements but most pneumatic instruments and amplifiers require air supplies in the 20 to 25 psi (138 to 172 kPa) pressure range. The lower pressure supply is easily derived from the higher pressure supply, using a pressure reducing valve having an adequate flow capacity. In the case of hydraulic systems, it is necessary usually to construct a hydraulic power supply specially for these systems.

6.7.1 Hydraulic Power Supplies

Figure 22 shows a hydraulic circuit diagram for a typical hydraulic power supply, together with an electrical equivalent circuit.

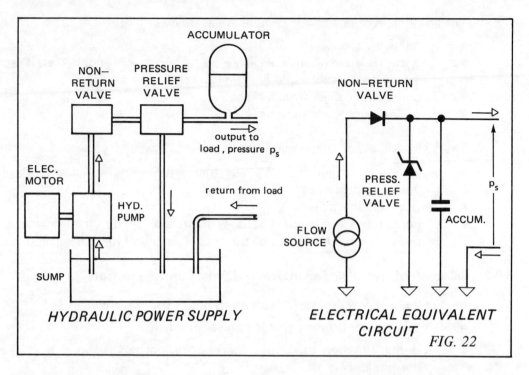

HYDRAULIC POWER SUPPLY

ELECTRICAL EQUIVALENT CIRCUIT

FIG. 22

The positive displacement pump is driven at constant speed, by the induction motor, and behaves as a constant flowrate source. The pressure relief valve returns oil to the sump whenever the developed pressure attempts to exceed the value manually set into the valve. The non-return valve ensures that the load cannot back-drive fluid to the pump, during transient operation.

The accumulator behaves as a hydraulic capacitor and smooths out any short-term fluctuations in output pressure. It can take a number of different forms, some of which are shown in Figure 23. All operate on the principle that the accumulator stores the potential energy of the oil, which is being held under pressure by an external force, acting against the forces arising from the dynamic behaviour of the hydraulic system.

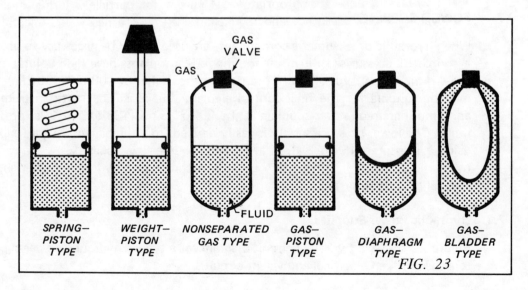

SPRING–PISTON TYPE   WEIGHT–PISTON TYPE   NONSEPARATED GAS TYPE   GAS–PISTON TYPE   GAS–DIAPHRAGM TYPE   GAS–BLADDER TYPE

FIG. 23

6.7.2 Pneumatic Power Supplies

Figure 24 shows a typical installation for a pneumatic power supply, where this has to be installed.

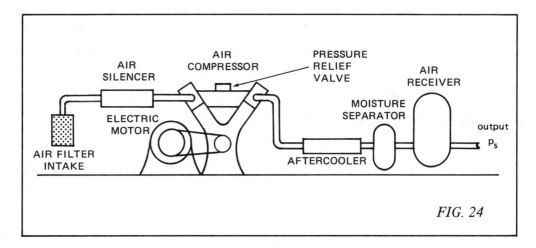

FIG. 24

The necessary components, taken in sequence, typically would be:

(1)   Air intake with particle filter.
(2)   Air silencer, to minimise acoustic noise.
(3)   Air compressor (a pneumatic piston pump) driven at constant speed by an induction motor.
(4)   Pressure relief valve, to determine output pressure.
(5)   Cooling heat-exchangers.
(6)   Moisture separator, to remove water which has condensed during the compression process.
(7)   Air receiver, which is a storage cylinder and is equivalent to the accumulator in the hydraulic system.

The electrical equivalent circuit would be similar to that for the hydraulic power supply. The distribution system which routes the compressed air to the various loads would include, at appropriate sites, means for particle filtering, moisture removal, pressure reduction and regulation, and, where necessary, injection of oil mist.

In the system shown, the pressure relief valve exhausts air to atmosphere, whenever the compressor begins to develop a pressure in excess of the pressure setting of the valve. This arrangement assumes that the electric motor and compressor are running continuously. An alternative, and less wasteful, arrangement is to instal a pressure-actuated switch, connected to switch the motor supply off whenever the output pressure reaches a preset value: this configuration, in effect, is a bang-bang closed loop pressure control system.

7

FLOW CONTROL VALVES, ACTUATORS AND POSITIONERS; PNEUMATIC PROCESS CONTROLLERS

7.1   FLOW CONTROL VALVES

In many process control loops, control of the system controlled variable is effected by manipulating the flow rate of a fluid in a pipeline. Where sufficient pressure head exists at the source of the flow, the rate of flow may be manipulated by inserting a variable, controllable restriction: that is, a fluid resistance. A flow control valve performs this task and is, in effect, an adjustable orifice.

There are many different styles of valve made for throttling the flow of liquids, slurries, gases and vapours, and they may be categorised as follows:

valves having a rectilinear motion —

- single and double seat globe
- split body globe
- 3-way globe
- angle
- diaphragm
- needle
- pinch
- gate
- wedge
- slide

valves having a (limited) rotary motion —

- butterfly
- ball
- plug .

Figure 1 shows the principles of operation of a number of these valves. Many valves installed in process plants will be operated manually, but in this volume we are concerned with those versions which can be actuated by pneumatic, electrical or hydraulic means. All of the valve types listed above can be configured to be signal actuated, either in a fully-activated/inactivated mode or in an infinitely variable mode. In practice, however, the control valves most commonly installed for automatic control use are the single and double seat globe types: further discussion will be restricted almost exclusively to these.

The construction of the globe valve may be separated into three principal parts:

ACTUATOR — this is the source of motive power to position the valve plug against the reaction of fluid forces on the plug, weight of the moving parts, and any spring force which may be introduced;

BODY — this is the case for the variable orifice, is usually a die-casting, and contains the valve trim;

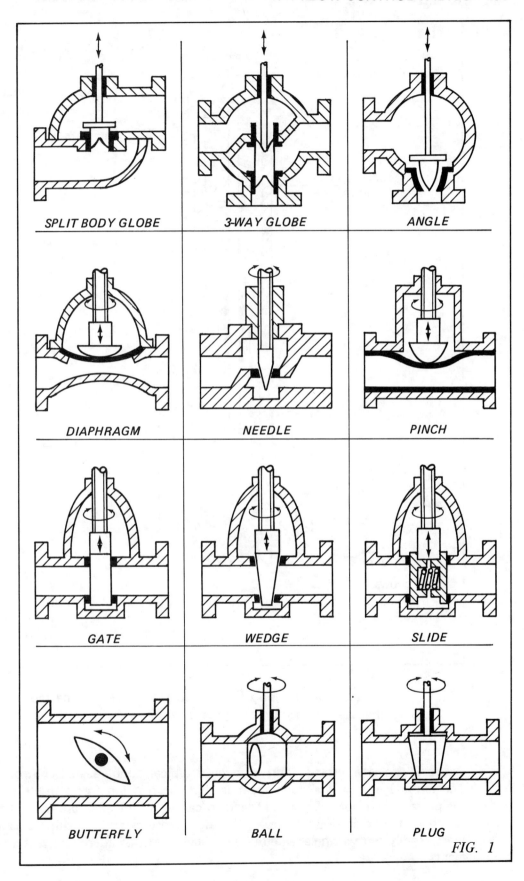

SPLIT BODY GLOBE   3-WAY GLOBE   ANGLE

DIAPHRAGM   NEEDLE   PINCH

GATE   WEDGE   SLIDE

BUTTERFLY   BALL   PLUG

FIG. 1

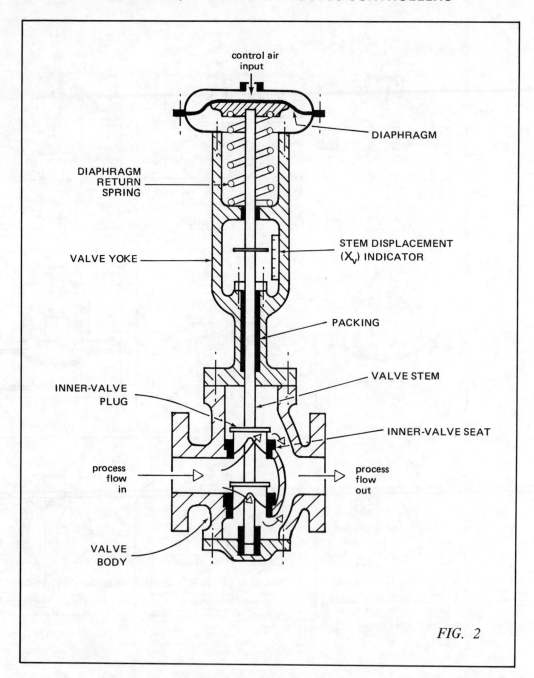

FIG. 2

TRIM — this is the combination of the fixed valve seat and the moving valve plug, the relative position of which determines the area of the adjustable orifice.

Figure 2 shows a cross-section through a typical double-seated control valve. The advantage with the double seat is that the reaction forces resulting from the pressure and flow of the fluid tend to cancel, so that the force requirements for the actuator are low; however, if a tight closure is desired, this is achieved more readily with a single-seated valve. Figure 3 shows alternative seat arrangements.

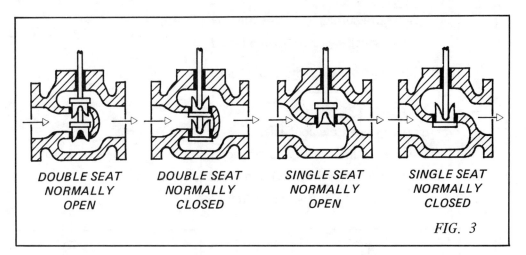

DOUBLE SEAT
NORMALLY
OPEN

DOUBLE SEAT
NORMALLY
CLOSED

SINGLE SEAT
NORMALLY
OPEN

SINGLE SEAT
NORMALLY
CLOSED

FIG. 3

The style, size, and material of the body and trim have to take into account:

● the maximum operating pressure in the fluid;

● the nature of the fluid, in terms of corrosive, toxic, and inflammable properties;

● the possibility of entrained solids being present in the fluid and of the building up of solid residues;

● the possibility of the occurrence of "cavitation", which arises from pressure recovery causing bubbles of vapour or gas to be reabsorbed spontaneously, in a liquid flow medium, by a process of implosion;

● the possibility of the occurrence of "flashing", which arises from pressure reduction causing the generation of bubbles of vapour or gas previously dissolved in a liquid flow medium;

● the type of installation;

● the properties of the fluid, such as the fluid phase, density, viscosity and vapour pressure;

● the range of flow rates required;

● dynamic performance requirements.

The engineering procedure for determining the correct size of a valve body is referred to as "control valve sizing", and this has been rationalised by use of a "valve flow coefficient", denoted by C_v. The definition of C_v may vary between manufacturers, but a common one is the number of US gallons of water which will flow through the wide-open valve in one minute, when the pressure drop across the valve is 1 psi. The corresponding flow formula for a liquid flow

medium would be $\qquad Q = C_v \sqrt{\dfrac{\Delta p}{G}}$,

where Q = volumetric flowrate through the fully open valve, in US gal/min,

Δp = pressure drop across the valve, in psi,

G = specific gravity of the liquid.

In the SI system of units, the equivalent flow formula takes the form

$$Q = A_v \sqrt{\Delta p / \rho}$$

where A_v = valve flow coefficient

Q   = volumetric flowrate through the fully open valve, in m^3/s,

Δp = pressure drop across the valve, in Pa,

ρ = density of the liquid, in kg/m^3.

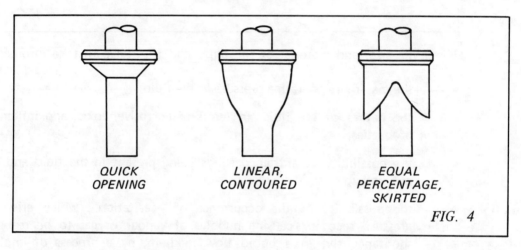

QUICK
OPENING

LINEAR,
CONTOURED

EQUAL
PERCENTAGE,
SKIRTED

FIG. 4

7.1.1   Valve Inherent Characteristic

The Inherent Characteristic of a control valve is the relationship between the flow Q through the valve and the valve position X_v (the displacement of the valve plug), with a constant pressure drop across the valve. Since the pressure drop across the valve will not be constant when the valve is in service, the inherent characteristic must be measured under specific test conditions. The shape of the characteristic is dependent upon the contouring of the valve plug, and examples of different contouring are shown in Figure 4.

Figure 5 shows the forms of inherent characteristic which can be obtained for representative plug types.

The quick opening characteristic provides a large change in flowrate for a small change in valve position, and is used in on-off applications requiring rapid opening or closure.

The linear characteristic normally is used in systems in which, when the valve is installed, most of the system pressure is dropped across the valve.

The equal percentage characteristic is one having a gradient proportional to the flowrate. It is used typically in applications where only a small proportion of the system pressure is dropped across the valve.

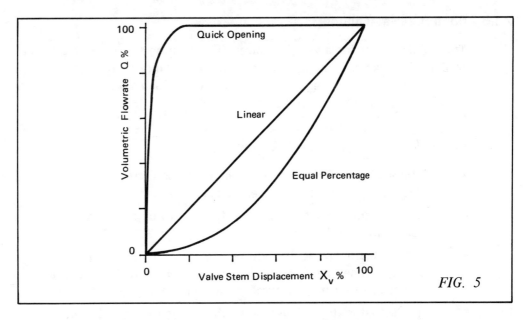

FIG. 5

The inherent characteristic, with a given plug profile, may be modified by using a valve positioner (see Section 7.1.4) having a nonlinear feedback, by virtue of the use of a suitably profiled cam in the positioner feedback path. Alternatively, the static characteristic of the controller driving the valve actuator may be modified appropriately.

7.1.2 Valve Installed Characteristic

The electrical analogy to the control valve is a variable nonlinear resistance. When installed in a flow line, the complete line would resemble a set of series-connected nonlinear resistances, as shown in Figure 6, each one representing a pipeline component presenting a resistance to flow. (The nonlinearity occurs because pressure drop is proportional to the square of the flowrate).

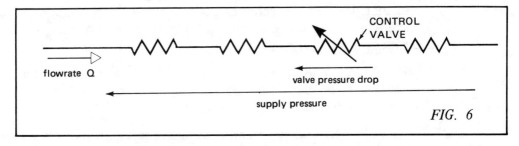

FIG. 6

The Installed Characteristic will be the relationship between the installed flowrate Q and the valve position X_v, when the supply pressure is constant: this obviously will be dependent upon the combination of the inherent characteristic and the properties of the other components in the flow line.

Except in on-off applications, the most desirable installed characteristic usually is a proportional (linear) relationship. Note, however, that the process engineer will need to supply, to the valve manufacturer, his inherent characteristic requirements and obviously these will be affected by the nature of the installation.

7.1.3   Control Valve Actuators

The requirements for a valve actuator depend upon the type of valve being controlled. For example, a globe type valve will require rectilinear motion, whereas a butterfly valve will require rotary motion. Each type of actuator possesses certain merits, in relation to the others.

Factors Involved in Actuator Selection

- The actuator must be compatible with the controller or valve positioner, depending upon which is the signal source.

- The actuator must generate sufficient force to overcome the reaction forces imposed by the valve.

- The actuator must be appropriate to the operating environment: for example, pneumatic actuators would be preferred in potentially explosive atmospheres or in environments requiring high levels of hygiene.

- The actuator stroke must match the requirements of the valve.

- The actuator must meet the speed of response requirements.

- The actuator must leave the valve in the most desirable state, should the power supply fail.

Sources of Reaction Force

The causes of components of reaction force, to be overcome by the actuator, are as follows:

WEIGHT AND INERTIA. These are the unbalanced weight and associated inertia of all the moving parts of the valve and its actuator. Except for very large valves, the inertia forces are not significantly large.

FRICTION. This is due to the action of the sealing gland on the valve stem and also sometimes to the actuator itself. This is a combination of stiction and coulomb friction, and contributes to mechanical hysteresis and hence positioning accuracy of the valve.

FLUID PRESSURE. This is the pressure of the fluid on the valve plug and the associated force can be considerably diminished by the use of double-seated arrangements.

DIAPHRAGM SPRING. Many actuators include a spring, the function of which is to return the valve to its new position when the actuating signal is reduced.

Types of Actuator

Actuators may be categorised as follows:

- pneumatically operated diaphragm actuators;

- piston actuators, pneumatically or hydraulically operated;

- electrohydraulic actuators;
- high performance servo actuators;
- electromechanical actuators;
- manually operated handwheel actuators.

By far the most common variety of actuator is the pneumatically operated diaphragm type. This consists of a synthetic rubber diaphragm sandwiched between the flanges of two circular pressed-steel dishes, as shown in Figure 2, in cross-section. The 3 to 15 psi (20 to 100 kPa) control air signal may be applied either to the top or the bottom face of the diaphragm, depending upon requirements; a restoring force will be provided by a calibrated spring placed in the other chamber (that is, the one not supplied with control air). Various combinations of actuating action and valve action (which depends upon the orientation of the valve trim) are illustrated in Figure 7. A cast yoke attaches the actuator to the valve body, as shown in Figure 2.

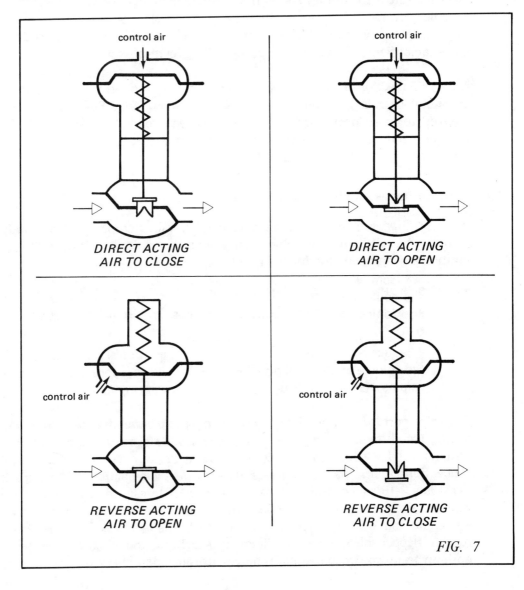

FIG. 7

The cylinder of a piston actuator is made from a casting or a pressing and can withstand much higher control pressures than can the diaphragm type. For this reason, piston actuators are particularly useful in applications where the pipeline pressure is high. The cylinder is mounted, with the piston axis aligned with the valve stem, vertically above the valve yoke. Pneumatic piston actuators normally are used in combination with valve positioners, which are described in Section 7.1.4.

With an hydraulic piston actuator, the piston may be controlled by an electro-hydraulic servovalve. Typically, the valve and actuator will be part of a position servosystem, with valve stem position feedback provided by a mechanically coupled rectilinear servo potentiometer or LVDT feeding an electronic amplifier which in turn drives the servovalve. Extremely higher operating forces and speeds of response can be generated.

Electric motors sometimes are used as actuators, driving the valve stem through a suitable gear reduction. A position servo feedback loop may be added around this, using a servo potentiometer or LVDT and an electronic preamplifier and power amplifier. The speed of response will be relatively low.

Note that position feedback loops are applied only around valve actuators when infinitely variable positioning of the valve is required. Such a loop may be referred to as a "positioner", although this term tends to be applied mainly to position (and force) feedback loops associated with diaphragm types of pneumatic actuator, which are discussed in the next section.

7.1.4 Valve Positioners for Pneumatic Actuators

Valve positioners often are applied to control valves employing pneumatic actuators, when infinitely variable positioning is required. The addition of a positioner can provide the following advantages:

- an increase in the speed of response;

- an improvement in the linearity of the stem displacement versus control signal characteristic;

- a reduction in the drain on pneumatic control signal sources, because the volume of a typical positioner input bellows is very much less than the volume of a typical diaphragm actuator, for example.

The valve positioner is, in effect, the controller in a closed feedback loop arrangement. The differential amplifier is a flapper-nozzle type, the air output driving a pneumatic relay which in turn controls the actuator. The input and feedback connections to the flapper plate result in differencing action. Where the input signal is a 3-15 psi control air pressure, the input transducer will be a bellows or capsule; where the input is a DC current or voltage, the input transducer will be a solenoid and armature type of force motor. The feedback from the valve stem to the flapper plate may be direct (through suitable linkages), representing position feedback, or sometimes it may be through a spring (and suitable linkages),

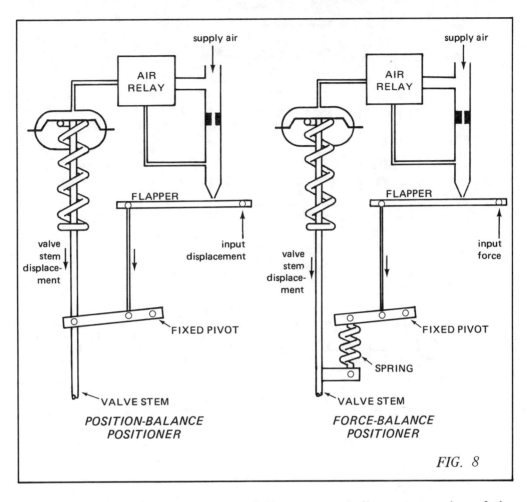

supply air

supply air

AIR RELAY

AIR RELAY

FLAPPER

FLAPPER

valve stem displace- ment

input displacement

valve stem displace- ment

input force

FIXED PIVOT

FIXED PIVOT

SPRING

VALVE STEM

VALVE STEM

POSITION-BALANCE POSITIONER

FORCE-BALANCE POSITIONER

FIG. 8

representing force feedback. Figure 8 shows a symbolic representation of the alternative configurations.

With any of these types, the feedback may be converted from linear to nonlinear by the insertion of a suitably contoured cam and follower into the coupling to the valve stem: the resulting nonlinear closed loop static characteristic then will supplement the installed characteristic of the control valve.

7.2   PNEUMATIC PROCESS CONTROLLERS

Section 8.3 will give a detailed account of the configuration of general purpose process controllers, treated in general terms. The specific implementation of these controllers, using pneumatic hardware, will be covered at this stage, in order to complete the exposition on pneumatic devices.

A typical application of a pneumatic process controller is shown in Figure 9. The function of the controller is to open and close the control valve so as to manipulate the inflow rate, in the presence of fluctuations in outflow rate. It does this in order that the liquid level in the tank, as measured by the transducer, shall match as closely as possible the desired value, as determined by the manually adjusted set point.

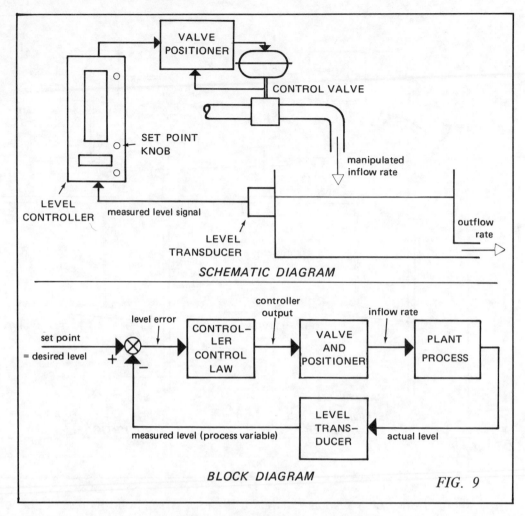

The functions of the pneumatic controller are:

- to enable the set point signal to be generated;
- to receive the feedback signal representing the measured level;
- to generate an error signal by comparing the above two signals;
- to amplify the error signal and to incorporate dynamic terms, in generating the controller output signal.

The control law can incorporate one or more of the terms known as Proportional Action, Integral Action, and Derivative Action, which are described in Chapter 8.

Figure 10 is a symbolic representation of a controller containing only proportional action. In practice, the PV and set point bellows may be coupled (differentially) to the flapper through fairly complex linkage arrangements. The flapper-nozzle amplifier is the pneumatic equivalent to the electronic operational amplifier and its output pressure responds, nonlinearly, to minute changes in flapper displacement. The air relay behaves as a unity follower, so that its output pressure tracks the amplifier output pressure, but with a significant increase in volumetric flow capacity. The feedback bellows completes a high gain negative

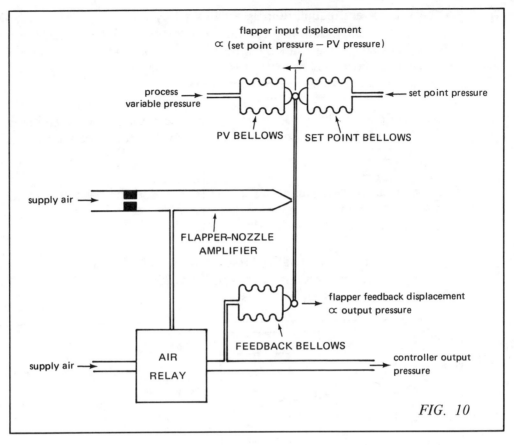

FIG. 10

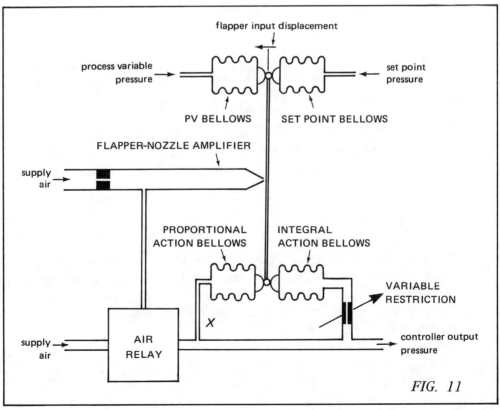

FIG. 11

feedback loop, and equilibrium is established by a force balance at the flapper. Thus, the controller output pressure is proportional to the difference between the set point and process variable pressures. The constant of proportionality may be adjusted by manually changing the moment arm ratios of linkages (not shown) which couple the feedback bellows to the flapper.

Integral action may be incorporated by adding a series connected combination of variable restriction and (integral action) bellows in the feedback path, as shown in Figure 11.

The restriction is analogous to a variable resistor and the bellows is analogous to a capacitor, so that adjustment of the restriction will cause the integral action time constant to be "tuned".

If a second, variable, (derivative) restriction is added at point X on Figure 11, in series with the proportional action bellows, adjustment of this restriction will cause the derivative action time constant to be tuned.

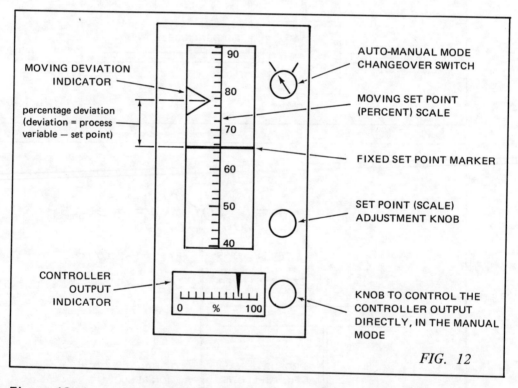

FIG. 12

Figure 12 shows the faceplate of a typical pneumatic indicating process controller, and the features shown are common to all general purpose analog process controllers.

8

ELECTRONIC AND ELECTRICAL CONTROLLERS

8.1   CLASSIFICATION

This chapter will deal specifically with electronic and other electrical controllers. Some of the principles to be described will also be applicable to certain equivalent pneumatic controllers, but detailed descriptions of these will not be included at this point: refer to Section 7.2 for details of pneumatic process controllers.

Commercially available general purpose controllers can be subdivided into four categories, which will be considered in detail. Any other types of controller not described here are unlikely to be available off the shelf and would need to be custom designed and constructed.

The four principal categories of controller are On-Off Temperature Controllers, General Purpose Process Controllers, Motor Speed Controllers, and Sequence Controllers. These controllers may include provision for indicating the various signals involved (Indicating Controllers) and/or provision for chart-recording specific signals (Recording Controllers). Indicating instruments will have either circular-arc scales or "thermometer" scales; however, in modern installations the instrument may be replaced physically by a simulation on a video display, which may include provision for setting the controller parameters from a keyboard and for displaying the values thereby selected. Recording instruments usually take the form of strip chart recorders, although some circular chart recorders are still in service; again, strip chart displays can also be simulated on video displays, in modern installations.

8.2   ON–OFF TEMPERATURE CONTROLLERS

8.2.1   Temperature Sensors

The simplest sensor is the bimetal strip, which may be either a flat or a coiled flexure. The change in shape of the strip, resulting from changes in temperature, typically causes electrical contacts to be either closed or broken, as required. Mechanical adjustments can be used to cause a change in the pre-stressing or pre-positioning of the strip, resulting in a change in the temperature at which the contacts just close (or open). Alternatively, motion of the strip can be used to shift the moving member of a displacement transducer.

Another class of device involves using the expansion of a fluid in a container (for example, a Bourdon tube), resulting from applied heat, to activate either electrical contacts or a displacement transducer.

Thermocouples may also be used, with the emf produced being used either to move a coil in a magnetic field or to provide the input signal of an amplifier. In similar fashion, resistance thermometers and thermistors may be used in a Wheatstone bridge circuit, with the unbalance voltage (resulting from temperature change) being used to move a coil or drive an amplifier.

8.2.2   Control Laws

The simplest law involves switching on and off a heat supply, with switching in both directions occurring at the same (preset) temperature. This results in a cycling of the load temperature, as shown by Figure 1. The magnitude and frequency of the temperature cycling will depend upon the magnitude of the heat source and the dynamics of the thermal load: in many installations, the thermal load will be such that the cooling interval is much longer than the heating interval, especially where cooling occurs entirely as a result of heat transmission to atmosphere.

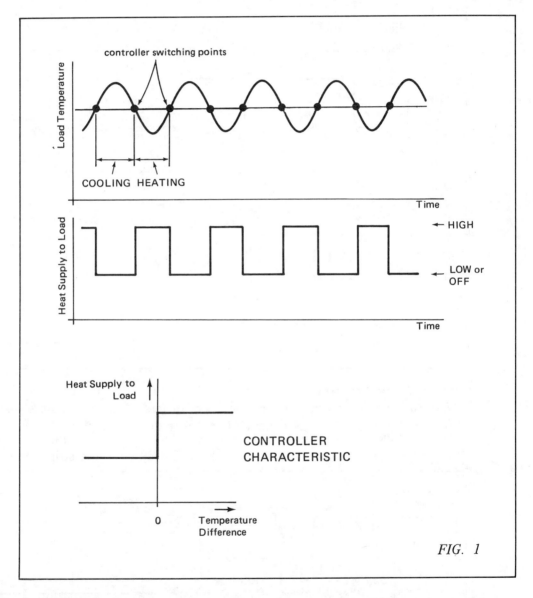

FIG. 1

A greater degree of control over the temperature cycling can be effected by designing the control law such that the switching point during heating occurs at a higher temperature compared with the switching point during cooling, as shown in Figure 2. This type of law property sometimes is referred to as "overlap" or "hysteresis". Increasing the overlap zone will result in a reduction in the frequency of the temperature cycling, but this will be accompanied by an increase in the temperature excursion.

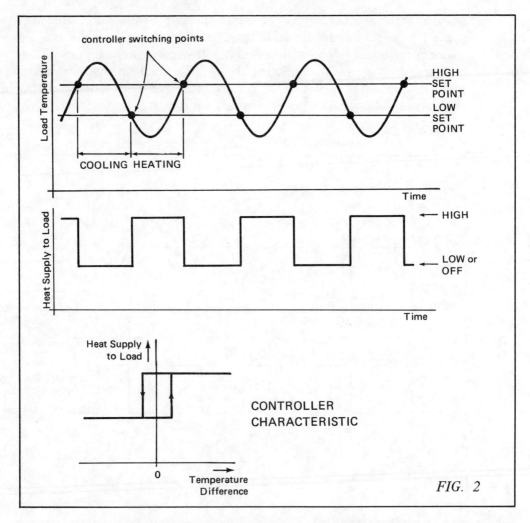

FIG. 2

With "multistep" control, the hardware makes provision for three or more switching temperatures, resulting in an equal number of different applied heat levels. Such a controller inevitably is more complex but can result in a significant reduction in the temperature excursion.

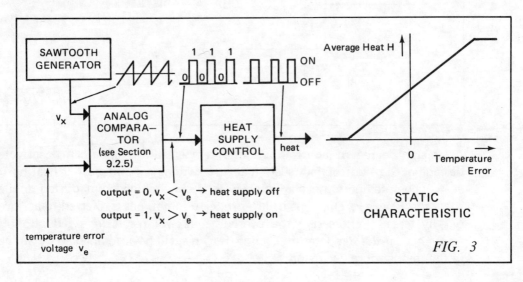

FIG. 3

Proportional control may be effected, using on-off switching hardware, with the type of arrangement shown in Figure 3. The mark-space ratio of the controlled heat supply changes as a function of the value of the temperature error voltage v_e, such that the average value of the heat delivered varies linearly with the temperature error. In this manner, proportional action is achieved, although the hardware does not require a linear power amplifier. If provision is made for offsetting the sawtooth waveform, the quiescent value of average heat, which is generated when the temperature error is zero, may be adjusted.

8.2.3 Heat Control

The function of a temperature controller is to switch on and off a source of heating or cooling. This is undertaken most readily with relays and/or contactors, in the case of electric heaters; however, the simplicity of the hardware must be traded against reduced reliability and maintainability. An alternative is to use Triac or SCR networks, with the thyristors being gated on and off by a suitable drive network: since the source of electrical energy usually is AC and there is no advantage to be gained from rectification, it follows that Triacs would be preferable to SCRs. Reliability and maintainability will be high with power semiconductors, provided that they are protected against excessive transients: the fact that a heater is almost purely resistive assists, in this respect.

Where the controller is concerned with the switching of steam or refrigerant flow, this can be effected by using an solenoid actuated pneumatic pilot valve switching air to the diaphragm actuator of a control valve in the flow line.

8.3 GENERAL PURPOSE PROCESS CONTROLLERS

8.3.1 History

General purpose process controllers originated in pneumatic form about forty years ago. Subsequently, these were superseded by electronic versions, to a large extent, using firstly discrete component and then integrated circuit analog technology. Because of cost and reliability, recent trends have been towards synthesising the controllers with digital hardware, with the control law either hardwired or represented by program statements in software. The progressively increasing degree of complexity and sophistication has presented potential problems, in terms of maintenance, fault location, and repair, and these become significant factors when selecting a controller.

8.3.2 Types of Control Action

General purpose process controllers can be subdivided into Feedback, Cascade, Feedforward, and Ratio controllers, depending upon the type of action which each is required to provide. In some cases, the type of action may need to be specified at the time of ordering, whereas, in other cases, it may be possible to configure one particular controller for any of these roles, at the time of commissioning. Refer to Section 13.7 for descriptions of typical applications for the various controller types.

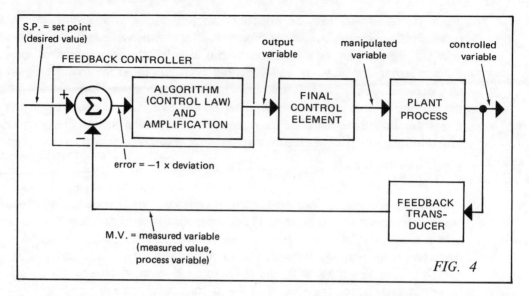

FIG. 4

The application of a Feedback controller is shown in Figure 4. Such a controller makes provision for setting the desired value (called the "set point"), accepting the measured value from the feedback transducer, determining the difference (called the "error" or "deviation"), and thereby generating an output signal which is related to the deviation by a preset algorithm. This algorithm usually includes time-dependent terms, thereby providing dynamic compensation of the control loop. This type of controller is providing feedback control in the conventional sense.

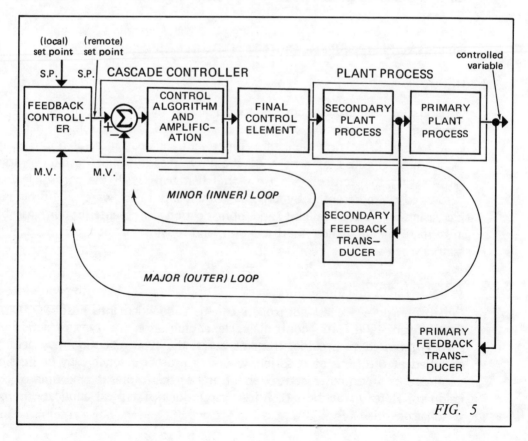

FIG. 5

The application of a Cascade controller, in conjunction with a Feedback controller, is shown in Figure 5. It will be seen that the two controllers must be similar, with the exception that the output signal from the Feedback controller becomes the (variable) set point of the Cascade controller, so that this set point would normally not be adjustable manually: it is said to be a "remote" set point, as opposed to a "local set point", which is set manually. The configuration represents a dual loop system, with the outer (major) loop having greater authority than the inner (minor) loop. The purpose of the inner loop will relate to one or more of the following factors, provided that the gain of this loop is made sufficiently high:

- the closed inner loop will have a faster transient response than that of the secondary section of the process, on its own, with the result that the speed of response of the outer loop will be enhanced;

- the closed inner loop will be relatively insensitive to changes in the properties of the secondary section of the process, so that this loop becomes an element having stationary properties, as far as the outer loop is concerned;

- the closed inner loop will be relatively linear in its behaviour, despite possible departure from linearity in the characteristics of the secondary section of the process, with the result that the linearity of the outer loop will be enhanced;

- parasitic disturbances occurring within the secondary section of the plant will have a minimal effect on the output of the primary section of the plant process.

The choice of control algorithm for Cascade controllers usually is made the same as that for Feedback controllers, as discussed in Section 8.3.4.

A Feedforward controller is used in order to anticipate, and correct for, large parasitic disturbances in a plant process, for which a Feedback controller, on its own, proves to be inadequate. The output from the Feedforward controller is used to augment the output from the Feedback controller: typically, the output from the Feedback controller is used as a remote input for the Feedforward controller, as shown in Figure 6. In the absence of the Feedback controller, there ceases to be any feedback action, because no longer is there a closed loop. Ideally, the Feedforward controller should be tuned so that the component of output signal which it generates from the measurement of the disturbance precisely cancels the direct effect of the disturbance upon the plant process. In practice, only an approximate cancellation is necessary, because the feedback action of the closed loop completed by the Feedback controller should cope with any residual effect of the disturbance. The usual control algorithm provided by a Feedforward controller takes the form of a "lead-lag" law, corresponding to a transfer function of the type $(1 + sT_1)/(1 + sT_2)$.

A Ratio controller is used for controlling a process involving the mixing of two components A and B. The set point of the controller represents the desired value for the ratio A/B (say). Figure 7 represents two alternative configurations which theoretically could be used to achieve this end; however, the first configur-

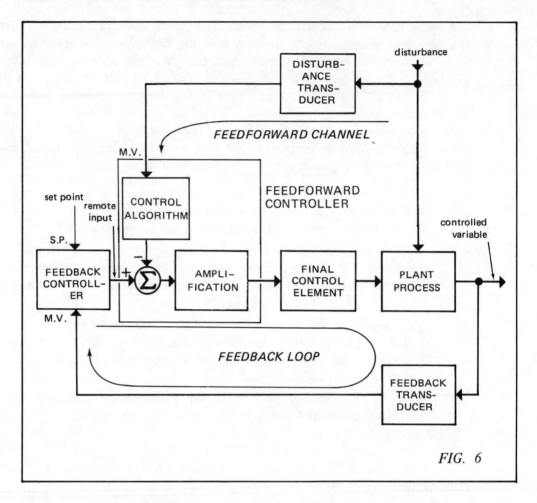

FIG. 6

ation is not practicable, because both of the transducer signals form part of the loop, with the result that the loop gain varies with signal level and therefore is far from constant in value. In the second system, the B transducer signal is external to the feedback loop, which therefore has a much more invariant loop gain: in this practical configuration, B is known as a "wild variable", because it is assumed that it is this variable which is not being affected by the action of the final control element. The choice of control algorithm for Ratio controllers usually is made the same as that for Feedback controllers, as discussed in Section 8.3.4.

8.3.3   Signal Levels

With electronic controllers, the range 4–20mA is by far the most common for the process signals. The offset datum to some extent is inherited from the need, for an offset datum, with pneumatic signals but it does have the merit of preserving a high signal/noise ratio and also provides means for detecting a broken connection. However, the control algorithms usually are processing voltage signals, referenced to signal common, rather than current signals, so that internal I/V and V/I conversion, together with datum offsetting, normally is incorporated into any controller designed for DC current transmission. For this reason, there almost certainly will be a steady trend towards DC voltages for transmission signals, especially now that more controllers are becoming digital: there is little sense in performing

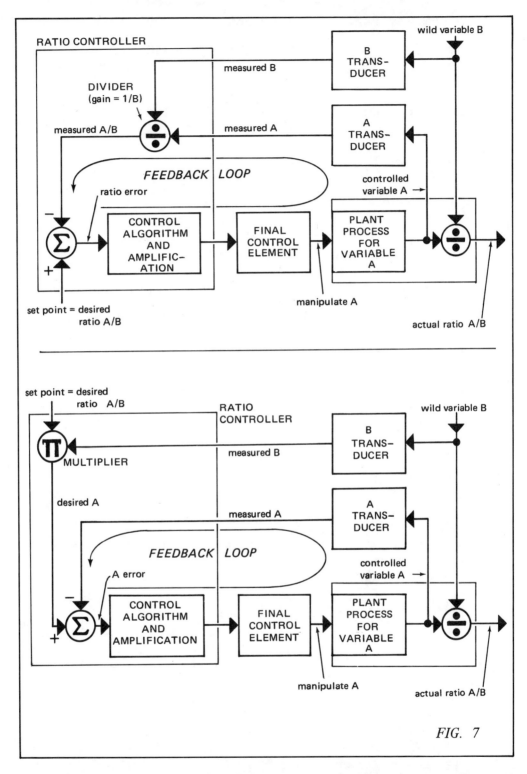

FIG. 7

firstly an I/V conversion and then an A/D conversion at the input side, if one conversion can be eliminated by changing to voltage signals for transmission; a similar argument applies to the output side. Alternative, less common, transmission signal ranges include 0–20mA, 10–50mA, 0–10 V, 0–1 V, and 1–5 V DC.

8.3.4   PID Feedback Controller Configuration

Figure 8 shows schematically the internal organisation of a typical analog Three Term Feedback Controller. The algorithm is said to be "three term" because it takes the typical form

$$\text{controller output} = \frac{1}{K_p}\left[e + \frac{1}{T_I}\int e\,dt + T_D\frac{de}{dt}\right]$$

where   controller steady state gain = $\dfrac{1}{K_p}$,

controller "proportional band" = $100K_p\%$,
T_I = "integral action time", or "reset time",
T_D = "derivative action time", or "pre-act time",
e = system error = $-1 \times$ "deviation".

The proportional term e/K_p results in a component of output proportional to error; the integral action term $\left[\dfrac{1}{K_p T_I}\displaystyle\int e\,dt\right]$ results in a ramping component of output if the error is constant, and the derivative action term $\left[\dfrac{T_D}{K_p}\cdot\dfrac{de}{dt}\right]$ results in a steady component of output if the error is ramping. This last term tends to amplify any parasitic noise components which may be present in the signal representing error e, and therefore should be used with great caution whenever signals from feedback transducers are noisy: this is because noise may exhibit high values for instantaneous rates of change even when the peak value of the noise signal may be quite small.

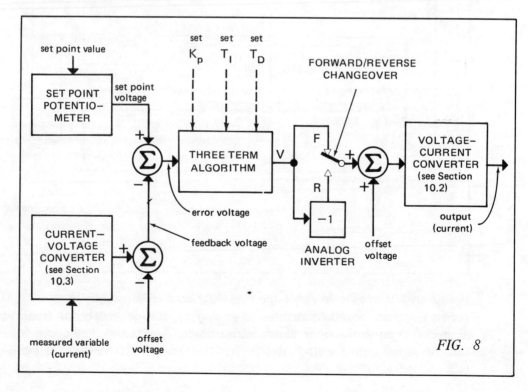

FIG. 8

The derivative action term $\left[\dfrac{T_D}{K_p} \cdot \dfrac{de}{dt}\right]$ will generate an impulsive component of output, should the set point be changed suddenly, and, for this reason, some manufacturers prefer to connect the derivative action in the feedback path, upstream of the error generation point, so that the set point component of the error signal can no longer be differentiated. This is shown in Figure 9.

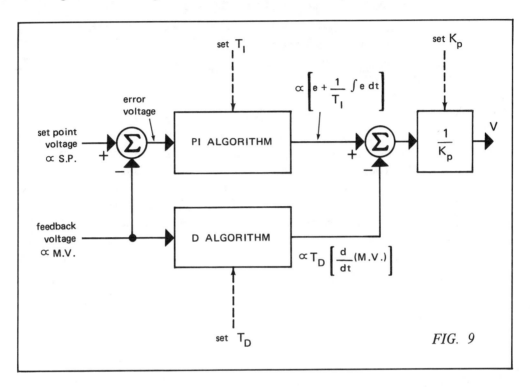

FIG. 9

If the coefficients K_p, T_I and T_D can be adjusted independently of each other, each by means of its own potentiometer (say), the control law is said to be "non-interacting": most modern electronic controllers are like this. In older electronic controllers, and in all pneumatic controllers, one control adjustment will change one coefficient in a major way but will also affect the value of at least one of the other coefficients to a minor extent: such controllers are said to be "interacting". Depending upon the chosen method of tuning the controller (see Section 15.7.2), it is likely that the control engineer will find it easier to tune the non-interacting type.

With some controllers, especially the pneumatic types, the actual control law may only approximate the three term law defined above. This factor would be taken into account automatically, when the controller is tuned.

In many instances, not all of the terms would be used, in a particular loop. For example, derivative action can be eliminated by setting $T_D = 0$, whilst integral action can be removed by setting $T_1 = \infty$. Thus, it is possible to configure P, PD, PI, and PID control, and in some cases I control only (called "floating control"). Roughly speaking, the effect upon loop performance of the three terms can be summarised as follows:

- Proportional action will reduce steady state error and increase the step response overshoot, as the proportional band K_p is reduced.

- Integral action will eliminate steady state error arising from most causes (refer to Section 15.2) and, as the integral action time T_I is reduced, increase the step response overshoot; it is unlikely to be required whenever the plant process contains an inherent integration term, since the resulting loop would then contain two integrations.

- Derivative action will reduce the step response overshoot, as the derivative action time T_D is increased.

- It is difficult to generalise about the effect of the terms upon step response settling time.

The controller output will only be related to the system error by a linear control law whilst the output is within the normal limits of excursion. The steady state relationship (which would be measured experimentally by selecting proportional action alone) between the controller output and the system error is indicated in Figure 10. The quiescent level of controller output, generated with zero system error, often is adjustable and, in that case, should be set to that value which causes the plant to operate at the nominal value of controlled variable: if this is not known at the time of commissioning, the quiescent controller output probably is best set to 50% of the excursion — that is, 12mA in the case of a 4—20mA signal range.

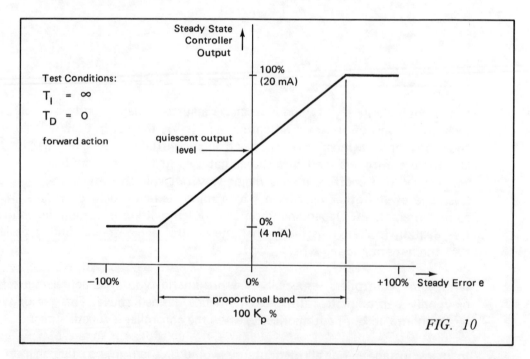

FIG. 10

Many controllers also incorporate "Forward/Reverse Action" selection, as indicated by the changeover switch in Figure 8. This makes it possible to include or omit a sign inversion, which can be used as necessary to ensure that the total number of sign inversions around the closed loop is an odd number, thus achieving negative feedback rather than positive feedback.

8.3.5 **Auto/Manual Transfer**

Often, when tuning a loop or when starting up or shutting down a plant, it is convenient to operate a system in an open loop mode (that is, with the feedback path rendered ineffective) rather than a closed loop mode. This is achieved by means of "Auto/Manual Transfer": in the Manual mode, the set point adjustment directly manipulates the value of the controller output signal, by-passing the three term control law (as shown in Figure 11), thereby eliminating the feedback action. Problems can arise when switching between the Manual and Auto modes, if this results in a discontinuity in the value of the controller output. Modern electronic controllers incorporate "bumpless transfer" (or "bumpless changeover") which, by electronic means, eliminates the possibility of a discontinuity in the output signal. Earlier controllers required manual "balancing", whereby the new value of the output had to be adjusted manually before switching to the new mode, in such a way that no change in output value would occur at changeover. On very early controllers, the step in output value was unavoidable.

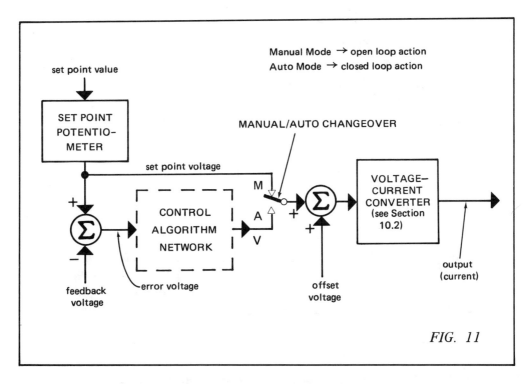

FIG. 11

With some older controllers, it was possible for the hardware mechanising the integral action term to accumulate a non-zero value, when the controller was in the Manual mode. This has been called "reset wind-up", and can prevent a bumpless transfer. In a modern controller, the output of the integral action term will be clamped at zero whenever the controller is in the Manual mode. Note that the term "reset windup" also may be applied to the integration of sustained values of error variable which might occur in the Auto mode (when the loop is closed). This situation can arise when either large changes in set point or large changes in plant load are applied. The controller may include components to limit the value of the output signal generated by the network mechanising the integral action term.

8.3.6   Analog Controller Displays

Wherever displays are incorporated into the faceplate of an analog process controller, these usually are provided by moving coil instrument movements travelling over a strip scale, calibrated linearly in terms of percentages of full signal excursion. Figure 12 of Chapter 7 showed a typical layout of the faceplate of a pneumatic process controller, and a similar arrangement would be typical for an analog electronic counterpart. Some modern controllers employ solid state "thermometer" types of scale, indicating 1% or ½% increments, using sets of parallel light emitting diodes or miniature gas discharge indicators, each taking the form of a very short bar to represent a specific signal level. The variables usually displayed are set point, deviation, measured variable (process variable), and controller output. Controllers often include means to indicate when the deviation exceeds manually preset upper and lower limits and, in addition, simultaneous output signals may be generated in order to activate remote alarm annunciators: alternatively, the alarm indication may be monitoring either the measured variable or the controller output.

8.3.7   Digital Process Controllers

The availability of digital hardware has introduced the possibility of improved reliability and flexibility to the production of general purpose process controllers.

Where the number of control loops for a particular plant is small, it is becoming common practice to instal, in the place of an analog controller, an equivalent digital controller. With this approach, the digital controller would be designed to synthesise its analog counterpart and would resemble it physically, in terms of packaging, external connection, and commissioning procedures. Such controllers are microprocessor based, with a separate microprocessor being dedicated to each controller.

Where the number of control loops for an installation exceeds a figure in the vicinity of (say) eight, a more efficient approach is to use an electronic system in which the microprocessor is shared between a number of controllers, and this technique often is used in "distributed control". This approach offers much greater flexibility, because the controllers need not be configured until the commissioning stage, provided that a correct estimate of the quantity of controllers required has been made beforehand. Moreover, the configuration can be revised easily at a later stage, should this so be desired. Configuring is undertaken either at a dedicated keyboard allocated to a set of these controllers, or by means of a centralised keyboard console which normally would be sited in a control room.

The creation of a distributed control system is undertaken in stages: taken in chronological sequence, these would involve controller configuration, followed by the specification of ranges and alarm limits of variables, the values of the control law parameters, and the values of the set points. All such data would be entered manually, in the form of an alphanumeric code, and stored in protected semiconductor memory. Typically, communication between controllers and plant would be by means of analog signal transmission; communication between controllers situated within the same logical grouping would be by means of parallel digital data transmission; communication between logical groups of controllers, central control stations, and process computers would be by means of serial digital data transmission: refer to Section 16.6 for discussion on digital data transmission formats.

In addition to synthesising all of the functions available with analog process controllers (Sections 8.3.2 to 8.3.6 inclusive), the distributed control configurations typically offer the following additional types of function, all of which would be implemented digitally:

● Nonlinear static characteristics, involving such nonlinearities as dead-space, square laws, etc.

● Summation, multiplication, division, square-rooting, etc., of data values.

● Gain constants and time constants which can be made variable functions of specified input signals.

● Supervisory Control, in which the (remote) set point values can be set electronically, using data generated by an on-line process computer — see Section 16.1 for further discussion on this topic.

● Direct Digital Control (DDC), in which the operation of the microprocessor based controller now is taken over by an on-line process computer, with the controller relegated to providing back-up capability in the event of computer failure — again, refer to Section 16.1.

The ability to introduce nonlinearities into controller static characteristics can effect the following types of improvement:

● control loops can be made less sensitive to parasitic noise;

● the settling times of control loops, following set point or load disturbances, can be minimised;

● loops can be made less sensitive to load disturbances;

● the dynamic behaviour of loops can be made less sensitive to control law parameter settings, set point values, and load values;

● compensation can be made for the effects of nonlinearities occurring in the final control element, plant process, or feedback transducer;

● the effect of interaction with other control loops can be minimised.

The ability to make gain constants and time constants signal dependent enables a simple form of adaptive control to be introduced, whereby the form of the control law can be modified to accommodate sensed changes in plant operating conditions. This capability also facilitates improved start-up and shut-down procedures, whereby the controller settings ideally should be "scheduled" to follow a predetermined sequence: typically, this scheduling would be supervised by a process computer or, in some cases, a Programmable Logic Controller (see Section 8.5.3).

Because of the increased flexibility afforded by digital process controllers, the following types of decision may need to be included, when the hardware is being selected:

- In the event of a failure in a supervisory computer, should the controller stay in the Auto mode, holding the last value of the set point?

- In the event of a failure in the controller, should the output line hold the last value of the controller output?

- Should each controller be self contained or can controller hardware be distributed and shared between various printed circuit assemblies?

- Should each controller have its own independent power supply?

- If power supplies are shared, should there be back-up power supplies?

- What integrity should data highways have, in terms of protection against damage and susceptibility to electrical noise?

- Should controllers be separate physically from the supervisory computer, or be an integral part of the computer interface?

- Should controllers be self monitoring, and should provision be made for their duplication, for failure survival purposes?

- Should controllers have their own manual controls and displays, or can these be integrated into a centralised control console?

- Should controller internal configurations be modular, to facilitate rapid fault isolation and rapid return to service, using possibly low grade personnel?

It can be seen that the introduction of digital controllers can involve a number of types of decision which are not relevant to the selection of their analog counterparts.

8.4   SPEED CONTROLLERS

8.4.1   General Purpose Speed Controllers for DC Motors

Figure 12 is a generalised representation of the various alternative arrangements used in DC motor speed control systems. The normal practice with large motors is to configure for armature control, with the armature power being derived from the AC mains and rectified to DC using a suitable Converter. The type of Converter to be used will depend to some extent upon the power rating of the motor: Converters employing either bipolar power transistors or power MOSFETs can now be built to control motors having ratings up to many tens of kilowatts; SCR Converters have been used extensively for all motor sizes up to several megawatts, although they are less likely to be used in the future at the lower end of the power range, due to the increasing competitiveness of transistor and MOSFET alternatives. The design of the Converter will take into account the following factors:

- the motor rating;
- the motor duty cycle;
- the possible need for reversibility of the direction of rotation;

- the type of braking action required;

- the waveform of the AC line current, which will have a "chopped" appearance — this waveform may be made to approach the desirable sinusoid by progressively increasing the pulse number created for the Converter supply;

- the possible need for electrical isolation between the AC mains and the motor circuit, so that the latter may be earthed at that point most convenient from controller design or safety aspects.

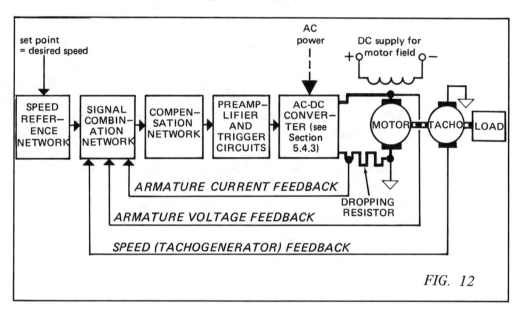

FIG. 12

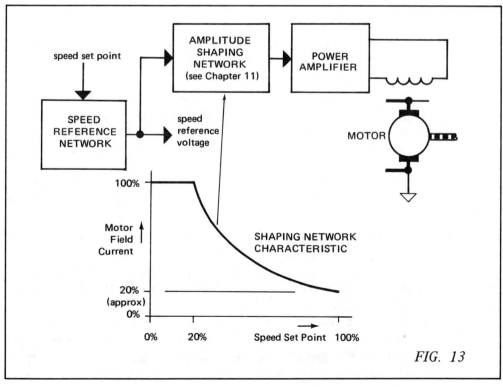

FIG. 13

When the motor is operated under conditions of constant excitation, a speed range in the region of 20:1 generally is regarded as being a maximum. The lower speed limit is determined by the slow running performance of the motor, which is subject to "cogging": this means that the motion is jerky, due to the effect of the armature slots on the time-variation in the magnetic flux distribution. The speed range may be extended to (say) 100:1, relative to the base speed, by weakening the field as a function of the set point (the desired speed), using the technique indicated in Figure 13.

The feedback paths shown in Figure 12 have the following properties:

- The primary (negative) speed feedback is obligatory and normally is derived from a DC tachogenerator. If reduced accuracy can be tolerated, the motor back-emf can be measured, using the bridge arrangement described in Section 2.4.5, and the derived voltage used as the feedback signal: this technique is not appropriate when field weakening is incorporated, since the emf then is no longer a function of speed alone.

- Negative armature current feedback can be used to change the Converter into a current source, as opposed to a voltage source: this can result in improved motor dynamic performance. (Refer to Section 5.5.3 for a detailed discussion). One disadvantage with the voltage source is that, if the armature supply voltage is subjected to a sudden change (arising from a sudden change in speed error), this can generate potentially damaging current levels circulating through the motor armature. This situation occurs whenever the motor back-emf is significantly different in value from the applied armature voltage. If the gain around the current feedback loop is sufficiently high, it will have a linearising effect upon the Converter which, on its own, can possess a nonlinear relationship such as would result, for example, from the law associated with the phase control of SCRs, as is discussed in Section 5.4.3.

- Negative armature voltage feedback may be switched in, on standby (when the set point will have been switched to zero), to ensure that the armature voltage, and hence the motor speed, is held rigidly at zero. In some systems, negative armature current feedback may be omitted (so that the output from the Converter probably will then behave as a voltage source), in which case negative armature voltage feedback may be connected permanently, to act as a minor (compensation) feedback path.

- A negative armature current feedback path incorporating a deadspace element, as shown in Figure 14, may be provided, to effect automatic armature current limiting so as to protect the motor against possible overload. The network is designed to block the feedback signal until the armature current exceeds a preset level of, for example, 125% of rated current: above this level, the feedback path has a very high incremental gain associated with it, which effects a very low incremental closed loop gain for the current loop. As a result, the current is held within virtually the limit value, irrespective of the value of the speed error signal.

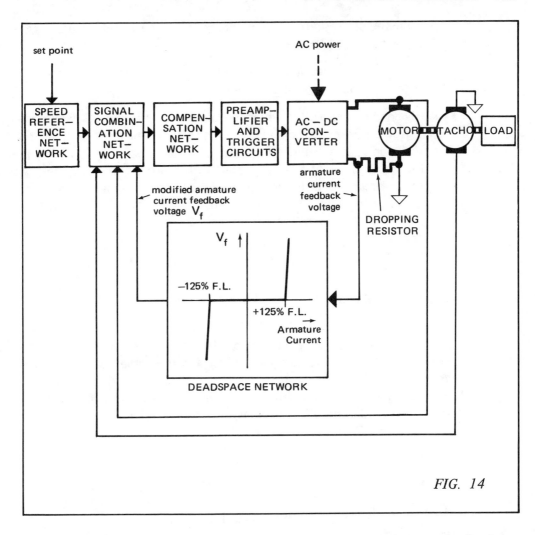

FIG. 14

- In those systems not employing negative armature current feedback, so that the output of the Converter then behaves as a voltage source, a small level of positive armature current feedback may be connected at all times. This can be designed to compensate for the voltage dropped across the armature circuit resistance, so that the motor back-emf is no longer significantly affected by load changes. This type of feedback is known as "IR compensation" and it cannot be 100% effective, because of the additional (nonlinear) effect of armature reaction upon the motor back-emf.

Other facilities which often are built into commercial speed controllers include the following:

- Selectable set points, facilitating sequence control of speed. Refer to Section 2.3.1 for details.

- Dynamic limiting of set point changes, to limit demanded motor acceleration. This is achieved by inserting an R—C filter (see Sections 12.2 and 12.3) between the speed reference network and the speed error generation point.

- Adjustment of minimum and maximum speed set points. Again, refer to Section 2.3.1 for details.

- Adjustment of compensator parameters, equivalent to the tuning of general purpose process controllers.

- Regenerative braking, which requires that the directional sense of the motor torque be controlled in a manner causing a return of energy to the AC supply, when this is required. Such an arrangement, whilst increasing the complexity of the Converter, will improve the system response time to a demanded reduction in speed and/or a demanded reversal in the direction of motion. An alternative is dynamic braking, with which a high dissipation resistor is switched across the motor armature, in order to provide a sink for the energy stored in the motor and load, but this method is unacceptably wasteful, except for small motors.

8.4.2   General Purpose Speed Controllers for AC Motors

In terms of capital cost, a DC motor is much more expensive than an AC motor of comparable rating; conversely, a speed controller for an AC motor has, until recently, been much more expensive than a comparable speed controller for a DC motor, because of the greater complexity associated with the former. In terms of total capital outlay, DC drives have had the financial edge over AC drives, although against this should be weighed the greater reliability and maintainability associated with AC motors. Recently, however, technological improvements and reduced device costs have made AC motor controllers much more competitive, especially when the combined cost of the controller and the motor is considered: when reliability and maintainability are also taken into account, the AC drive is becoming increasingly the more attractive of the alternatives, especially in the power range from 1kW to several tens of kilowatts.

Conventional AC motors can be divided into four categories, all of which can be subjected to electronic speed control: induction motors, AC commutator motors, synchronous motors, and reluctance motors, the last named being a type of synchronous-induction motor. However, AC commutator motors are not competitive when employed with electronic speed control, so that they will not be considered further, here.

With induction motors, the usual value of standstill inrush current can be limited with electronic control, by exciting the stator with reduced voltage or reduced frequency during starting. With electronic control, synchronous and reluctance motors need not be started in an induction machine mode, because of the variable frequency action inherent with electronic controllers for these types of motor.

Electronic controllers for conventional induction motors can be divided into three categories. In each case, the converter and inverter networks used may employ SCRs or, certainly at the low end of the power range, bipolar power transistor or power MOSFET networks may be used as alternatives. The three alternative control strategies are as follows:

A.   MANIPULATION OF STATOR VOLTAGE

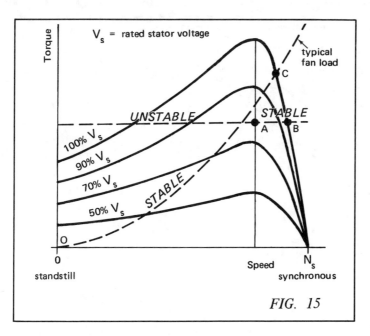

FIG. 15

Figure 15 shows a family of torque vs speed characteristics for varying levels of stator voltage, for a conventional induction motor. For a load exhibiting a constant torque, the speed range would be limited to the region between the operating points A and B, which usually would be unacceptably restricted. However with fan types of load, the speeds represented by the region between points O and C can cover a wide range, so that this type of strategy can be suitable for fan loads. Efficiency is low and internally generated heat is high at low speeds, because of the correspondingly high slip frequencies, so that this control technique is not appropriate for large motors. Figure 16 represents a speed control system using stator voltage manipulation: other (minor) feedback channels may also be present in a practical system, but these have been omitted from the diagram.

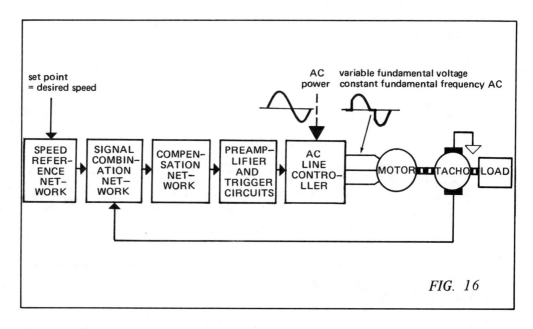

FIG. 16

The AC Line Controller blocks part of each half cycle of the AC supply waveform, so that the fundamental component of the (constant frequency) motor voltage waveform is manipulated.

B.   MANIPULATION OF STATOR VOLTAGE AND FREQUENCY

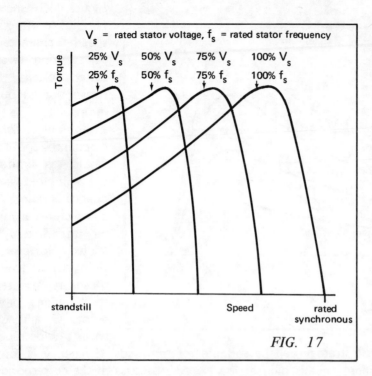

FIG. 17

Figure 17 shows a family of torque vs speed characteristics for varying levels of stator voltage and frequency, with both being varied in the same proportion. With this strategy there is almost no restriction upon matching the motor to the load requirements, within the available torque and speed ranges, and the motor will be operated at low values of slip for all levels of excitation, yielding high efficiency and low heat generation.

Because of the low operating levels of slip, (imprecise) open loop control of induction motor speed can be produced using this strategy, with the stator supply frequency determining the instantaneous value of synchronous speed. However, precise control demands that compensation be made for the slip speed, so that a system like that in Figure 18 would then be required: again, minor feedback paths have been omitted.

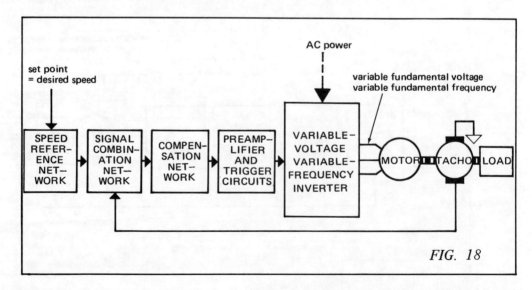

FIG. 18

Figure 19 shows the most commonly used alternative configurations for generating variable-voltage variable-frequency inverters. As other alternatives, some types of Cycloconverter may be used for performing the same task.

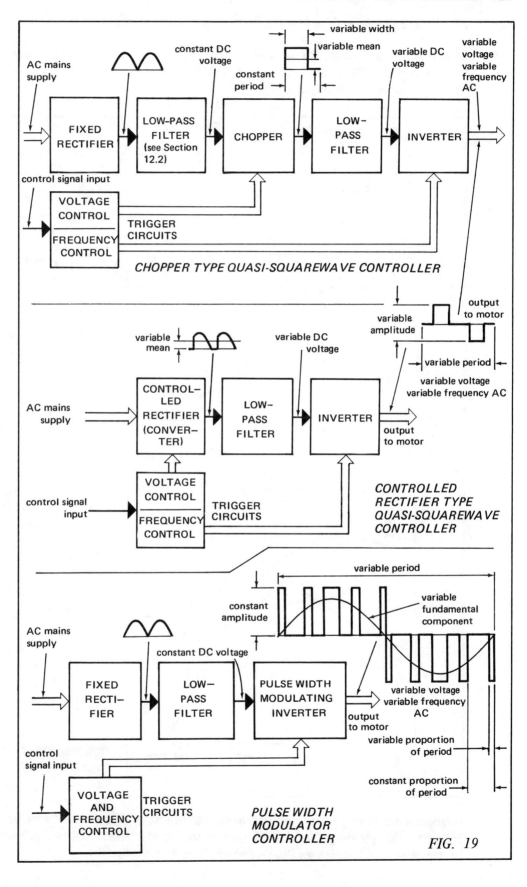

CHOPPER TYPE QUASI-SQUAREWAVE CONTROLLER

CONTROLLED RECTIFIER TYPE QUASI-SQUAREWAVE CONTROLLER

PULSE WIDTH MODULATOR CONTROLLER

FIG. 19

C.   MANIPULATION OF ROTOR ENERGY

This method is suitable for wound rotor induction motors, for which the transfer of energy from the rotor back into the AC mains is manipulated by means of a line commutated inverter, as shown in Figure 20.

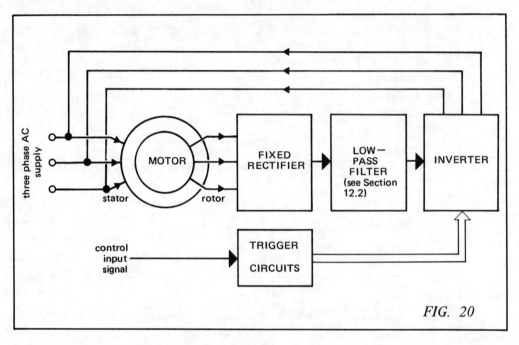

FIG. 20

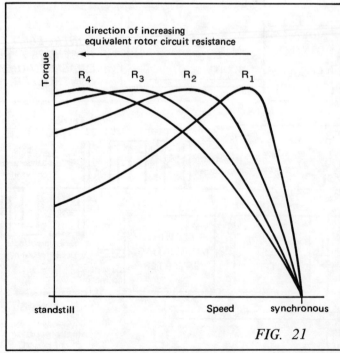

FIG. 21

The effect, upon the family of torque vs speed characteristics, of transferring increasing levels of energy out of the rotor is comparable to that of increasing the rotor circuit resistance, which is demonstrated in Figure 21. However, electrical energy no longer is dissipated as heat in the rotor but is transmitted back to the supply, so that the power efficiency is high despite the fact that high values of slip can occur during operation. In more complex arrangements, energy transfer between the mains and the rotor can be made bidirectional, yielding families of torque vs speed characteristics equivalent to both positive and negative values of rotor circuit resistance.

Synchronous motors and reluctance motors are controlled by manipulation of frequency but not voltage. For these motors, therefore, simplified versions of the controllers of Figure 19 can be used, omitting the variable voltage facilities. In the absence of control over the full frequency range, a synchronous motor is not self-starting and then requires to be operated in an induction motor mode during starting: the necessary hardware can be produced using an integral AC brushless exciter, a fixed rectifier network, and solid state switching circuits, all mounted upon the rotor assembly. With both types of motor, open loop action will yield precise speed control, because of the exact relationship between rotor speed and stator supply frequency, once synchronous operation has commenced. It may be possible to operate several motors from the one controller, with the rotors remaining in precise synchronism with each other, once synchronous action has started.

AC motors may be braked using one of the following alternative techniques:

- Alternately reversing the phase sequence of the stator connections, a procedure known as "plugging". This is unsuitable for synchronous motors.

- Disconnecting the normal AC supply from the stator and, instead, applying a DC voltage. This represents a form of dynamic braking, and is suitable for induction motors.

- Disconnecting the normal AC supply from the stator and, instead, connecting suitable resistors across the stator terminals. This represents a form of dynamic braking, and is suitable for synchronous motors.

- Disconnecting the normal AC supply from the stator and, instead, connecting the stator through a fixed rectifier network into a suitable DC source. This is a form of regenerative braking, and is suitable for synchronous motors.

- Gradually reducing the frequency of the stator supply. This is a form of regenerative braking, and is suitable for all three types of AC motor.

In all cases involving switching, the braking circuitry can be implemented using either electromechanical or solid state switches.

8.4.3 Incremental Controllers for Stepper Motors

The control of a stepper motor (described in Section 5.6.3) involves the DC excitation of the stator windings, in a predetermined sequence. Each manufacturer of stepper motors has tended to adopt individual standards, so that the multiplicity of stepper motor types which has resulted means that there are no universal controllers for these motors: each motor tends to require its own controller design.

Certain properties of stepper motors are common:

- The speed of rotation will be proportional to the frequency of the pulse train applied to the drive circuits, provided that a specified maximum frequency and load torque are not exceeded.

- The position of the motor rotor will depend upon the number of pulses which have been applied previously to the drive circuits, provided that the motor has been able to develop sufficient torque to enable it to respond to every pulse.

- The direction of rotation can be reversed by reversing the sequence in which the motor coils are energised and de-energised.

- The motor coils are highly inductive, so that the drive transistors must be protected against voltage spikes whenever a coil is de-energised.

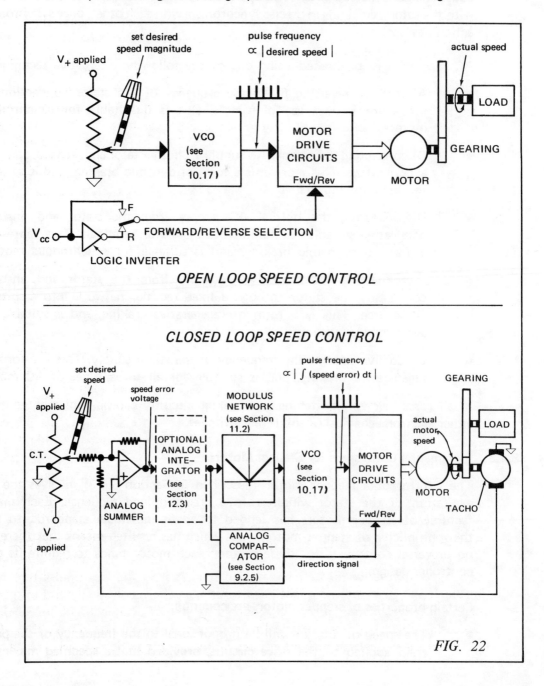

FIG. 22

●   By energising two adjacent motor coils simultaneously, the rotor step size may be halved in value. The consequent reduction in kinetic energy will result in less overshoot of each step position. The frequency of the pulse train will need to be doubled, in order to restore the original stepping rate.

●   Motor efficiency can be improved by reversing the current in each motor coil, as an alternative to switching the current off. With such a bipolar drive (which requires greater circuit complexity), the total input power to the motor may be half that required for the corresponding unipolar drive, for approximately the same motor performance.

Figure 22 shows representative configurations for open loop and closed loop speed controllers. The motor drive circuits receive a pulse train having a frequency proportional to the voltage applied to the voltage-controlled oscillator. In the case of the open loop configuration, the Forward/Reverse switch would not be required for a unidirectional drive. More precise control of speed might be achieved with the closed loop configuration, which almost certainly would require the analog integrator in order to achieve satisfactory operation: in the steady state, this integration will develop that steady output voltage required by the oscillator in order that the motor may be stepped at precisely that speed corresponding to zero speed error. In Section 13.4.3, the application of stepper motors to position control systems is described, and further examples of speed control applications are given in Section 13.5.3.

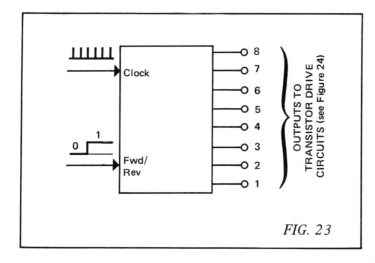

FIG. 23

The pulse train from the V C O would be applied to a purpose-designed ring counter, an example of which is indicated in Figure 23. Typically, at any time one output would be high whilst all other outputs would be low, although the reverse situation might be preferable for some designs. The input pulse train would cause the high signal to be stepped around the outputs in numerical sequence: 1, 2, 3, 4, 5, 6, 7, 8, 1, 2, etc. when the Fwd/Rev input is high (say), and 8, 7, 6, 5, 4, 3, 2, 1, 8, 7, etc. when the Fwd/Rev input is low. In other cases, two outputs might need to be high at any one time, with the others driven low, and these two high outputs would be circulated in sequence by the input pulse train. In further cases, the outputs might need to be high alternately singly and in pairs: many different combinations are possible. (Refer to Section 10.14 for further discussion about counters). Typical pulse frequencies would be in the 300 — 400 Hz range for permanent magnet stepper motors and the 700 — 800 Hz range for variable reluctance stepper motors; however, stepping rates as high as 20 kHz have been reported, the upper limit on speed being dependent upon the time constant of the stator coil circuits.

The outputs from the ring counter are used to excite transistor drive circuits, there being one for each motor coil or for each pair of coils, typically. To limit the effect of the winding inductance, it is preferable that each winding circuit should present a switched current source to the coil. In the case of variable reluctance motors, some current must be retained when the motor is required

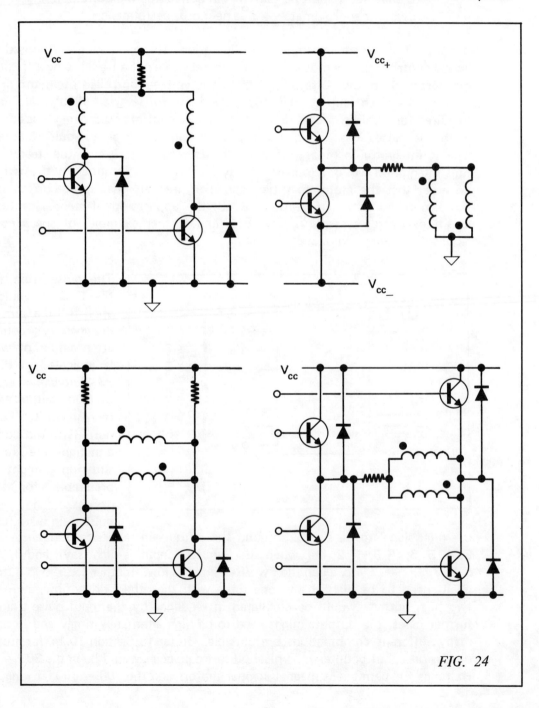

FIG. 24

to remain stationary, if a holding torque is required. In the case of permanent magnet motors, however, some holding torque is present without energisation, so that current pulses of controlled mark-space ratio can be used to excite the motor coils, with the resulting reduction in the mean level of current being used to minimise the heat developed by the motor. Figure 24 shows representative transistor drive circuits, some of which allow for two windings to be energised simultaneously; many other configurations are possible. Diodes, zener diodes, and resistors may be incorporated into the circuits, to provide protection for the transistors, to provide discharge paths for the coil inductances, to alter the circuit time constant, and to modify (that is, dampen) the typically oscillatory response of the motor rotor to a step in the position of the stator flux.

Any gearing and/or couplings in the drive between the motor and the load will be subjected to a hammering type of action, and allowance must be made for this. If the gearing is omitted, most applications would require the use of a motor designed to provide many steps per revolution: the large number of coils occurring in many such motors would then result in the need for an equally large number of transistor drive circuits.

Stepper motors are prone to overheating, if subjected to continuous high speed operation, so that the duty cycle is an important facet of their use. The fact that significant energy can be wasted, in the form of heat dissipation, is an indication that the power efficiency of these devices can be low in value.

8.5   SEQUENCE CONTROLLERS

8.5.1   Motor Driven Electromechanical Timers

These represent the simplest form of sequencer. Usually, the motor runs at constant speed and turns a bank of rotary switches. The sequence is predetermined, to some extent, by the configuration of the switch wafers, but the sequence can be modified by changing the external wiring to the switch wafers. This type of sequencer has the merit of simplicity but life, reliability, and maintainability will be limited. This type also has the merit of making it easy to combine various types of voltage supply and various types of load, and to easily obtain isolation between the various supplies.

8.5.2   Relay and Contactor Networks

These networks normally employ straightforward "ladder" arrangements of relay/contactor contacts and coils. Adjustable time delays can be a problem, especially if long periods of dwell are required. These networks have the advantages of ease of combination of types of supply and types of load, together with ease of electrical isolation of supplies. Life, reliability, and maintainability can be good, depending upon the type of environment and the switching duty required of the contacts. These three factors can be improved by using either dry reed relays or mercury wetted relays, at lower power levels, and improved still further by using solid state relays and contactors, which employ power MOSFETs, SCRs, and Triacs. In the case of solid state devices, problems may arise with signal isolation requirements (which can be alleviated by using optoisolated components), with breakdown due to voltage spikes, and with false switching caused by crosstalk.

8.5.3   Programmable Logic Controllers (PLCs)

Usually, these controllers are designed around dedicated microprocessors, and their principal function is to provide a solid state replacement for relay and contactor networks. Some of these processors have the ability to digitally process numerical data, in addition to their switching role, and, when this is the case, they tend to be known more simply as "Programmable Controllers" (PCs).

A typical PLC system would consist of a Processor, one or more Interface Units, and a Programming Unit. The Processor would be a microprocessor-based central processing unit with semiconductor memory, with the memory storing the programming language and diagnostic software, the program defining the switching sequence (as determined by the operation of the Programming Unit), and the data currently being processed. The memory would be protected against mains power failure, by means of long-life battery back up. A large installation might have provision for connection to a process computer, general purpose process controllers, and computer peripherals such as line printers, disc memory, etc.

The function of the Interface Unit is to enable the Processor to communicate with the plant, the sequence of operations of which is to be controlled. The type of interface circuitry used would be similar to that employed in general purpose process computer interfaces, which are discussed in detail in Chapter 16. A typical interface would be expandable up to a preset upper limit and would include many of the following signal handling capabilities:

- DC on/off voltage or current input signals;
- AC on/off voltage or current input signals;
- serial digital input signals;
- parallel digital input signals;
- DC on/off voltage or current output signals;
- AC on/off voltage or current output signals;
- serial digital output signals;
- parallel digital output signals.

Typically, the Programming Unit would comprise a keyboard and video display, and this would be used for entering the programs into the Processor. Usually, the programming would take the form of entries of symbols and data into a visually displayed relay ladder diagram, an example of which is shown in Figure 25. However, some Programmers would provide for entry of sets of Boolean equations: this latter technique is more economical with storage but requires more programming expertise. Some languages include provision for processing numerical data, such as the contents of registers and counters, and code conversion; a few include some digitally synthesised general purpose process controller algorithms.

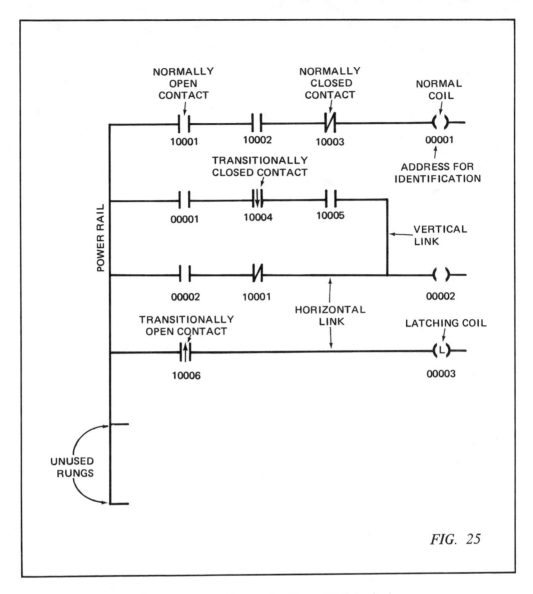

NORMALLY OPEN CONTACT 10001
NORMALLY CLOSED CONTACT 10003
NORMAL COIL 00001
ADDRESS FOR IDENTIFICATION
TRANSITIONALLY CLOSED CONTACT 10004
POWER RAIL
00001 10005
VERTICAL LINK
00002 10001 00002
HORIZONTAL LINK
TRANSITIONALLY OPEN CONTACT 10006
LATCHING COIL 00003
UNUSED RUNGS

FIG. 25

Factors to be taken into account when selecting a PLC include:

- input and output signal capacity;
- the availability of suitable interface hardware;
- the degree of difficulty involved with formulating programs;
- the facilities available for entering and displaying programs and system status;
- the ability to expand subsequently the system size;
- the ability to modify the program easily;
- ease of fault identification (including fault diagnostics) and isolation, and of return to service;
- survival of power supply failure;
- reliability and maintainability.

When correctly used, PLCs offer the advantages of long life, high speed of operation, compactness, ease of modification, and minimal power requirement.

9

HARDWARE TO GENERATE SUM AND DIFFERENCE DATA; MECHANICAL COMPONENTS

9.1   THE COMBINATION OF DATA

In any closed loop system, it becomes necessary to combine data. For example, it is always necessary to compare the controlled variable data (representing actual value) against the reference variable data (representing desired value). In systems containing multiple feedback paths, the minor feedback data must be added or subtracted at appropriate points in the forward path of the system, in the usual arrangement.

In many instances, it is more convenient to add, rather than subtract, the signals representing the data required to be compared. The summation of data can be arranged to implement the subtraction of data by firstly inverting the sign of the data to be subtracted. This is demonstrated by the equivalence of the two diagrams shown in Figure 1.

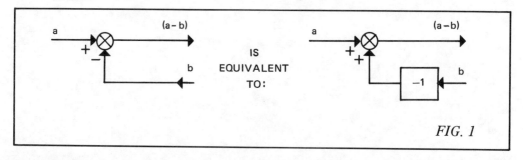

FIG. 1

The inversion required for data b typically would be implemented by the insertion of sign-inverting hardware or, alternatively, by modifying either the input connections or the output connections of the transducer generating b (assuming this to be feasible).

Often, it is not practicable to combine data in one–to–one proportions. This situation can be demonstrated by making reference to Figure 2.

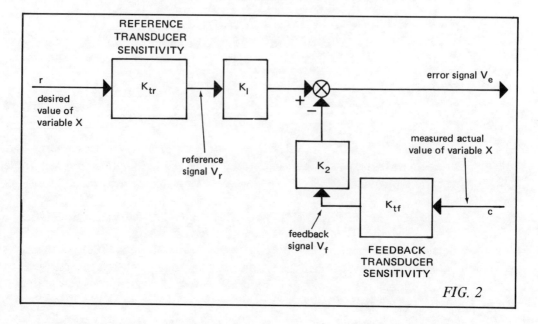

FIG. 2

Suppose, for example, that the diagram represents the instrumentation of an analog speed control system, with the reference transducer being a potentiometer and the feedback transducer a tachogenerator. Therefore, both K_{tr} and K_{tf} will have units of volts per rad/s. Suppose, also, that these sensitivities are such that, when a full speed of 200 rad/s is both demanded and achieved, $V_r = 10\ V$ and $V_f = 100\ V$. In this situation, the error $e(= r - c)$ is zero, so that the error signal V_e also must be zero.

Now $V_e = K_{tr} K_1 r - K_{tf} K_2 c$

$$= K_1 V_r - K_2 V_f$$

$$= 0$$

It follows that $10\ K_1 - 100\ K_2 = 0$

so that $\dfrac{K_1}{K_2} = 10$

Thus, the two signals should be combined in inverse proportion to the sensitivities of their transducer sources:

$$K_{tr} = \frac{10}{200}, \quad K_{tf} = \frac{100}{200}, \quad \frac{K_{tr}}{K_{tf}} = \frac{1}{10} = \frac{K_2}{K_1}$$

It should be noted that the calibration of the reference transducer relates to the scale arbitrarily marked in units of rad/s (or rpm), against which the operator manually sets his desired speed, by adjusting the shaft of the potentiometer. Normally, full scale deflection would represent maximum desired speed.

Note that the diagram of Figure 2 can be rearranged mathematically to represent one–to–one mixing of data, as shown in Figure 3, which represents a unity feedback system: that is, one with unity gain in the feedback path.

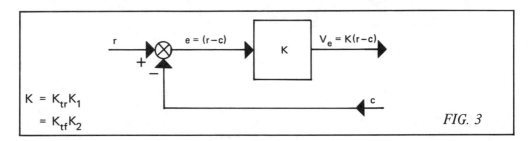

$K = K_{tr}K_1$

$\quad = K_{tf}K_2$

FIG. 3

Having established that data may be both added and subtracted and that they will need to be mixed in varying proportions, the hardware which can implement this can be investigated.

9.2 ELECTRICAL METHODS FOR COMBINING ANALOG SIGNALS

Electrical signals can be combined in terms of combining either voltages, currents or electro-magnetic fields. In modern technology, voltages and currents usually are combined using analog computing networks based on integrated circuit operational amplifiers, and some representative examples will be given.

9.2.1   Inverting Summer Configuration

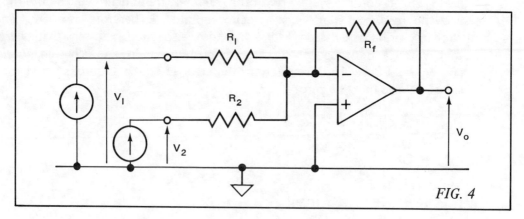

FIG. 4

Referring to Figure 4 and assuming an "ideal" operational amplifier, it is shown readily that

$$V_o = -\frac{R_f}{R_1}V_1 - \frac{R_f}{R_2}V_2 = -(K_1V_1 + K_2V_2)$$

This network is suitable for adding both DC and AC voltages. The loads on the input signal sources will be R_1 and R_2 ohms, respectively, provided that the amplifier output is not driven into saturation. Both input signal sources need to be single-ended and referenced to common.

9.2.2   Non-Inverting Summer Configuration

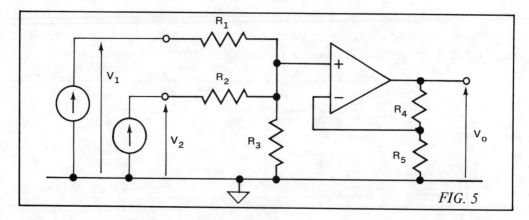

FIG. 5

Referring to Figure 5, it is readily shown that

$$V_o = \frac{\left(\dfrac{V_1}{R_1} + \dfrac{V_2}{R_2}\right)\left(1 + \dfrac{R_4}{R_5}\right)}{\left(\dfrac{1}{R_1} + \dfrac{1}{R_2} + \dfrac{1}{R_3}\right)} = K_1V_1 + K_2V_2$$

This network is suitable for adding both DC and AC voltages. The loads on the input signal sources will be approximately

$$\left(R_1 + \frac{R_2 R_3}{R_2 + R_3}\right) \quad \text{and} \quad \left(R_2 + \frac{R_1 R_3}{R_1 + R_3}\right) \quad \text{respectively,}$$

irrespective of whether the amplifier is saturated or not. Both input signal sources need to be single-ended and referenced to common. R_3 may be omitted physically and replaced by infinity in the above expressions.

9.2.3 Differential Amplifier Configuration

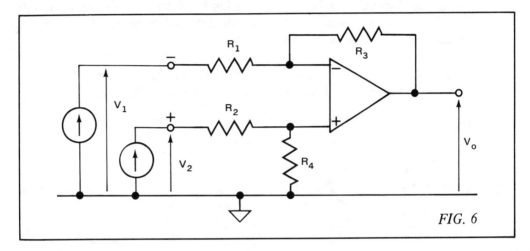

FIG. 6

Referring to Figure 6, it is shown readily that

$$V_o = -\frac{R_3}{R_1} V_1 + \frac{R_4}{(R_2 + R_4)} \cdot \frac{(R_3 + R_1)}{R_1} V_2 = -K_1 V_1 + K_2 V_2.$$

This network is suitable for subtracting both DC and AC voltages. The loads on the input signal sources will be R_1 and $(R_2 + R_4)$ respectively, provided that the amplifier output is not driven into saturation. If the resistors are matched so that $R_1 = R_2 = r$ and $R_3 = R_4 = R$, then $V_o = K(V_2 - V_1)$, where $K = R/r$, and the signal sources can be referenced to a potential different from the amplifier common: the effect on V_o will be subject only to the common-mode rejection ratio of the amplifier.

9.2.4 Series Addition and Subtraction

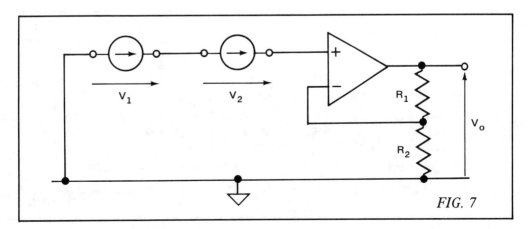

FIG. 7

Referring to Figure 7, it is shown readily that

$$V_o = \left(1 + \frac{R_1}{R_2}\right)(V_1 + V_2) = K(V_1 + V_2), \quad K > 1.$$

This network is suitable for adding both DC and AC voltages. The loads on the input signal sources will be almost infinitessimal, being due to the (very high) input impedance of the amplifier and to the (very low) input offset current of the amplifier. The first signal source must be single-ended and therefore connected to common, whilst the second (and any additional) signal source must be floating. The network can be modified to subtract signals, by reversing one of the signal sources, where appropriate.

Where the range of V_1 and/or V_2 is too great for the amplifier, these signals may be attenuated prior to being mixed, as shown in Figure 8.

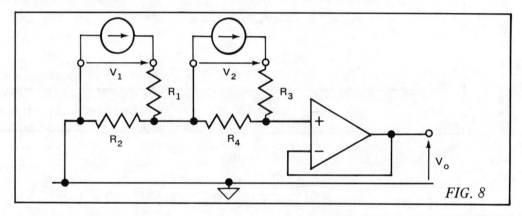

FIG. 8

In this example, $V_o = \left(\dfrac{R_2}{R_1 + R_2}\right)V_1 + \left(\dfrac{R_4}{R_3 + R_4}\right)V_2$

$$= K_1 V_1 + K_2 V_2, \quad K_1 < 1, K_2 < 1.$$

The loads on the signal sources are now $(R_1 + R_2)$ and $(R_3 + R_4)$, respectively.

9.2.5 Analog Comparators

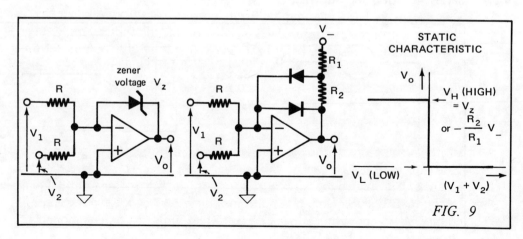

FIG. 9

The purpose of an Analog Comparator is to generate a digital signal to indicate the relative state of two analog signals. In theory, at least, any of the networks featured in Figures 4 to 7 inclusively may be configured to this end, by choice of appropriate values for specified resistors, as follows:

Network Figure No.	Necessary Resistor Values	Input State for $V_o = V_{sat-}$	Input State for $V_o = V_{sat+}$
4	$R_f = \infty$	$(V_1 + V_2) > 0$	$(V_1 + V_2) < 0$
5	$R_5 = 0$	$\left(\dfrac{V_1}{R_1} + \dfrac{V_2}{R_2}\right) < 0$	$\left(\dfrac{V_1}{R_1} + \dfrac{V_2}{R_2}\right) > 0$
6	$R_3 = \infty$	$\left(\dfrac{R_4 V_2}{(R_2 + R_4)} - V_1\right) < 0$	$\left(\dfrac{R_4 V_2}{(R_2 + R_4)} - V_1\right) > 0$
7	$R_2 = 0$	$(V_1 + V_2) < 0$	$(V_1 + V_2) > 0$

V_{sat+} and V_{sat-} are the output saturation levels of the operational amplifier, the values of which will depend upon the values of the amplifier supply rail voltages. For high speed switching, it is not good practice to drive the output voltage into saturation, but to limit its excursion by means of appropriate components: Figure 9 shows two typical arrangements.

Far superior in performance to these networks are dedicated Analog Comparator ICs, such as the LM311, which offer the following advantages:

- relatively high differential input voltage range;
- unipolar supply rail voltage requirement;
- low response time (200 ns is typical);
- very high input impedance;
- low input offset current;
- open collector output.

The advantage with the open collector output arises from the fact that the HIGH level V_H of output voltage can be chosen to suit the application, with an appropriate "pull-up" resistor being connected between the output terminal and a suitable V_H supply rail. Note that most analog comparator ICs respond to an input voltage differential, as opposed to an input voltage sum.

9.2.6 Use of Bridge Networks for Subtracting Signals

In the arrangement shown in Figure 10, which is, in effect, an unbalanced Wheatstone bridge, it can be shown that $V_o = K(\theta_i - \theta_o)$, where K is the V/rad sensitivity of the feedback potentiometer. The network performs equally well for DC and AC signals. Only one point in the network supplying the amplifier can be connected to common: either one amplifier input can be commoned or one side

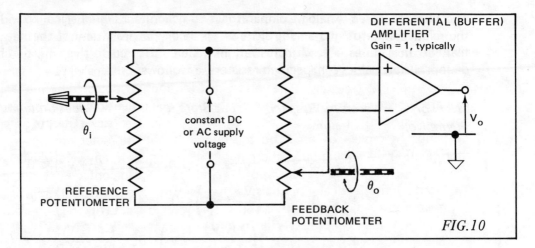

FIG.10

of the supply can be commoned, but they must not both be commoned, because this will short circuit one limb of the bridge. The formula for V_o is only precise provided that the potentiometers are not loaded significantly.

9.2.7   Use of Tapped Continuous Track Potentiometers for Subtracting Signals

A development of the previous method employs a pair of special toroidal servo potentiometers each having a continuous track, multiple equi-spaced tappings, and dual brushes set diammetrically opposite to one another. Each of the set of tappings on one potentiometer is joined to the corresponding tapping on the other, as indicated in Figure 11: most of the links have been omitted for clarity.

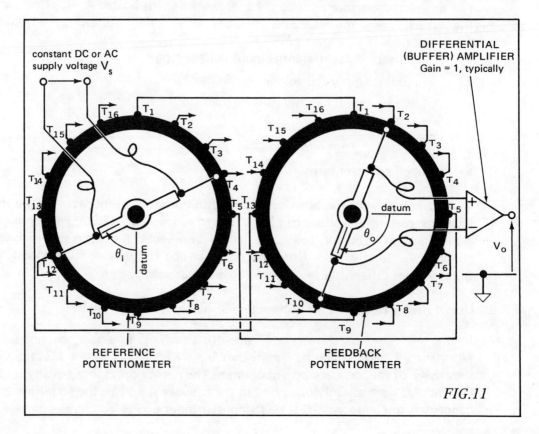

FIG.11

Using slip rings (not shown), a fixed DC or AC voltage, usually from a floating source, is applied to the two brushes of the reference potentiometer. This causes two identical linear voltage distributions to be established along the two 180° sectors of the track. The alignment of these two distributions will be determined by the value of θ_i selected. The voltage distributions are detected by the tappings and are transferred to the tappings on the feedback potentiometer. The resulting voltage distributions imposed upon the track of the feedback potentiometer will be almost a replica of those on the reference potentiometer, the accuracy of reproduction depending upon the number of tappings. In any case, when $\theta_o = \theta_i$ the two brushes of the feedback potentiometer will be in contact with two points on the track at identical potentials, so that the output potential difference, which is transferred to the amplifier via slip rings (again not shown), will be zero. Note that θ_i and θ_o are calibrated relative to datums separated by 90°. When $\theta_o \neq \theta_i$, it is shown readily that

$$V_o \cong V_s \cdot \frac{2}{\pi} \left(\theta_i - \theta_o \right) \qquad \text{when} \quad -\frac{\pi}{2} < (\theta_i - \theta_o) < \frac{\pi}{2}$$

$$\text{and} \quad \cong -V_s \cdot \frac{2}{\pi} \left(\theta_i - \theta_o \right) \qquad \text{when} \quad -\pi < (\theta_i - \theta_o) < -\frac{\pi}{2}$$

$$\text{and when} \quad \frac{\pi}{2} < (\theta_i - \theta_o) < \pi$$

V_s is the supply voltage and $(\theta_i - \theta_o)$ is in radians.

9.2.8 Use of Electromagnetic Fields for Adding and Subtracting Signals

An alternative method for combining data represented by electrical signals is to cause these signals to establish magnetic fields, to combine these fields, and to sense the value of the nett flux, the output signal normally being a voltage. A typical technique is to employ multiple field windings on a DC generator, which is being used as a power amplifier, as shown in Figure 12.

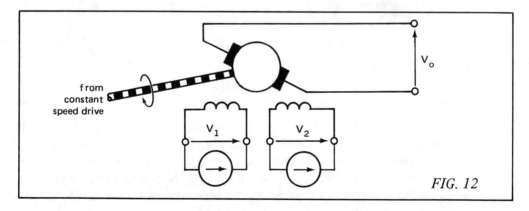

FIG. 12

The separate field windings provide full isolation between the input signal sources. Reversing a signal source converts additive action to subtractive action, and vice-versa. Assuming a linear magnetisation characteristic, the configuration shown in Figure 11 will yield an expression of the form $V_o = K_1 V_1 + K_2 V_2$, where the relative values of K_1 and K_2 will depend upon the relative numbers of turns and the relative resistances of the two windings.

The technique which has been described here is suitable only when the signal voltages are DC. When the sources are AC, transformer action between windings having a common magnetic circuit would result in each AC voltage source inducing high circulating currents in the other input circuits, which would not be tolerable.

The use of synchro differentials and control transformers in chains of synchros, as described in Section 2.2.4, presents an electromagnetic technique for the addition and subtraction of angular data. Resolvers, discussed in Section 2.2.5, provide an alternative set of components which can be applied in similar fashion. In these cases, all of the electrical signals are AC voltages.

9.2.9 Additional Techniques with AC Signals

One of the advantages with using AC signals arises from the fact that signal transformers can be introduced into the signal paths, prior to signal combination. Signal transformers can provide some or all of the following facilities:

- electrical isolation of signal sources from loads;

- signal level and impedance level conversion;

- improvement in signal-to-noise ratio.

For an example of the application of signal transformers, refer to Figure 13.

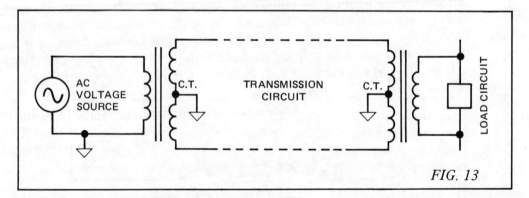

FIG. 13

The centre-tapped windings of the two signal transformers form a balanced bridge and common-mode noise picked up by the two conductors in the transmission path will cancel in the second transformer, and therefore will not be transmitted to the load. In addition, the two conductors may be twisted together and the twisted pair may be screened, with the screen connected to common (ground). Electrically, the transmission circuit is completely symmetrical relative to common. The signal source and the load are completely isolated from each other electrically, the signal source need only be single ended, and the transformer turns ratios can be selected for signal level and impedance level requirements.

9.3   ELECTRONIC NETWORKS FOR COMBINING DIGITAL DATA

The application of arithmetic operations to digital data is most easily undertaken when the data are represented in some form of weighted code, as defined in Section 2.2.7. Unless otherwise stated, the operations to be described here assume that a natural binary code is used during the processing, and this is by far the most common format: however, the techniques may be adapted to accommodate other weighted formats. The networks to be described involve the application of hard wired logic to arithmetic operations, although a suitable digital processor may be programmed to perform the same tasks.

9.3.1   Natural Binary Representation

With a word length of eight bits, for example, all eight bits can be allocated to the representation of a numerical value, if the value always has the same polarity. In those cases where the polarity can assume either sign, one of the bits must be used to indicate the sense of the polarity, and thus becomes the "sign bit". The most common convention used is one which allocates, to the most significant bit, binary 0 to represent a positive value and binary 1 to indicate a negative value.

Thus, a positive integer might be represented by the word 0100 1101 which, according to the basis for the discussion so far, is to be interpreted as

$$+[(1\times2^6)+(0\times2^5)+(0\times2^4)+(1\times2^3)+(1\times2^2)+(0\times2^1)+(1\times2^0)] = +77_{10}$$

In order to facilitate arithmetic operations, the magnitude of a negative value of data usually would be represented in "complement" form, the most common being "two's complement format". The two's complement of a number is formed by inverting every digit and then adding a 1 to the result: thus, to encode -77_{10} one would need to invert 0100 1101, yielding 1011 0010, and then add 1, so that the final code is 1011 0011.

In those cases where a fractional number is required to be represented, the binary digits now acquire weightings which are negative powers of the base 2. Thus, a positive fraction might also be represented by the word 0100 1101 which, using a comparable basis for interpretation, would denote a value

$$+[(1\times2^{-1})+(0\times2^{-2})+(0\times2^{-3})+(1\times2^{-4})+(1\times2^{-5})+(0\times2^{-6})+(1\times2^{-7})]$$

$$= +0.6015625_{10}.$$

The two's complement technique can also be applied to the representation of negative fractions, so that -0.6015625_{10} would be coded by inverting every digit of the word 0100 1101, yielding 1011 0010, and then adding 1 to the least significant bit, to produce 1011 0011, as for the integer case.

Arithmetic operations are much more easily undertaken using integer numbers alone or fractional numbers alone and, wherever possible, digital control hardware should attempt to scale the data to this effect. Where the range of values to be processed cannot be accommodated in this manner (not even with the use of multiple length words), mixed numbers then must be used, in which case the representation normally adopted is "floating point format". In this format, a mixed number typically is represented in the form $M \times 2^E$, where M is a signed fractional "mantissa" (normally adjusted to lie between 0.5_{10} and 1 in magnitude) and E is a signed integer "exponent". Multiplication and division of two floating point numbers $M_1 \times 2^{E_1}$ and $M_2 \times 2^{E_2}$ (say) are relatively easy operations, because

$$(M_1 \times 2^{E_1}) \times (M_2 \times 2^{E_2}) = (M_1 \times M_2) \times 2^{(E_1 + E_2)} \text{ and}$$

$$(M_1 \times 2^{E_1}) / (M_2 \times 2^{E_2}) = (M_1 / M_2) \times 2^{(E_1 - E_2)}.$$ Thus, these two types of operation involve the multiplication and division of fractional numbers and the addition and subtraction of integer numbers. Addition and subtraction of two floating point numbers require that the two numbers have the same value of exponent, so that provision must be made for adjusting exponents and mantissae accordingly, before processing can proceed further: thus, for example

$$(+0.8 \times 2^{+10}) + (-0.6 \times 2^{+8}) = (+0.8 \times 2^{+10}) + (-0.15 \times 2^{+10})$$

$$= (+0.8 - 0.15) \times 2^{+10} = +0.65 \times 2^{+10}$$

After any processing operation, including multiplication and division, it will be usual to adjust, where necessary, the mantissa and exponent of the result, so that the former finally lies within the range 0.5_{10} to 1 in magnitude.

The addition of two signed integer numbers can follow the rules of binary addition, with the sign bit handled in the same manner as any other bit. For example,

Decimal	Natural Binary
+16	010000
+(−3)	+ 111101
+13	(1)001101

↑   ↑
    sign bit
discard carry bit

Subtraction of a signed integer number usually is implemented by firstly complementing the number to be subtracted (the "subtrahend") and then adding the result to the "minuend".

In the addition and subtraction processes described here, any leftmost carry bit always is discarded, provided that two's complement arithmetic is used. Thus, for example:

Decimal	*Natural Binary*
+3	000011
−(+16)	+ 110000
− 13	(0) 110011

sign bit
zero carry bit

Decimal	*Natural Binary*
−29	100011
−(+2)	+ 111110
− 31	(1)100001

sign bit
discard carry bit

The need for multiplication and division operations in digital control processes may arise where it is required to apply a gain constant to a variable or, in rarer cases, where two variables need to be multiplied or divided.

The multiplication of two signed integer numbers can follow the rules for binary multiplication, provided that the sign bits are processed separately. For example

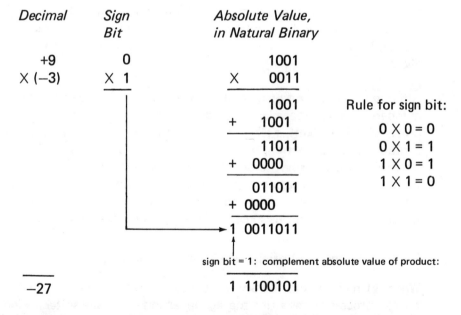

Decimal	*Sign Bit*	*Absolute Value, in Natural Binary*	
+9	0	1001	
X (−3)	X 1	X 0011	
		1001	Rule for sign bit:
		+ 1001	0 X 0 = 0
		11011	0 X 1 = 1
		+ 0000	1 X 0 = 1
		011011	1 X 1 = 0
		+ 0000	
		1 0011011	

sign bit = 1: complement absolute value of product:

−27	1 1100101

It will be seen that the word length of the product is double that of the multiplicand and the multiplier, and provision would need to be made for this situation.

The division of two signed integer numbers can follow the rules for binary division, provided that the sign bits are handled separately. For example:

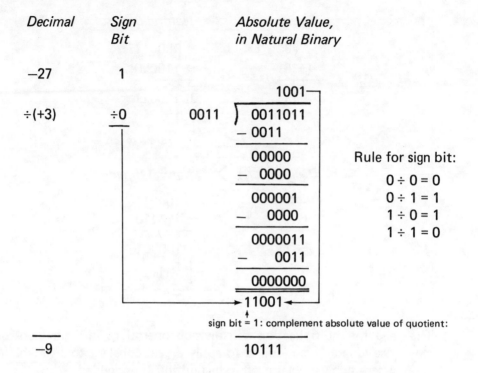

	Decimal	Sign Bit	Absolute Value, in Natural Binary

-27   1

÷(+3)   ÷0   0011

$$
\begin{array}{r}
1001 \\
0011\ \overline{)\ 0011011} \\
-\ 0011 \\
\hline
00000 \\
-\ \ \ 0000 \\
\hline
000001 \\
-\ \ \ \ \ 0000 \\
\hline
0000011 \\
-\ \ \ \ \ \ \ 0011 \\
\hline
0000000
\end{array}
$$

Rule for sign bit:

$$0 \div 0 = 0$$
$$0 \div 1 = 1$$
$$1 \div 0 = 1$$
$$1 \div 1 = 0$$

→ 11001 ←

sign bit = 1: complement absolute value of quotient:

-9   10111

It can be seen that multiplication involves a sequence of shifting and addition, whereas division involves a sequence of shifting (in the opposite direction) and subtraction, so that these two processes have fundamental similarities. However, the result from the division of integers can be an integer, a fractional number, or a mixed number, depending upon the relative values of the dividend and the divisor.

Although the operations shown above have been demonstrated for integer numbers they can be adapted to cope with either fractional or mixed numbers, provided that account is taken of the position of the radix point. Complementing, addition, and subtraction, together with straight comparison, can be implemented relatively easily, using hardwired logic; although such implementation also is possible for multiplication and division, the complexity involved makes these last two processes more easily handled with a programmable digital processor, with the arithmetic operations specified in terms of program statements.

9.3.2 Hardwired Logic for Forming the Two's Complement

When an n-bit natural binary word has to be translated into two's complement form, a process representing the sign inversion of data, a suitable algorithm for the jth bit is $B_j = A_j \oplus [A_{j-1} + A_{j-2} + ... + A_2 + A_1]$, $j > 1$, and $B_1 = A_1$, where A_n .... A_1 are the bits of the word before it is converted and B_n .... B_1 are the corresponding bits of the word after conversion. This algorithm is valid whether A_n and B_n represent sign bits or not. The symbol $\oplus$ signifies the Exclusive—OR (modulo − 2 addition) process. Figure 14 shows one possible logic network for implementing this algorithm for an 8-bit word.

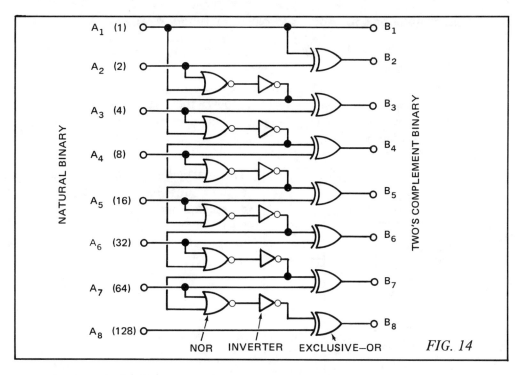

FIG. 14

9.3.3   Hardwired Logic for Comparing Two Binary Words

The logic to be described here represents the digital counterpart of the analog comparator of Section 9.2.5, and so could be used in the formation of a digital on-off controller, for example. Medium-scale ICs are available for generating a comparison between two digital words of limited length. An example in the TTL range is the 7485, which can be used to compare two 4–bit words: these ICs can be cascaded, in order to compare two natural binary or B C D words having lengths which are integer multiples of four bits, as shown in Figure 15.

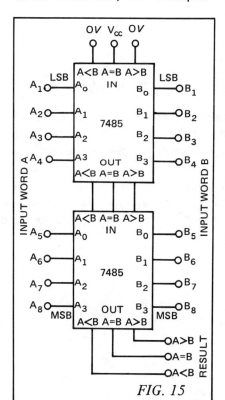

FIG. 15

Because this particular logic is comparing magnitudes, it cannot cope with complemented data. Thus, if it is to be used with data which can have both negative and positive values, the negative values would best be converted to sign bit plus (uncomplemented) absolute data format. Separate logic would be required for comparing the sign bits, and the result of this comparison would then be used in the interpretation of the absolute value comparison.

Any unused IC data inputs would be connected to logic LOW.

9.3.4   Hardwired Logic for Adding Two Natural Binary Words

The logic to be described here represents the digital counterpart of the non-inverting analog summer of Section 9.2.2, scaled for unity gain. Medium-scale ICs are available for generating the sum of two binary words of limited length. An example in the TTL range is the 7483, which can be used to add together two words having lengths which are integer multiples of four bits, as shown in Figure 16.

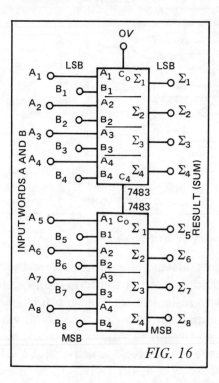

This particular logic is designed to handle either unsigned or signed — and — complemented data, so that no special treatment is required for the latter case. Any unused IC data inputs should be connected to logic LOW.

FIG. 16

9.3.5   Hardwired Logic for Multiplying Two 4-Bit Natural Binary Words

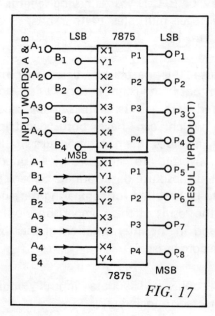

Figure 17 shows two particular ICs which can be connected to generate the 8-bit product of two 4-bit natural binary words. The configuration represents a (limited) hardwired logic arrangement for multiplying unsigned 4-bit words. For handling data of any greater complexity, a digital processor probably would be used.

FIG. 17

9.4   MECHANICAL METHODS FOR COMBINING SIGNALS

Mechanical devices can be used to generate the sum and difference between linear displacements or forces, for the rectlinear case, and between angular displacements or torques, for the rotary case. The advantages of these devices are their simplicity, ruggedness and independence from power supplies. Possible disadvantages include:

- frictional, mechanical hysteresis, inertia, and deflection (bending) effects;

- bulkiness;

- inflexibility of the configurations, in contrast to electronic networks.

Some typical mechanical devices will be described.

9.4.1   The Lever and the Walking Beam

In the application shown in Figure 18, the Walking Beam is a lever which effects a mechanical negative feedback path around an hydraulic servovalve-power cylinder combination.

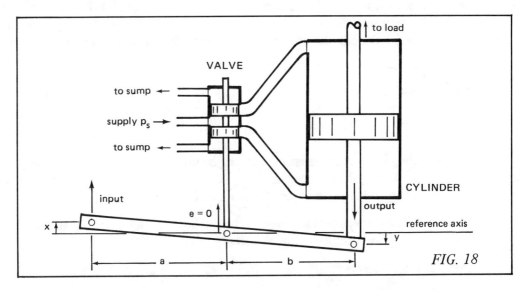

FIG. 18

The quiescent position of the lever is indicated by the reference axis. When e = 0, the valve spool is central, so that no oil flows into the cylinder and the piston will be stationary. Applying similar triangles,

$$\frac{y}{b} = \frac{x}{a}.$$

If the input x is changed, the beam pivots about the output joint at y, because the large holding forces initially prevent the piston from moving. This results in e changing, and the displaced valve spool causes the piston to be driven until the subsequent change in y has reduced e back to zero. This condition corresponds to a new equilibrium state.

For small variations about the quiescent position,

$$\Delta e = \frac{\partial e}{\partial x} \cdot \Delta x + \frac{\partial e}{\partial y} \cdot \Delta y .$$

$\partial e/\partial x$ can be derived from the relationship between e and x with the output end unmoved: using triangles,

$$\frac{\partial e}{\partial x} = \lim_{\substack{\Delta e \to 0 \\ \Delta x \to 0}} \left[\frac{\Delta e}{\Delta x} \right] = \frac{b}{(a+b)} .$$

By similar reasoning, for the other end $\frac{\partial e}{\partial y} = - \frac{a}{(a+b)}$.

Thus, $\Delta e = \frac{b}{(a+b)} \cdot \Delta x - \frac{a}{(a+b)} \cdot \Delta y = K_1 \Delta x - K_2 \Delta y$.

With the above configuration, the equilibrium state corresponds to a "displacement balance" condition. As an alternative, it is possible to configure the hardware to generate a "force balance" condition in the equilibrium state: in such a case, the output will deflect by an amount such that the resulting force applied to the load balances the input force applied to the beam, in the proportion of a:b.

By applying forces to different points along the beam, and reversing the sense of application of forces, it is possible to effect the addition and subtraction of forces, with adjustable proportions.

A controlled force may be applied to the beam input using, for example:

- a controlled pressure applied to a bellows;

- a controlled current passed through the solenoid of a solenoid-ferrous armature assembly (force motor);

- a spring extended by a controlled displacement of one end.

These techniques form the basis of differential-pressure to pressure and differential-pressure to current transmitters (Section 4.2) and control valve positioners (Section 7.1.4). The advantages arising from using the force balance technique are that effects such as those due to mechanical hysteresis, deadband, and static friction are minimised.

9.4.2   The Differential Gear

Angular displacements may be added or subtracted (depending upon the sense of the displacement) using the type of differential gear shown in Figure 19.

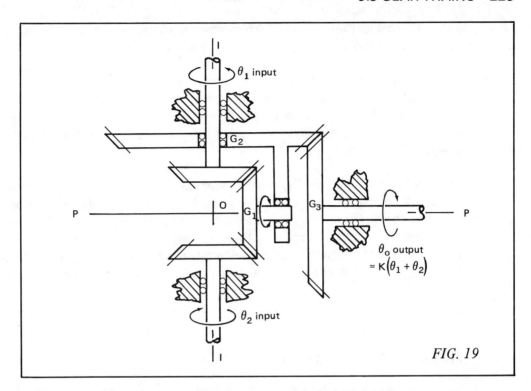

FIG. 19

If there is relative motion between the two input shafts, so that $\theta_1 \neq \theta_2$, then the axis of gear G_1 will be rotated bodily about IOI in a plane through POP and perpendicular to the page. This will result in rotation of gear G_2 which will be transmitted, throught gear G_3, to the output shaft.

$\theta_o = K(\theta_1 + \theta_2)$, where the value of K depends upon the gear ratios.

9.5   GEAR TRAINS

In many servomechanisms, it is commonplace to use one or more gear trains in the vicinity of the servomotor (or actuator), the mechanical load, and the feedback transducer. There are many possible reasons for this, amongst which feature the following:

- to enable a high speed-low torque motor (or actuator) to be coupled to a low speed-high torque load, in order to minimise motor (or actuator) size;

- to convert rectilinear motion to rotational motion, and vice-versa, using rack–pinion or screw–nut configurations;

- to reverse the direction of motion of a drive;

- to provide a change in the direction of a shaft drive (for example, to turn a drive through 90°);

- to enable a transducer to be coupled to an otherwise inaccessible shaft, the selection of gear ratio providing means for mechanically altering the system loop gain;

- to enable shaft angular displacements to be added or subtracted (see Section 9.4).

In the last two cases, the gears usually are transmitting data at very low power levels and, as such, would be termed "instrument gears". Instrument gear trains are available commercially in pre-packed form, covering a wide range of alternative gear ratios; often they are packaged in synchro-style cases and then are known as "gearheads".

It is possible to make backlash-free instrument gears, by "splitting" pinions into two parallel plates. These are sprung apart, in an angular sense, so that one is in contact with the "leading" edges of the teeth of the mating gear, whilst the other is in contact with the "trailing" edges, so that no out-of-mesh state can ever exist. Against the advantages of backlash-free gearing must be traded the disadvantages of added complexity and a significant increase in frictional forces.

9.6   BRAKES, CLAMPS AND CLUTCHES

In a number of servosystem applications, there may be a requirement for the drive to be capable of holding the load rigidly stationary, against the action of reactive load forces. One example would be when the drive is hoisting a load and must then hold the load at a given height. A second example would be in a machine-tool drive, where the workpiece and table must be held rigidly stationary during a machining operation (for example, during a milling cut or a gear hobbing operation).

Electric motors, in particular, require to be in motion, in order that the ventilating action can provide adequate cooling, if the motor is developing significant levels of torque. Thus, most electric motors are not rated to sustain significant torque levels when crawling or stationary: to be so would necessitate a significant increase in frame size.

Hydraulic and pneumatic drives usually can be designed to have an inherent capacity for developing high holding forces/torques. Where this requirement is specified for an electric drive, usually it becomes necessary to supplement the motor with a brake or clamp.

In certain motors, electromagnetically actuated brakes are built into the motor frame, as an integral part of the armature assembly. If such a motor is not available, it becomes necessary either to include a brake in the shaft-gearing-load assembly or physically clamp the load to a base. Brakes and clamps, under automatic control, would be actuated by either electromagnetic, hydraulic, or pneumatic actuators.

Clutches can be used, in an on-off manner, in 'bang-bang' speed control systems. A typical arrangement is shown symbolically in Figure 20.

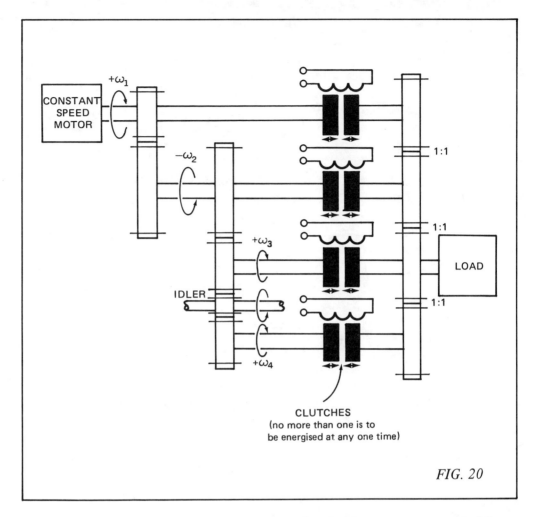

CLUTCHES
(no more than one is to
be energised at any one time)

FIG. 20

In this arrangement, with the motor assumed to be run at constant speed $+\omega_1$, the load could be driven at alternative speeds of $+\omega_1$, $+\omega_2$, $+\omega_3$, $-\omega_4$, depending upon which clutch is energised. With no clutch energised, the load would be stationary (and might require to be clamped). Such on-off clutches may be electromagnetically, hydraulically, or pneumatically actuated.

It also is possible to create a (unidirectional) variable speed drive using a constant speed motor, if a coupling capable of controllable slip is introduced. (Note that normal clutches would burn out if allowed to slip for any length of time). One possible coupling for this application is the type of fluid flywheel coupling used in automotive transmissions. An alternative is an electrical equivalent, one of which is the "magnetic particle clutch": the two clutch faces are separated by a "plasma" of magnetic particles, and the degree of slip between the two faces is determined by the degree of magnetisation to which the particles have been subjected. This is controlled by manipulating the DC current passed through a stationary solenoid. Another electrical alternative is the "eddy current clutch", which is based upon a metal disc being rotated within the field of a rotating electromagnet, with manipulation of the current being passed through the winding: the currents generated within the disc react with the magnetic field, to produce a (controllable) coupling torque and controllable slip.

10

SIGNAL AND DATA CONVERSION

TABLE 1.   SIGNAL CONVERSION HARDWARE

TO \ FROM	DC voltage	DC current	AC voltage (single)	AC synchro voltage pattern	AC resolver voltage pattern	Serial digital data	Parallel digital data	Pneumatic pressure (3–15 psi control air)
DC voltage	—	E	G			O	P	X
DC current	A	—						Y
AC voltage (single)	B		—	H	L	Q	R	
AC synchro voltage pattern				—	I	S	T	
AC resolver voltage pattern				I	—	U	V	
Serial digital data	C			J	M	—	W	
Parallel digital data	D			K	N	W	—	
Pneumatic pressure (3–15 psi control air)		F						—

Note: a blank entry signifies that no component exists to effect a conversion directly. Conversion may be achieved by cascading two or more of the listed devices.

KEY:

A	current feedback around a high gain amplifier	:	refer to Section 10.2
B	modulator; phase-sensitive, where necessary	:	refer to Section 10.4
C	analog-digital converter (ADC) with serial output	:	refer to Section 10.6
D	analog-digital converter (ADC) with parallel output	:	refer to Section 10.6
E	resistor; with bufferred load, where necessary	:	refer to Section 10.3
F	current-to-air converter (transducer)	:	refer to Section 10.19
G	demodulator (rectifier); phase-sensitive, where necessary	:	refer to Section 10.5
	or RMS-to-DC converter	:	refer to Section 10.13
H	synchro control transformer with locked rotor, or use one line-to-line voltage	:	refer to Section 2.2.4
I	Scott-Tee connected transformer pair	:	refer to Section 10.10
J	synchro-digital converter with serial output	:	refer to Section 10.11
K	synchro-digital converter with parallel output	:	refer to Section 10.11
L	resolver control transformer with locked rotor, or use one line-to-line voltage	:	refer to Section 2.2.5
M	resolver-digital converter with serial output	:	refer to Section 10.8
N	resolver-digital converter with parallel output	:	refer to Section 10.8
O	digital-analog converter (DAC) with serial input	:	refer to Section 10.7
P	digital-analog converter (DAC) with parallel input	:	refer to Section 10.7
Q	digital-analog multiplier (DAM), with sinewave reference and serial input	:	refer to Section 10.7
R	digital-analog multiplier (DAM), with sinewave reference and parallel input	:	refer to Section 10.7
S	digital-synchro converter with serial input	:	refer to Section 10.12
T	digital-synchro converter with parallel input	:	refer to Section 10.12
U	digital-resolver converter with serial input	:	refer to Section 10.9
V	digital-resolver converter with parallel input	:	refer to Section 10.9
W	shift register or counter	:	refer to Section 10.14
X	gauge pressure transducer with voltage output	:	refer to Section 4.4
Y	air-to-current converter (transducer)	:	refer to Section 10.18

Sections 10.15, 10.16 and 10.17 contain descriptions of code converters, frequency-voltage converters and voltage-frequency converters, respectively, which cannot logically be entered into Table 1 but which sometimes feature in data conversion.

10.1   INTRODUCTION

It is commonplace for the output signal of one element in a control loop to be incompatible with the input signal requirements of the element which it is intended to drive. It therefore becomes necessary to interpose special hardware, in order to convert the characteristics of the driving signal to the appropriate form. Examples of configurations in which this would be necessary are the following:

- a transducer with a pneumatic output signal required to drive into an electronic controller;
- a digital transducer required to drive into an analog electronic controller;
- a synchro control transformer required to drive a DC servoamplifier.

Many other examples are easily conceived. Hardware which is capable of providing signal conversion of this nature will obviously be very varied in nature, depending largely on the forms of the input and output signals of concern, and, for this reason, a survey of the alternative elements available must necessarily be limited in extent, in this particular volume. (Note, for example, that complete books have been devoted just to analog-digital and digital-analog conversion techniques).

The range of hardware available for signal conversion is summarised in Table 1, which should be interpreted by making reference to the Key. It should be noted that, if necessary, signal converters may be cascaded: thus, for example, an AC voltage signal may be converted into a set of signals representing parallel digital data by cascading together a demodulator and an analog-digital converter having parallel digital outputs. The types of hardware to which reference is made in the key of Table 1 will now be described in detail.

10.2   VOLTAGE TO CURRENT CONVERTERS

Section 5.5.3 described how negative feedback may be used in order to create a voltage-controlled current source. A specific application of this technique is shown in Figure 1.

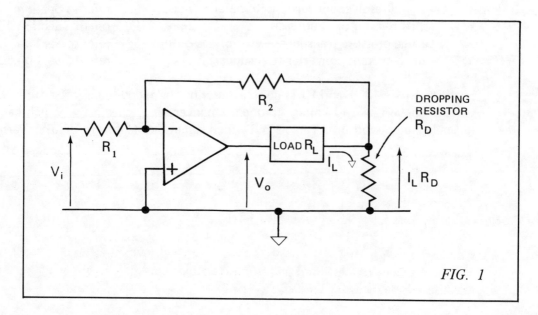

FIG. 1

It is readily shown for this configuration that, provided the amplifier output V_o is not saturating and the amplifier can be regarded as "ideal",

$$\frac{V_i}{R_1} + \frac{I_L R_D}{R_2} = 0$$

Solving for I_L yields $I_L = -\dfrac{R_2}{R_1 R_D} V_i$

The limiting value for I_L is related to the saturation value of $V_{o_{sat}}$ of the amplifier by $I_{L_{max}} = -\dfrac{V_{o_{sat}}}{R_D + R_L}$ and $V_{o_{sat}}$ will usually be 1.5 to 2V in magnitude less than the voltage of the amplifier supply rails (which is typically 12V, 15V, or 18V).

The principal disadvantage with the network of Figure 1 lies in the fact that the load must "float", because the network requires the dropping resistor to be tied to signal common. This problem can be eliminated by interchanging R_D and R_L and feeding back the voltage drop $I_L R_D$ through a differential amplifier stage, as shown in Figure 2.

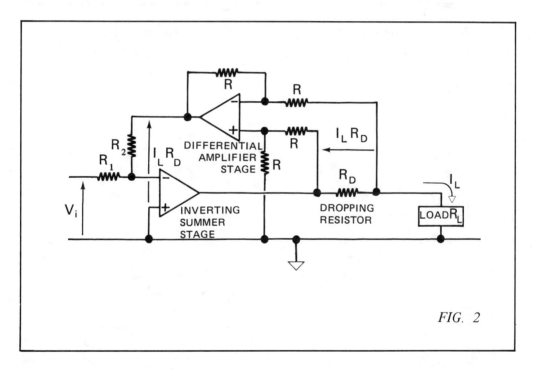

FIG. 2

The operation of the differential amplifier stage has been described in Section 9.2.3 and the version shown here has a voltage gain of unity. The formulae quoted above for I_L therefore still apply.

Where the range of I_L is required to be offset (by, for example, 4 mA), this can be effected by injecting an appropriate bias current into the negative input terminal of the inverting amplifier.

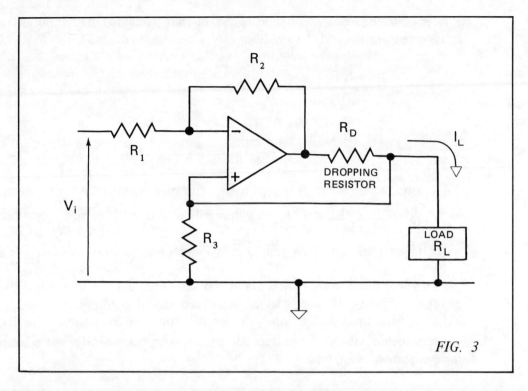

FIG. 3

Figure 3 shows a simpler version (which only uses one operational amplifier) of the network of Figure 2. Analysis shows that, provided the relationship $R_2 R_3 = R_1 R_D$ is satisfied and the amplifier is not saturated, the output current I_L is related to the input voltage V_i by the expression $I_L = V_i/R_D$. In this case, the limiting value of I_L is given by

$$I_{L_{max}} = \frac{V_{o_{sat}}}{\left(R_D + \dfrac{R_3 R_L}{(R_3 + R_L)} \right)}$$

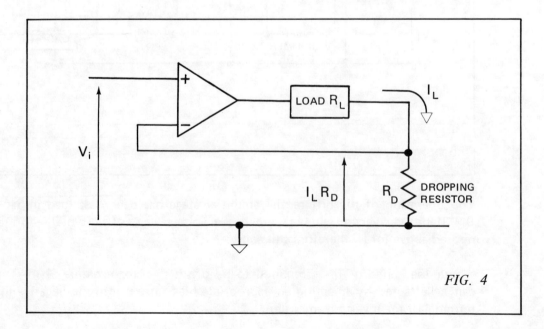

FIG. 4

Figure 4 shows a non-inverting alternative to the network of Figure 1. For this arrangement, $I_L R_D = V_i$, so that $I_L = V_i/R_D$. Again, R_L and R_D may be interchanged if a differential amplifier stage is inserted into the feedback path. If required, I_L may be offset by adding a suitable bias to the input of the non-inverting amplifier, using the type of input resistor network described in Section 9.2.2.

The configurations shown here will be suitable for converting either DC or AC signals: the operational amplifier must be supplied for bipolar operation, in the latter case.

Where the source of V_i has a low internal resistance and sufficient current drive, it may be possible to drive the load R_L directly from the source (yielding $I_L = V_i/R_L$, rendering unnecessary the amplifier stages.

10.3 CURRENT TO VOLTAGE CONVERTERS

The usual method for converting a current signal into a voltage signal is by use of an appropriate dropping resistor. Figure 5 shows one possible configuration, which assumes that it is appropriate to connect one side of the resistor R_D to signal common.

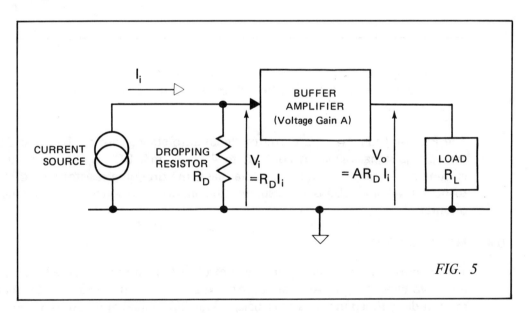

FIG. 5

The buffer amplifier must be included where the load resistance R_L is likely to vary and is sufficiently low so as to create a significant shunting effect on R_D. The amplifier may be inverting or non-inverting, as required, typically using the configurations discussed in Section 9.2: referring to these networks, $R_D I_i$ becomes the voltage source V_1 and the other source V_2 is redundant unless required as a bias source to offset V_o.

Where the dropping resistor cannot be tied to signal common, for whatever reason, it may be floated and allowance made for this by use of a differential amplifier network of the type described in Section 9.2.3: this is shown in Figure 6.

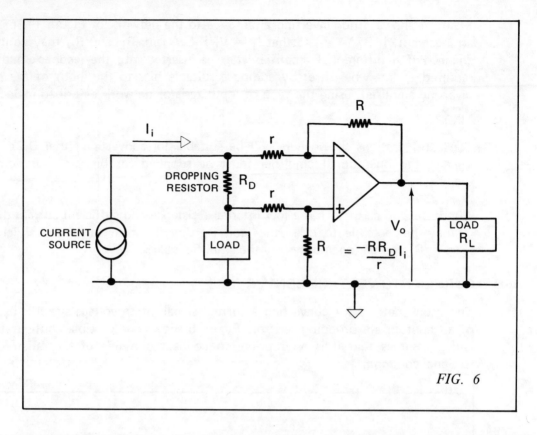

FIG. 6

The configurations shown here will be suitable for converting either DC or AC signals: the operational amplifier must be supplied for bipolar operation, in the latter case.

The Process Industries are currently tending to standardise on 1 to 5 V DC for the voltage signal range, in contrast to 4 to 20 mA DC for the most common current signal range: in this particular case, the dropping resistor would require to have a value of 250 ohm, assuming the amplifier stage to have a voltage gain of unity.

10.4   MODULATORS

The function of a modulator, in the control system context, is usually to convert a DC voltage into an AC voltage of fixed (carrier) frequency, such that the magnitude (defined in terms of either peak or RMS value) of the AC is proportional to the magnitude of the DC. This process, in a Telecommunications context, is referred to as "suppressed – carrier amplitude modulation".

Wherever the DC voltage is going to reverse in polarity, corresponding to a reversal in the sense of the data being represented by the DC signal, it is usual to cause the AC voltage to reverse its phase, relative to the phase relationship pertaining before the occurrence of the DC sign reversal. The type of modulator which can achieve this phase reversal is said to be "phase-sensitive". Figure 7 shows typical waveforms for various input signal conditions and assumes that the output waveform is required to be sinusoidal.

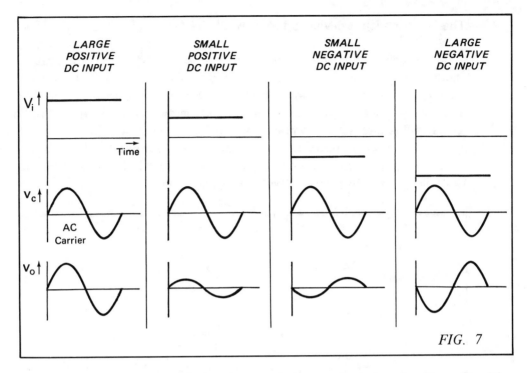

LARGE POSITIVE DC INPUT   SMALL POSITIVE DC INPUT   SMALL NEGATIVE DC INPUT   LARGE NEGATIVE DC INPUT

V_i

Time

V_c

AC Carrier

V_o

FIG. 7

Figure 8 represents the static characteristic required for the Phase-Sensitive Modulator (PSM).

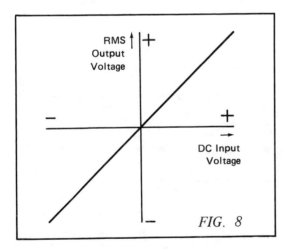

RMS Output Voltage

DC Input Voltage

FIG. 8

The negative RMS output voltage values are to be interpreted as a reversal in the relative phase of the output voltage waveform.

The most common type of PSM network currently uses a monolithic analog multiplier: such a device is capable of multiplying together two analog voltages, as indicated in Figure 9. Not shown in this diagram are external components usually necessary for setting output nulls, sensitivity, and for providing output power boosting: refer to Section 11.4.2 for further details.

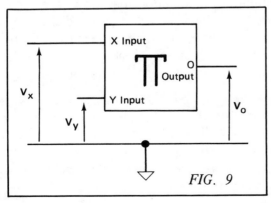

X Input

O Output

V_x

Y Input

V_y

V_o

FIG. 9

The law for such a device is typically of the form $v_o = \dfrac{v_x v_y}{10}$, where v_x, v_y and v_o are in volts. Thus, $v_o = 10V$ when $v_x = v_y = 10V$. It is commonplace for the excursions of v_x, v_y and v_o to be limited to the vicinity of $10V$, so that external attenuation or amplification of signals may be necessary, depending on the particular application. In PSM applications, the multiplier is required to handle all four possible alternative combinations of input signal polarity (i.e. $++$, $+-$, $-+$, and $--$), so that it needs to be configured for "four-quadrant" operation. Figure 10 shows such a multiplier being used as a PSM: it behaves according to the formula $v_o = kV_i V_{ref_m} \sin\omega_c t$, where k is a constant.

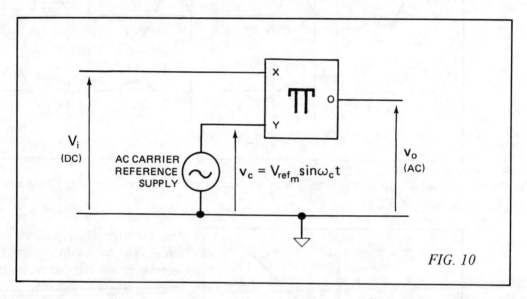

FIG. 10

The phase-sensitive relationship may be expressed more clearly by rewriting the equation in the form:

$$v_o = k|V_i|V_{ref_m}\sin\omega_c t, \qquad V_i > 0$$

and
$$v_o = k|V_i|V_{ref_m}\sin(\omega_c t + \pi), \quad V_i < 0.$$

Occasionally, a square output waveform is an acceptable alternative to the sinusoidal waveform. In this situation, modulation may be effected by causing the carrier, after being converted to a squarewave, to "gate" digitally-controlled analog switches. A suitable network is exemplified by Figure 11: the analog switches are assumed to provide a low resistance analog path when the digital signal v_s is in the 1 state and an open circuit when the digital signal v_s is in the 0 state.

$$v_o = +V_i , \qquad v_c > 0$$
$$v_o = -V_i , \qquad v_c < 0;$$

in other words, $v_o = V_i \, \text{sgn}(v_c)$.

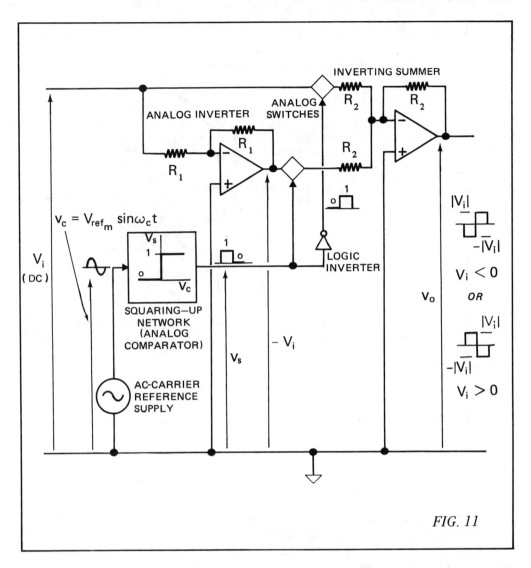

FIG. 11

Whilst a squarewave modulator can be more accurate (in terms of linearity, offset nulls, etc.) than a sinewave modulator, it should be borne in mind that the harmonic content of the squarewave may be detrimental to the control elements being fed by the modulator. It is conceivable that some of this harmonic content could be reduced by the application of a low-pass output filter (see Section 12.2).

Squarewave modulators have been constructed using special diode bridges, but these are no longer commonplace in modern equipment, due to the inaccuracies introduced by the forward characteristics of the diodes. Figure 12 shows a typical diode-ring modulator.

For the half cycle of the reference supply when v_c is positive, diodes D_1 and D_2 conduct and behave (ideally) as short-circuits, so that nodes A and C are at the same potential, with the result that $v_o = V_i$. For the alternate half cycle when v_c is negative, diodes D_3 and D_4 conduct and behave (ideally) as short-circuits, so that nodes B and C are at the same potential and $v_o = -V_i$.

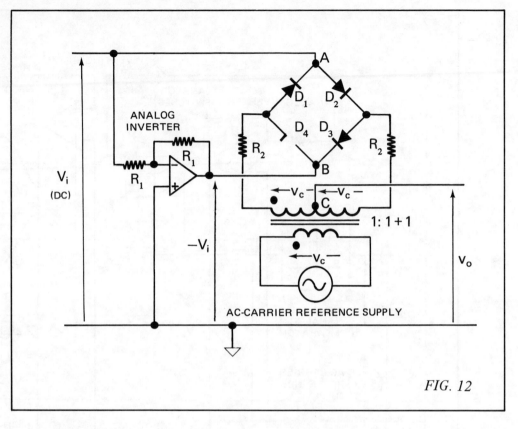

FIG. 12

Thus, $v_o \cong +V_i,$ $v_c > 0$

and $v_o \cong -V_i,$ $v_c < 0.$

Investigation will show that the network ceases to function as described should V_i exceed one half the peak value of v_c.

10.5   DEMODULATORS

The function of a demodulator, in the control system context, is the reverse of that of a modulator: that is, usually to convert an AC voltage of fixed (carrier) frequency into a DC voltage, such that the magnitude of the DC is proportional to the magnitude (defined in terms of either peak or RMS value) of the AC. Wherever the AC voltage is going to reverse in phase (relative to the carrier reference), corresponding to a reversal in the sense of the data being represented by the AC signal, it is usual to cause the DC voltage to reverse in polarity.

The type of demodulator which can achieve this phase reversal is said to be "phase-sensitive". Figure 13 shows typical waveforms for various input signal conditions and assumes that the input sinewave is precisely inphase or antiphase, relative to the AC-carrier reference.

Figure 14 represents the static characteristic required for the Phase-Sensitive Demodulator (PSD), which is alternatively known as a Phase-Sensitive Rectifier (PSR).

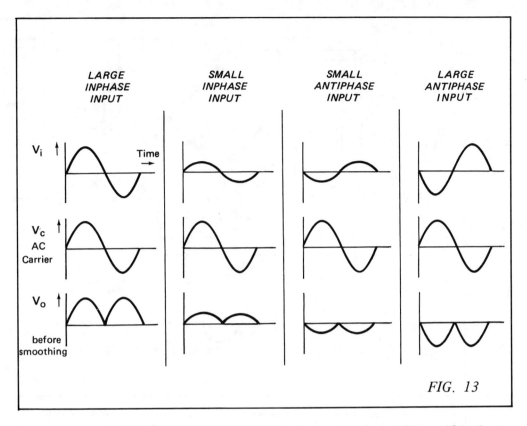

FIG. 13

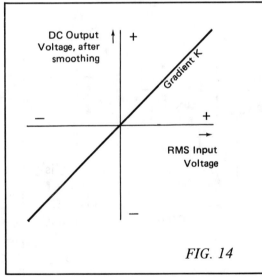

FIG. 14

Interpretation of Figure 13 indicates that, before v_o is smoothed, the PSD is required to implement the relationship

$$v_o = + v_i \, , \, v_c > 0$$

$$v_o = - v_i \, , \, v_c < 0; \text{ in other}$$

words, $v_o = v_i \, \text{sgn} \, (v_c)$.

A diode-ring PSD can be constructed along the lines of the diode-ring PSM, but with the AC and DC signals interchanged, as shown in Figure 15.

It will be left to the reader to derive the principle of operation of this network. It can also be shown that the network will cease to function as required should the peak value of v_i exceed one half the peak value of v_c. This type of PSD is no longer commonplace, because of inaccuracies introduced by the forward characteristics of the diodes and the availability of superior circuits.

A more accurate PSD can be created using digitally-controlled analog switches, similar to the network of Figure 11. This type of PSD is shown in Figure 16.

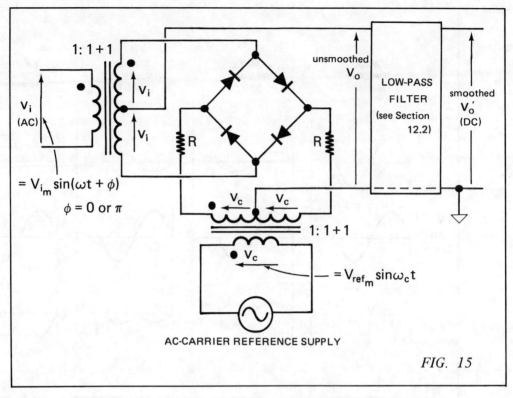

FIG. 15

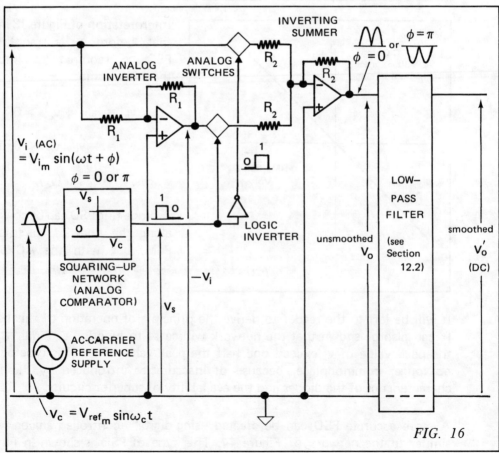

FIG. 16

This circuit operates in the same way as the Figure 11 network, so that, before smoothing, $v_o = + v_i$, $v_c > 0$ and $v_o = - v_i$, $v_c < 0$.

It is quite usual for the source of the AC input voltage v_i to introduce a parasitic phase shift ϵ so that, in practice, $\phi = \epsilon$ or $(\epsilon + \pi)$. This has the effect of diminishing the sensitivity K, which is represented by the gradient of the characteristic of Figure 14, according to the relationship $K = K_m \cos \epsilon$, where K_m is the "ideal sensitivity", obtained when $\epsilon = 0$. Thus, when $\epsilon = \pi/2$, the output from the PSD is zero for all input signal levels and the network becomes unusable: parasitic phase shifts must therefore be kept to a minimum or corrected for (by, for example, using power-factor correction techniques).

10.6 ANALOG–DIGITAL CONVERTERS (ADCs)

Most contemporary ADCs are either monolithic (that is, achieved within single integrated circuit chips) or are supplied as plastic or metal encapsulated plug-in circuit modules. This is not to say that each device is complete in itself: to enable it to function, separate sample-hold amplifier, clock-pulse generator, precision voltage reference source, control logic, and (possibly) output logic will almost certainly need to be added externally to the basic device.

Several alternative conversion techniques, which will be described, are employed by ADC manufacturers. However, suppliers often do not identify the particular principle employed in a specific converter, although, in fact, this principle can often be inferred from the specification for the converter. It is commonplace to discover an ADC described in terms such as "high-speed", "high-accuracy", "low-cost", etc. In practice, it is rarely necessary to have a knowledge of the principle of operation in order to be able to incorporate a particular ADC into a system: it is usually adequate to have a reasonably detailed specification (including waveforms) for the device.

The following are considered to be the most important terms in a specification for an ADC:

- *Input Voltage Range.* Typical bipolar input ranges are –5V to +5V, –10V to +10V, and –10.24V to +10.24V; typical unipolar input ranges are 0V to +5V, 0V to +10V, and 0V to +10.24V. It is important to appreciate that not all devices can be configured in all ranges: in some cases, a particular ADC may be suitable only for unipolar operation. In any case, the input range will bear a close relationship to the voltage value required for the external precision voltage reference source.

- *Conversion Time.* This will be closely related to the principle of operation employed, the clock-pulse frequency, and the word length (see below). "Conversion time" is defined as the time required for the ADC to generate a complete digital word representative, in code, of the value of an input voltage sample. Typical conversion times range from about 100 nanoseconds to 50 milliseconds. As a general rule for any particular type of converter, the conversion time will increase when the word length is increased: that is, an 8-bit converter can be expected to be faster than a 12-bit converter of the same type, for example.

- *Word Length.* This term denotes the number of bits in the digital output word which represents, in code, the value of the input voltage sample. The word length is closely related to the term "resolution", which is the smallest change in input voltage required to result in a change in the output code. Assuming a weighted type of binary code (see below), then, if the word length is represented by n and the nominal maximum input voltage which can theoretically be converted is represented by $V_{i_{max}}$, the resolution will be given by $V_{i_{max}}/2^n$ in the case of a unipolar converter, and by $V_{i_{max}}/2^{n-1}$ in the case of a bipolar converter. Resolution should not be confused with the term "accuracy", which is the degree of precision to which the digital word represents the analog input value: accuracy depends on the degree of precision to which the analog components of the ADC have been manufactured.

  It is possible for an ADC to achieve 12-bit resolution but with 10-bit accuracy, for example. If this converter is rated for 0V to −10V input range, then it can sense a change of $10/2^{12}$ V = 2.4mV in input value but the output word produced will only represent the input value to an accuracy of $10/2^{10}$ V = 9.8mV.

  Typical word lengths are 8, 10, 12, 14, and 16 bits, although a number of ADCs with greater lengths are manufactured. In addition to conversion time, price will increase with word length.

- *Output Code.* This is the relationship between the output bit pattern and the equivalent input voltage value. In the majority of cases, the code will be a form of weighted binary code: the term "weighted" means that a given bit in the output word is equivalent to the same value of input voltage increment, irrespective of the states of the other bits in the word. Coding of unipolar ADCs is relatively straightforward, because no (sign) bit needs to be allocated to represent the state (+ or −) of the input voltage polarity; in the case of bipolar ADCs, it will be necessary to allocate one output bit to indicate sign, so that the number of bits available for representation of voltage magnitude is reduced by one. Table 2 lists a number of alternative codes for a converter having an 8-bit word length.

It will be seen from Table 2 that many different output codes are available. Alternative codes not shown in the table include Binary-Coded Decimal (BCD) codes although, in general, these would more often be used for display purposes rather than in control loops. The need to represent 0V input can result in a slight asymmetry in the orientation of the code, as can be seen with some examples in the table.

10.6.1 Single Slope ADC

The internal organisation of a single slope ADC is shown in Figure 17.

TABLE 2. TYPICAL ADC OUTPUT CODES

Nominal Input Value	ADC TYPE						
	UNIPOLAR		BIPOLAR				
	Natural (Straight) Binary	Complementary Straight Binary	Sign & Natural Binary Magnitude	Offset Binary	Complementary Offset Binary	Two's Complement Binary	Complementary Two's Complement Binary
$+V_{i_{max}}$	—	—	—	—	—	—	10000000
$+(V_{i_{max}} - V_{LSB})$	11111111	00000000	01111111	11111111	00000000	01111111	10000001
· · · · · · ·	· · · · ·	· · · · ·	· · · · ·	· · · · ·	· · · · ·	· · · · ·	· · · · ·
$+V_{LSB}$	00000001	11111110	00000001	10000001	01111110	00000001	11111110
O	00000000	11111111	00000000	10000000	01111111	00000000	11111111
$-V_{LSB}$	—	—	10000001	01111111	10000000	11111111	00000000
· · · · · · ·	· · · · ·	· · · · ·	· · · · ·	· · · · ·	· · · · ·	· · · · ·	· · · · ·
$-(V_{i_{max}} - V_{LSB})$	—	—	11111111	00000001	11111110	10000001	01111111
$-V_{i_{max}}$	—	—	—	00000000	11111111	10000000	—

$$V_{LSB} = V_{i_{max}}/2^8 \ V \quad \text{for a unipolar converter.}$$

$$V_{LSB} = V_{i_{max}}/2^7 \ V \quad \text{for a bipolar converter.}$$

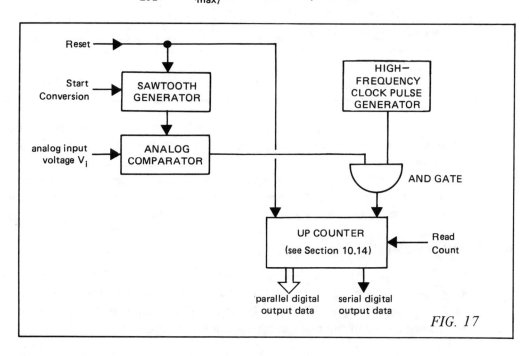

FIG. 17

The principle of operation of this network can be demonstrated by referring to the waveforms of Figure 18.

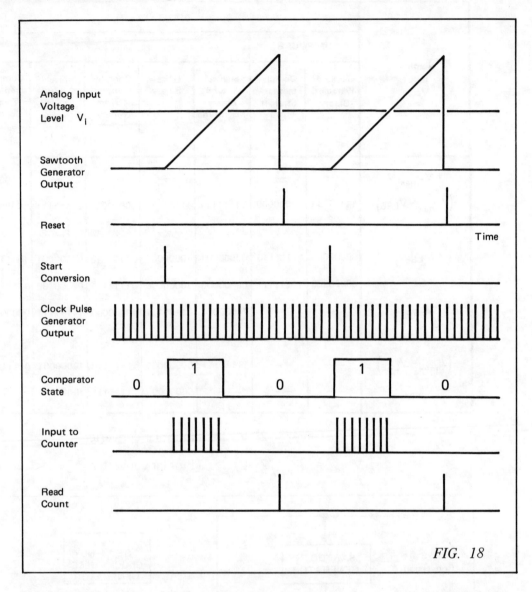

FIG. 18

Immediately prior to each reset pulse, the count size stored in the counter will equal the number of clock pulses counted during the previous period when the comparator was in the 1 state: this will therefore be proportional to the analog input voltage level. The accuracy of this ADC depends on the precision of the sawtooth gradient. The speed of this ADC will be relatively low, depending on the frequency of the clock and on the word length.

10.6.2 Dual Slope ADC

This is a variant of the ramp type of ADC (above) which obviates the effect in the latter of variations in the gradient of the sawtooth gradient. Using a system based on that of Figure 19, V_i is applied to the integrator, the output of which now ramps up, until the counter registers a full count.

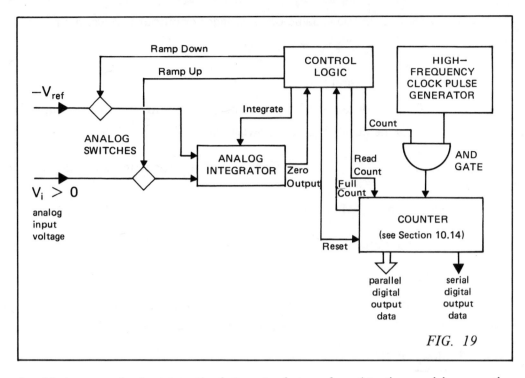

FIG. 19

At this instant, the input to the integrator is transferred to the precision negative voltage reference $-V_{ref}$ and the counter is reset to zero. The output of the integrator ramps down and, on reaching zero volts, causes the counter to stop: at this juncture, the count size will be representative of the value of V_i. Figure 20 shows waveforms which demonstrate the principle of operation.

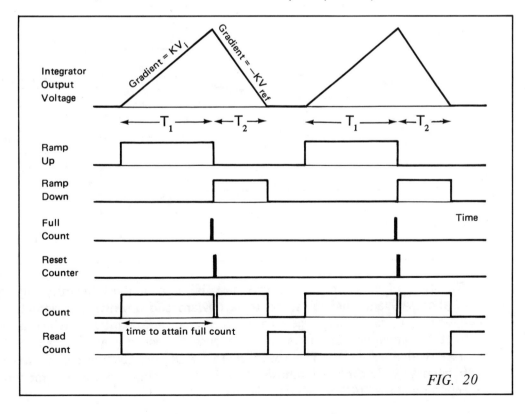

FIG. 20

If X represents the peak value of the integrator output voltage, then

$$X = K V_i T_1 = K V_{ref} T_2$$

where K is the integrator sensitivity, in second $^{-1}$

T_1 is the duration of the up ramp, the time to register full count

T_2 is the duration of the down ramp.

Thus, $T_2 = \dfrac{V_i}{V_{ref}} T_1$.   Since T_1 will be proportional to the full count size,

it follows that T_2 will be proportional to the count size registered during read-out.

Thus, digital output $= \dfrac{V_i}{V_{ref}} \times$ (full count), $0 \leqslant \dfrac{V_i}{V_{ref}} \leqslant 1$.

Since K does not feature in the final equations, it follows that, provided the integrator is stable, the absolute value of K is not critical.

10.6.3   Feedback ADC

This arrangement employs a digital-analog converter (DAC), to be described in Section 10.7, in a feedback loop as shown in Figure 21.

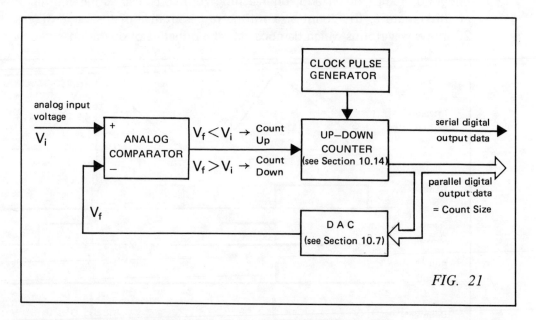

FIG. 21

This type of converter can be very fast, because of the inherently high speed of the DAC and the ability to track upward and downward variations in V_i. Basically, V_f is a DC voltage measure of the current count size, which is caused, by the comparator output state, to change in such a way as to enable V_f to track variations in V_i. The speed of this ADC will be limited by the clock frequency, which must be chosen to suit the maximum switching rates of the counter and the DAC.

A simplified version of this ADC employs only an up-counter; the counter must then be reset periodically and the count size read only when counting has ceased.

10.6.4 Successive Approximations ADC

This is the fastest type of ADC, because the speed depends only upon the switching times of the analog switches, comparators, and analog inverting and summing amplifiers. The first two stages of such a converter are shown in Figure 22.

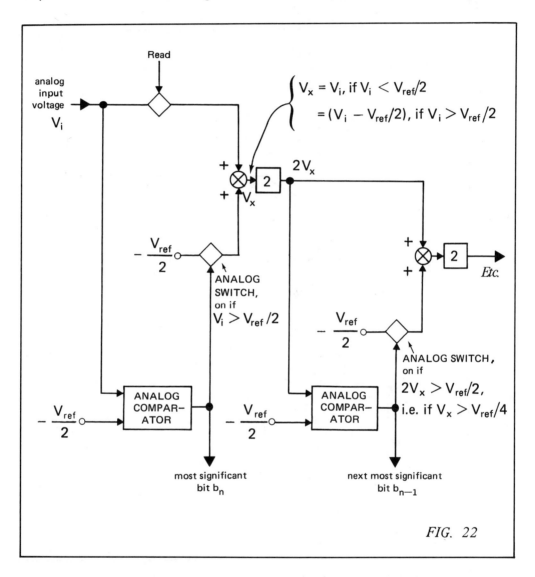

$$\begin{cases} V_x = V_i, \text{ if } V_i < V_{ref}/2 \\ = (V_i - V_{ref}/2), \text{ if } V_i > V_{ref}/2 \end{cases}$$

FIG. 22

The operation of this network can best be explained by means of the flow chart in Figure 23. In effecting the comparison XX (for example), the hardware in fact compares twice the balance with $V_{ref}/2$, so that the same reference voltage source can be used for all stages in the converter. Similarly, the subtraction of $V_{ref}/4$ from the balance, at ZZ, is effected by causing $V_{ref}/2$ to be subtracted from twice the balance. All stages in the converter thus use identical hardware and the same reference voltage signal and, as a result, considerably enhanced accuracy can be achieved.

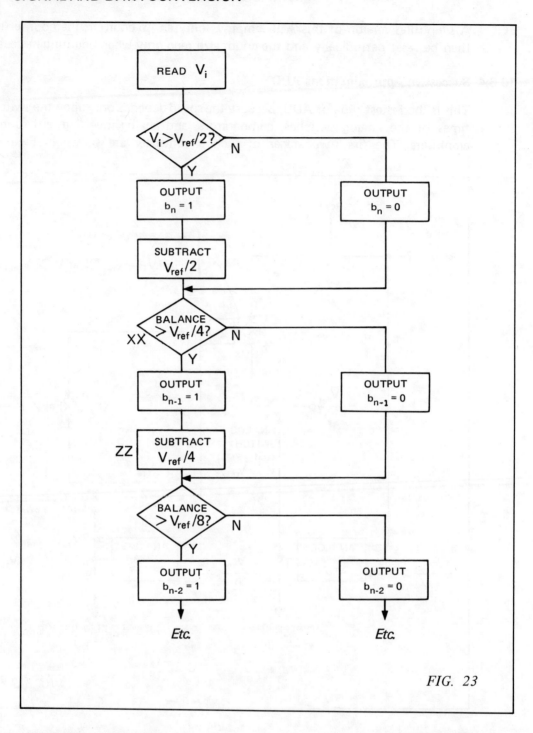

FIG. 23

10.6.5 Voltage/Frequency ADC

With this type of ADC, the input voltage V_i is converted into a pulse train by a voltage/frequency converter (voltage-controlled oscillator), so that the frequency of the pulse train is proportional to V_i. The pulse train is gated into a counter for a controlled period of time so that the final count size, which becomes the digital output, is proportional to the pulse frequency and hence is a representation of the value of V_i.

10.6.6 Typical ADC External Circuitry

Figure 24 shows the additional circuit elements which will typically be required before an ADC can be used within a control system.

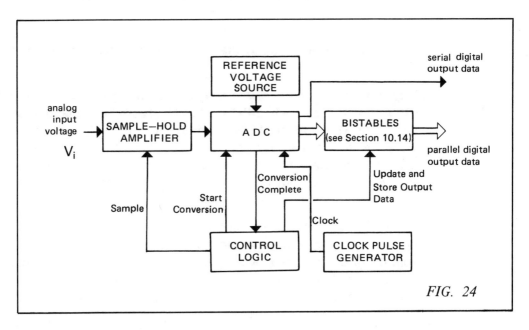

FIG. 24

The sample-hold amplifier is included so that the ADC is presented with a constant voltage for the duration of one conversion. If the converter is fast and V_i is changing only slowly, then this amplifier could be superfluous. Sample-hold amplifiers usually take the form of an integrated circuit requiring a high quality capacitor as the sole external component.

The bistables ("flip-flops") are often necessary when the ADC operates in such a way that its digital output states change sequentially rather than concurrently. The bistables provide temporary digital storage, so that all the output bits will remain constant during any conversion and will be updated concurrently whenever a conversion is completed.

The need (or otherwise) for the remaining elements of Figure 24 has already been explained for the particular types of ADC. In some cases, one or more of these elements may be incorporated into the ADC by the manufacturer.

10.7 DIGITAL–ANALOG CONVERTERS (DACs) AND DIGITAL–ANALOG MULTIPLIERS (DAMs)

The principal difference between the DAC and the DAM is that the former is associated with a fixed voltage reference source, whilst the latter is associated with a varying voltage reference. In the DAC case, the reference source may be incorporated into the device. In terms of the principle of operation, the DAC and DAM circuits behave identically, so that the following description, which will refer to DACs, will be equally applicable to DAMs.

Most contemporary DACs are either monolithic (that is, achieved with single integrated-circuit chips) or are supplied as plastic or metal encapsulated plug-in circuit modules. Only one conversion technique is used and this involves the switching of resistor networks using digitally-controlled analog switches.

The following are considered to be the most important terms in a specification for a DAC:

- *Output Voltage Range.* Typical bipolar output ranges are −5V to +5V, −10V to +10V, and −10.24V to +10.24V; typical unipolar output ranges are 0V to +5V, 0V to +10V, and 0V to +10.24V. It is important to appreciate that not all devices can be configured in all ranges: in some cases, a particular DAC may be suitable only for unipolar operation. In any case, the output range will bear a close relationship to the voltage value required for the external precision voltage reference source.

- *Settling Time.* This is the time required, following a change in digital input data, for the output voltage to change and settle to a value different from the prescribed value by an amount no greater than a voltage equivalent to one half of one least-significant bit. Because of the nature of the circuitry, settling times are very short, being in the range from 15 nanoseconds to 40 microseconds, typically.

- *Word Length.* This term denotes the number of bits in the digital input word, which represents, in code, the value required for the output voltage. The word length is closely related to the term "resolution", which is the smallest change in output voltage which can result from a change in the input code. Assuming a weighted type of binary code, then, if the word length is represented by n and the nominal maximum output voltage which can theoretically be generated is represented by $V_{i_{max}}$, the resolution will be given by $V_{i_{max}}/2^n$ in the case of a unipolar converter, and by $V_{i_{max}}/2^{n-1}$ in the case of a bipolar converter. Typical word lengths are 8, 10, 12, 14, and 16 bits, although a number of DACs with greater lengths are manufactured: price will increase with word length.

- *Input Code.* This is the relationship between the input bit pattern and the equivalent output voltage value, and, in the majority of cases, it will be a form of weighted binary code. Coding of unipolar DACs is relatively straight-forward because no (sign) bit needs to be allocated to represent the state (+ or −) of the output voltage polarity; in the case of bipolar DACs, it will be necessary to allocate one input bit to indicate sign, so that the number of bits available for representation of voltage magnitude is reduced by one. The codes listed in Table 2 (Section 10.6) for ADCs are equally applicable to DACs: the entries in the first column are now to be interpreted as "Nominal Output Value".

The principle of operation of a DAC is represented theoretically by Figure 25.

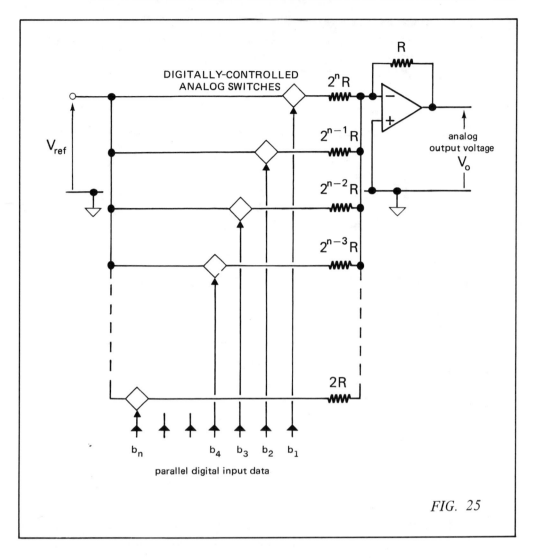

FIG. 25

The law for this configuration is:

$$V_o = -V_{ref} [2^{-1} b_n + \ldots + 2^{-(n-2)} b_3 + 2^{-(n-1)} b_2 + 2^{-n} b_1]$$

where bits $b_1, \ldots, b_n$ = 0 or 1, depending on the state of the input word. Thus, when $b_1 = b_2 = \ldots = b_n = 1$, $V_o = -V_{ref}(1 - 2^{-n})$, so that the nominal maximum value of V_o is slightly less than V_{ref} in magnitude.

Although feasible, this method of construction is not practicable, because high accuracy is precluded by the large range of resistance values which usually would be required.

For high accuracy, the resistors are designed to have comparable values, often precisely determined by laser trimming techniques. The resulting "ladder network" is sometimes contained in a package separate from the DAC although, currently, it is more common to incorporate the network in the DAC device. Figure 26 shows a suitable ladder network arrangement, in which there are only two different resistor values, related by a 2:1 ratio.

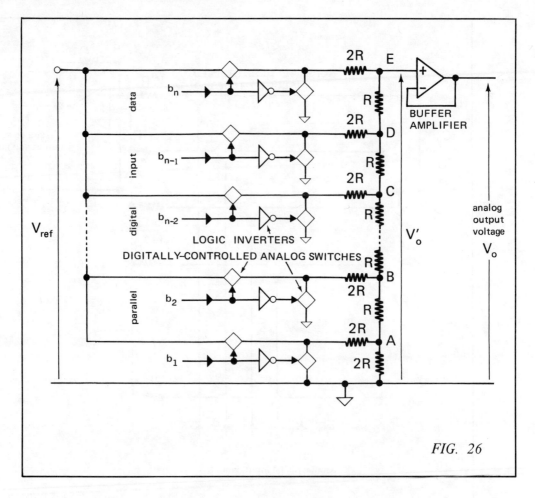

FIG. 26

Provided that the V_{ref} voltage source has a low output resistance, it can be shown that the resistance measured from every node A, B, C, D, E to ground is virtually R ohms, irrespective of the states of the analog switches. However, the magnitude of V_o' will depend on the states of the switches.

Increasing the number of bits does not change the weighting of each bit, starting with the most-significant, but it does increase the degree of resolution, since the least-significant bit is reduced in weighting by a factor of 2 for each bit added to the word length.

It can be shown that

$$V_o' = V_{ref} [2^{-1} b_n + \ldots + 2^{-(n-2)} b_3 + 2^{-(n-1)} b_2 + 2^{-n} b_1].$$

Additional switches may be incorporated in order to make the converter bipolar: for example, the state of a sign bit could be used to reverse the sign of V_{ref}. Alternatively, the polarity of V_{ref} could be fixed, and the output voltage offset by $-V_{ref}/2$, using external circuitry.

Figure 27 shows the additional circuit elements which typically will be required before a DAC can be used within a control system.

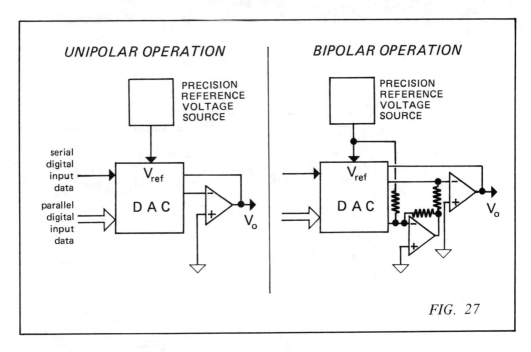

UNIPOLAR OPERATION | BIPOLAR OPERATION

FIG. 27

The operational amplifiers normally are external to the DAC and the quantity (1 or 2) will depend on whether the swing of the output voltage is unipolar or bipolar, respectively.

In the case of the DAM, the V_{ref} input signal will be derived from a variable (analog) DC voltage source so that, for this case also,

$$V_o = V_{ref} \times \text{(analog value represented by the digital input word)}.$$

10.8 RESOLVER–DIGITAL CONVERTERS

These converters are used for direct conversion of resolver AC voltages to digital data (representing a shaft angular displacement) and also often form the bases of Synchro-Digital Converters (see Section 10.11). Because of their nature, appropriate versions may be used as Inductosyn-Digital Converters. When a number of angular displacement transducers are required to be interfaced to a digital controller, it becomes economically advantageous to use resolvers or synchros, together with a time-shared converter of the appropriate type, in preference to using a set of digital transducers. Resolver-Digital Converters can assume two alternative forms: the tracking type and the sampling type.

10.8.1 Tracking Resolver — Digital Converter

The two output voltages V_1 and V_2 from a resolver transmitter can be represented by $V_1 = k\, V_{ref} \sin\theta$ and $V_2 = k\, V_{ref} \cos\theta$, where V_1, V_2 and V_{ref} are RMS values, θ is shaft angle, and k is the transformation ratio. Thus,

$$\theta = \tan^{-1}(V_1/V_2).$$

The tracking converter employs what is known as an "electronic servo", which is represented by Figure 28.

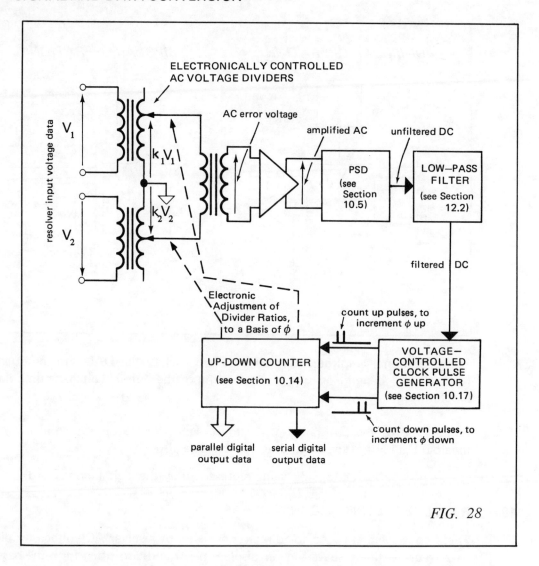

FIG. 28

The up-down counter increments an implied shaft angle ϕ and electronically adjusts the divider ratio according to the relationships $k_1 = \cos\phi$ and $k_2 = \sin\phi$.

Thus, when the null state is achieved (error voltage = 0), $k_1 V_1 - k_2 V_2 = 0$ so that $kV_{ref} \sin\theta \cos\phi = kV_{ref} \cos\theta \sin\phi$; whence, $\tan\phi = \tan\theta$ and $\phi = \theta$.

At any instant, the count size represents, in digital form, the current value of ϕ and hence of θ. Practical accuracies are in the region of 10 seconds of arc. The tracking converter is relatively immune to parasitic phase shifts in the resolver signals and to harmonics and noise; however, it is not particularly suitable for multiplexing (time-sharing) duties, due to limitations in maximum slew rate.

10.8.2 Sampling Resolver — Digital Converters

These converters usually sample the peak values of the resolver voltages and then manipulate these sample values. Figure 29 shows schematically the internal arrangement.

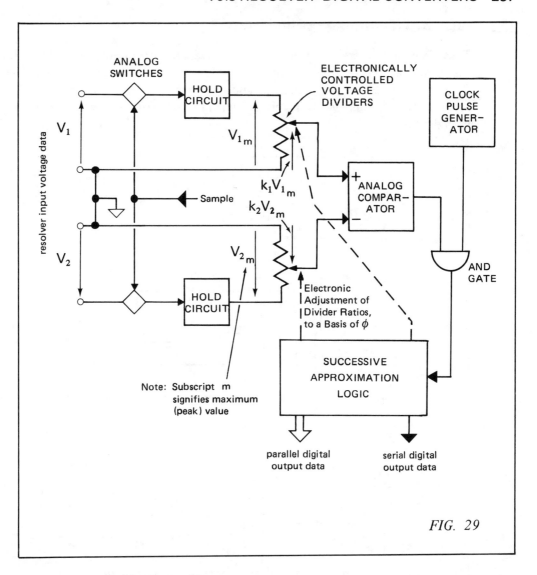

FIG. 29

Successive approximation techniques, similar to those indicated in Figure 23, are used to adjust the resistive divider ratios according to the relationships $k_1 = \cos \phi$ and $k_2 = \sin \phi$, where the value of ϕ is implied by the state of the logic.

A null is achieved when $k_1 V_{1_m} = k_2 V_{2_m}$, so that

$$kV_{ref_m} \sin \theta \cos \phi = kV_{ref_m} \cos \theta \sin \phi, \text{ whence}$$

$$\tan \phi = \tan \theta \text{ and } \phi = \theta.$$

Sampling converters are less accurate than their tracking converter counterparts and are sensitive to parasitic phase shifts, harmonics, and noise in the resolver signals, which may therefore necessitate accurate pre-filtering. However, sampling converters are suitable for multiplexing duty, being capable of sampling at up to twice the carrier frequency (the frequency of the reference supply).

10.9   DIGITAL–RESOLVER CONVERTERS

These converters are used for direct conversion of digital data (representing shaft angular displacement) and also often form the bases of Digital-Synchro Converters (see Section 10.12). These converters are, in effect, solid-state replacements for resolver transmitters, with the value of the input angle represented by a digital word.

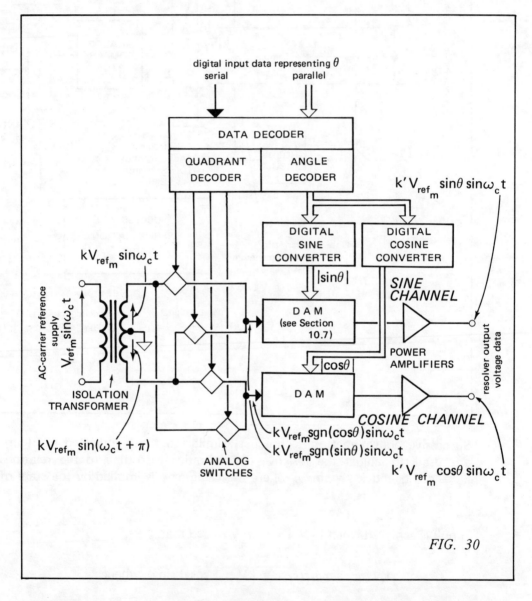

FIG. 30

Figure 30 shows a typical arrangement for a Digital-Resolver Converter. The decoder interprets the most-significant bits to sense the quadrant in which the angle lies: the quadrant decoding selects either inphase or antiphase AC reference voltage, as appropriate, for the sine and cosine channels. The decoder also converts the data to the equivalent first-quadrant value and this angular value is input to digital sine and cosine converters. The quadrant decoder thus selects the sign of the AC reference for the two channels, by gating the appropriate analog switches, according to the relationships + +, + −, − −, − + for the four quadrants. In each case, the two signs represent the required sign for the sine and cosine functions, respectively. The data representing equivalent first-quadrant angle are then converted to sine and cosine data, using hardware implementing the sine and cosine algorithms, so that the output data from these converters now represent the magnitudes of the sine and cosine functions.

The sine channel DAM (see Section 10.7) multiplies the AC analog input signal $k.V_{ref_m}$ .sgn (sinθ). sin $\omega_c t$ by the digital input representing $|sin\theta|$, to yield an AC analog output signal $k.V_{ref_m}$. sin θ.sin $\omega_c t$ which is then input to a power amplifier: this, in turn, outputs $k'.V_{ref_m}$. sinθ. sin $\omega_c t$. The DAM in the cosine channel causes the associated power amplifier, by the same reasoning, to output $k'.V_{ref_m}$.cos θ.sin $\omega_c t$.

The two AC output voltages thus represent a pair of resolver voltages, so that the converter is, in effect, a solid-state Resolver Transmitter. Because of its nature, it can also be arranged to function as a Digital-Inductosyn Converter.

10.10 SCOTT−TEE TRANSFORMERS

A pair of suitable signal transformers may be connected to enable 4-wire resolver data to be converted to 3-wire synchro data, and vice-versa. Such a configuration is traditionally known as a "Scott-Tee" connected pair of transformers, the need for which originated in 2-phase to 3-phase power conversion, and vice-versa.

The operation of the configuration will be explained in relation to synchro-resolver conversion, as indicated by Figure 31.

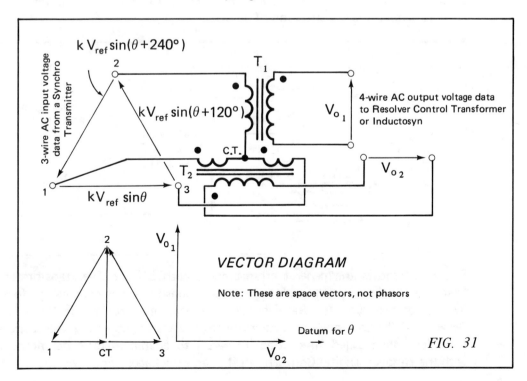

FIG. 31

All voltages are RMS values. By the application of simple trigonometry, it can be shown that

$$V_{2\,CT} = \frac{\sqrt{3}}{2} kV_{ref} \cos\theta \quad V_{3CT} = \frac{1}{2} k V_{ref} \sin\theta \quad \text{and} \quad V_{1CT} = -\frac{1}{2} k V_{ref} \sin\theta.$$

By giving transformer T_1 a turns ratio of $\frac{\sqrt{3}}{2}$: 1 and T_2 a ratio of $\frac{1}{2} + \frac{1}{2}$:1, it is readily seen that the output voltages will be given by

$$V_{o_1} = kV_{ref} \cos \theta$$

and $\quad V_{o_2} = kV_{ref} \sin \theta.$

The maximum values of these variable RMS voltages are equal but separated by 90° vectorially, and therefore the transformers provide a suitable data source for a resolver transmission system. Equally readily, it may be shown that the transformer pair will provide suitable resolver-synchro transformation, if the direction of input-output transmission is reversed

Scott-Tee transformer pairs are commonly used in Synchro-Digital and Digital-Synchro Converters, which are the subject of the next two sections.

10.11 SYNCHRO–DIGITAL CONVERTERS (SDCs)

Because it is relatively easier to process two AC voltages, as opposed to three AC voltages, to generate equivalent digital angular data, it is usual to convert synchro data to resolver data and subsequently to convert the latter to digital angular data, in the construction of an SDC.

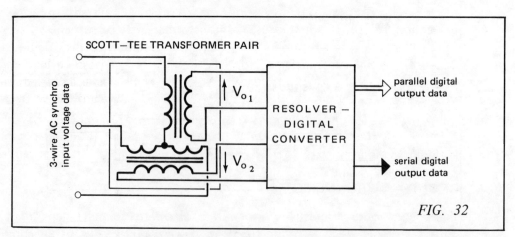

FIG. 32

Figure 32 shows the general arrangement, with a Scott-Tee transformer pair (refer to Section 10.10) performing the synchro-resolver conversion, followed by one of the types of Resolver-Digital Converter described in Section 10.8. Because of the low power levels involved, the transformers may be sufficiently small (and thus called "microtransformers") to enable them to be encapsulated with the Resolver-Digital Converter in the same package.

10.12 DIGITAL–SYNCHRO CONVERTERS (DSCs)

Because it is relatively easier to generate two AC voltages, as opposed to three AC voltages, it is usual to convert digital angular data to resolver data and subsequently to convert the latter to synchro data, in the construction of a DSC.

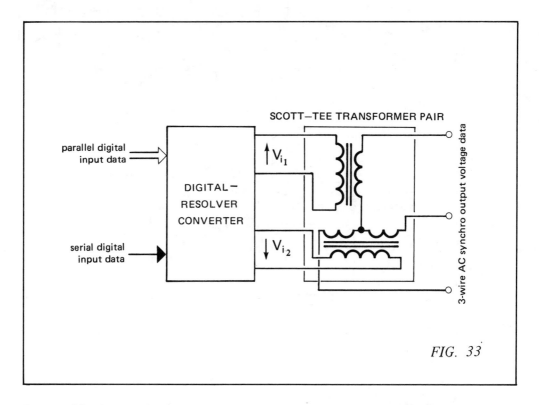

FIG. 33

Figure 33 shows the general arrangement, with a Digital-Resolver Converter (described in Section 10.9) being followed by a Scott-Tee transformer pair (refer to Section 10.10). In some cases, the transformers may be sufficiently small (and thus called "microtransformers") to be encapsulated with the Digital-Resolver Converter in the same package. However, because of the possible load demands, it may be necessary for the transformers and even the power amplifiers deriving V_{i_1} and V_{i_2} to be packaged separately. The Digital-Synchro Converter may be thought of as a solid-state Synchro Torque Transmitter (TX) or Control Transmitter (CX); in addition, these techniques have been extended to produce solid-state Differential Transmitters (TDXs and CDXs) and Control Transformers (CTs).

10.13 RMS–TO–DC CONVERTERS

These converters are usually monolithic integrated circuits generating a DC output voltage which is proportional to the true-RMS value of an applied AC input voltage. Because they do not sense the phase of the AC voltage, these converters can only be used either for instrumentation purposes (to enable a DC instrument to display the RMS value of an AC voltage) or as non-phase-sensitive demodulators in those AC-carrier control systems in which phase reversals are sensed by some alternative means. Figure 34 shows how an RMS-to-DC Converter could be used as part of a phase-sensitive detector network.

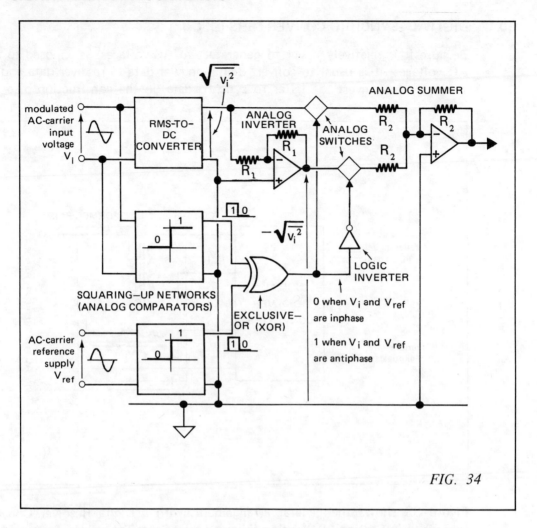

FIG. 34

The most common type of converter network mechanises the relationship $V_{RMS} = \overline{v_i^2}/V_{RMS}$ using the type of circuitry implied by Figure 35.

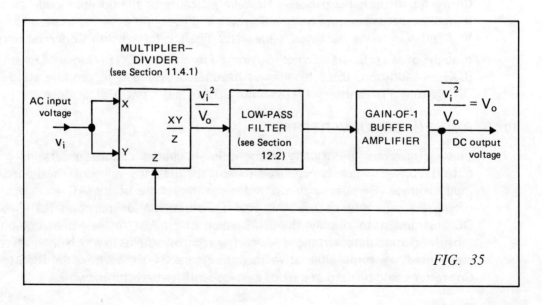

FIG. 35

Provided that the period of v_i is long in relation to the time constant of the low-pass filter, it is readily seen that V_o will be a good approximation to V_{RMS}: for a given filter time constant, there will be finite limits to the frequency range of v_i.

An alternative type of converter uses Log and Antilog circuits to implement the relationship $\log \dfrac{|v_i|^2}{V_o} = 2 \, \log|v_i| - \log V_o,$ as shown in Figure 36.

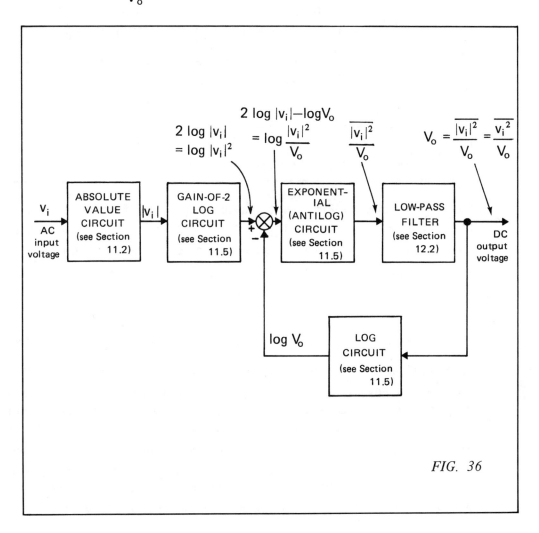

FIG. 36

10.14 SHIFT REGISTERS AND COUNTERS

A shift register is a set of logic "cells", each of which is capable of maintaining a binary 1 or a binary 0 state. A digital network or circuit which can be used to create a cell is known as a "Bistable", "Bistable Multivibrator", or "Flip-Flop". A bistable can be arranged to change its output state whenever its input signals change in an appropriate manner, in which case it is known as an "asynchronous" element, or it can be arranged to change its output state whenever its input signals are in an appropriate state and a pulse from a clock pulse generator is present, in which case it is known as a "synchronous" element.

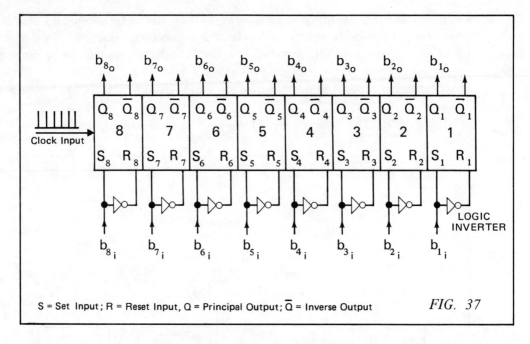

S = Set Input ; R = Reset Input, Q = Principal Output; $\bar{Q}$ = Inverse Output   *FIG. 37*

Figure 37 shows an 8-bit shift register constructed from eight synchronous bistables. When any input bit b_{1_i} .... b_{8_i} is set to a 1, the corresponding output bit b_{1_o} .... b_{8_o} will assume a 1 state on the next clock pulse and will maintain this state until the next clock pulse occurs. Thus, the register can store an 8-bit digital word for the duration of one clock interval. The register has been configured for parallel input and parallel output.

If Q_8 is linked to S_7, Q_7 to S_6, and so on to Q_2 linked to S_1, then a 1 bit applied to b_{8_i} will cause b_{8_o} to be set to 1 on the next clock pulse, b_{7_o} to be set to 1 on the following clock pulse, and so on until b_{1_o} is set to 1 after eight clock pulses have occurred. Thus, data can be caused to ripple through the register and it has been configured for serial input and parallel output, if all outputs Q_1 to Q_8 are used. If only output Q_1 is used and the clock pulse train is maintained then, after eight clock pulses have occurred, the sequence of 1s and 0s emerging from output Q_1 will be a replica of the sequence of 1s and 0s which were input to S_8, and the register has been configured for serial input and serial output.

If a full 8-bit input word is loaded in through b_{1_i} .... b_{8_i}, before the outputs are effectively cross-connected to adjacent Set inputs, then the time sequence of bits emerging from Q_1 will be a replica of the bit pattern loaded into the register initially, so that it has now been configured for parallel input and serial output.

Thus, a set of bistables, together with appropriate combinational logic, can be organised for storage of data, for temporarily delaying data, for conversion of data from serial to parallel format, and for conversion of data from parallel to serial format. Figure 38 summarises these various configurations.

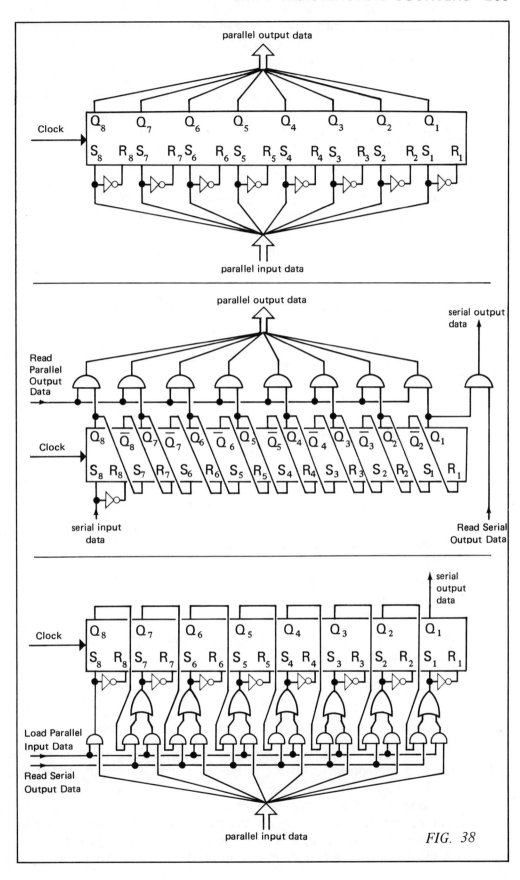

FIG. 38

If the outputs of a shift register are fed back, through appropriate combinational logic, in order to set and reset the shift register inputs, then the network can be configured to behave as a counter: for example, the output states of the register could be arranged to represent a count, in an appropriate binary code, of the number of pulses occurring on a serial data input line, commencing at a specific instant in time. The counter could be reset to zero, for example, by causing a logic 1 to be applied to all bistable Reset inputs simultaneously. Certain types of counter (for example, natural binary and binary-coded-decimal) are available already pre-configured, as monolithic integrated circuits.

Counters can also be arranged to convert the frequency of a periodic waveform into a digital word, and the result is a frequency-to-digital converter, which normally is referred to as a "Frequency Counter". Such an element is useful, for example, for converting the frequency of the pulse train produced by a digital velocity transducer (see Section 2.4.4) or a turbine type of flowmeter (see Section 4.5.4) into a parallel digital word.

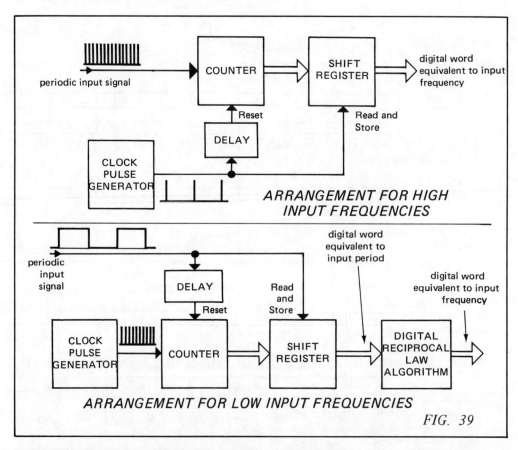

FIG. 39

Figure 39 shows two alternative arrangements, catering for both high and low input signal frequencies. In the former case, the number of input rising edges (say) occurring within one (fixed) period of the clock waveform is counted, and the count value is stored by the shift register. In the latter case, the period of the input waveform is measured initially, by counting the number of clock pulses occurring within one period of the input waveform, the count size being stored by the shift register; finally, the value of the period may be inverted, to yield frequency data, by means of digital hardware mechanising a reciprocal law algorithm (see Section 11.7).

Frequently, the input signal will need to be preconditioned, by suitable circuitry, to standardise the voltage levels and to "square-up" the rising and/or falling edges of the waveform: this may require amplifiers, attenuators, analog comparators, Schmitt triggers, etc.

10.15 CODE CONVERTERS

A code converter network would typically be used where the output code from a digital transducer is incompatible with the input code of the digital controller to which the transducer is to supply data. For example, a Gray code shaft encoder (see Section 2.2.7) might have to be interfaced to a digital controller configured to accept natural binary code, as indicated in Table 3.

TABLE 3. GRAY AND NATURAL BINARY CODES

Decimal Value	Network Input States (Gray Code)				Network Output States (Natural Binary Code)			
	A	B	C	D	E	F	G	H
0	0	0	0	0	0	0	0	0
1	0	0	0	1	0	0	0	1
2	0	0	1	1	0	0	1	0
3	0	0	1	0	0	0	1	1
4	0	1	1	0	0	1	0	0
5	0	1	1	1	0	1	0	1
6	0	1	0	1	0	1	1	0
7	0	1	0	0	0	1	1	1
8	1	1	0	0	1	0	0	0
9	1	1	0	1	1	0	0	1

One technique for generating the translation process is to devise a Boolean equation for each output E .... H, each in terms of the set of input states A .... D. Thus, in this simple example,

$$E = A$$
$$F = \bar{A}.B$$
$$G = \bar{B}.C + \bar{A}.B.\bar{C}$$
$$H = A.D + \bar{B}.\bar{C}.D + \bar{B}.C.\bar{D} + \bar{A}.B.C.D + \bar{A}.B.\bar{C}.\bar{D}$$

In these formulae, . represents a logical AND, + a logical OR, and the bar $^{-}$ a logical inversion (a NOT operation).

Provided that the number of input signals does not exceed preferably four or, at most, five, the process of formulating Boolean equations can be assisted by the construction of a Karnaugh map for each of the output signals. This is a particularly useful aid to minimising the quantity of hardware required, especially in those cases where not all combinations of input state can arise: for example, those states corresponding to 10 to 15 decimal, inclusive, in the above illustrative case.

Once the equations have been minimised, they can be mechanised by AND, OR, NAND, NOR, and inverter gates, using a suitable logic series. However, this simple approach does not take into account the fact that it might be possible to simplify the network further using one or more of the following techniques:

- rewriting the equations in terms of the other outputs, in addition to the inputs;
- sharing hardware between the logic channels implementing the equations;
- using other types of gate: for instance, the exclusive-OR.

It is possible to buy certain code converters (for example, binary-coded-decimal to natural binary converters) pre-configured in monolithic integrated circuits, although the choice is limited. In some cases, these ICs can be cascaded, in order to extend the word length.

One potential problem with combinational logic code converters arises from the variation in propagation delays through the different channels, which can result in short-lived (that is, of nanosecond duration) spurious output states occurring during input transitions. The circuitry being fed by the converter must be designed so that it cannot respond to these parasitic states.

An alternative technique for code conversion, which can be used when counters are available to operate in the two codes of interest, is illustrated symbolically in Figure 40.

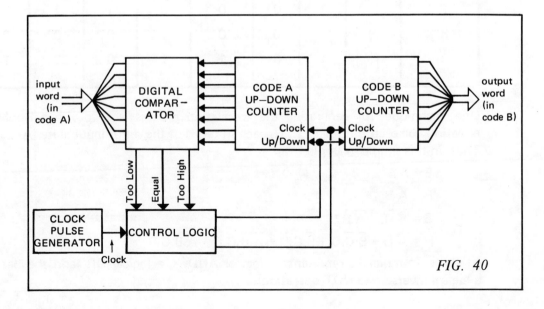

FIG. 40

The two counters are supplied with precisely the same number of pulses to count (up or down, as the case may be), so that they both register exactly the same count size, in terms of their respective codes. The state of the digital comparator senses any disparity between the input word and the count value in the code A counter, causing the control logic to require the two counters to increase or decrease their count size, according to requirements. Modern IC counters can count at frequencies up to 1 GHz, which means that conversions can be very fast.

It must be stressed that both combinational and sequential logic design can require considerable skill and experience. Many books are available to deal with these complex topics.

A third technique can achieve extremely fast code conversion if modern semiconductor memory is used. The input word is interpreted as the address of a location in read-only memory (ROM) and stored in this location, as a data word, is the corresponding output word required. All possible input states must be accommodated by a corresponding number of locations and the full set of corresponding output states must be stored, in the form of a look-up table, with the word length of each location equal to the output word length required. The conversion time will be equal to the access time of the memory, and this can be less than 350 nanoseconds.

10.16 FREQUENCY–VOLTAGE CONVERTERS

These are usually encapsulated circuits or monolithic integrated circuits. The purpose of the converter is to generate a DC voltage proportional in value to the frequency of an applied periodic input waveform. Typically, these circuits will operate over a frequency range from DC to the region of 100kHz and will function with a variety of input waveforms, including sinewave, squarewave, triangularwave and pulse train. In control systems, the principal application would be the conversion of a pulse train from a digital velocity transducer or the sinewave from a signal alternator or power alternator into a DC feedback voltage, for use in speed or frequency control.

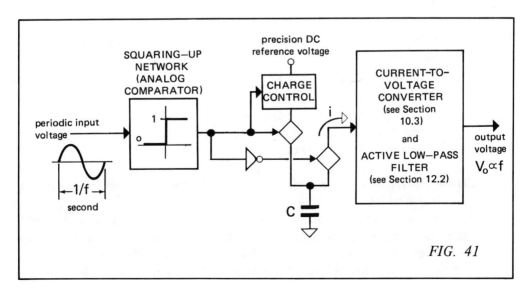

FIG. 41

The principle of operation is shown symbolically in Figure 41. The capacitor is charged from a precision voltage reference source, during the positive half-cycle of the input waveform, and discharges into the active low-pass filter, during the negative half-cycle. The capacitor C is arranged to accumulate a fixed quantity of charge, during any one charging interval, so that the average value of the current i flowing during the discharge interval will be proportional to the input frequency.

10.17   VOLTAGE—FREQUENCY CONVERTERS

These are usually encapsulated circuits or monolithic integrated circuits. The purpose of the converter is to generate a periodic output waveform having a frequency proportional to the magnitude of an applied (unipolar) DC input voltage. Since a "Voltage-Controlled Oscillator" (VCO) performs the same function, the two terms are synonymous.

Most VCOs are based on a triangularwave oscillator using a precision analog integrator which integrates positive and negative precision reference voltages: the gain of the integrator is made to be proportional to the DC input voltage, so that the integrator output voltage ramps up and down (with a gradient having a magnitude proportional to the DC input voltage), depending on whether the positive or the negative reference is being applied at the current instant in time. Analog comparator and amplitude shaping circuits enable the triangularwave to be translated into a sinewave, squarewave, sawtooth and pulse train.

The VCO will require external components, including a precision capacitor for the oscillator integrator: the value of this capacitor will determine the frequency range, which is unlikely to exceed three decades. By providing means to enable the integrator to have a different gain for the two different directions of charging, it becomes possible to distort the triangular waveshape in the direction of a sawtooth waveshape, to vary the mark/space ratio of the squarewave and the pulse width of the pulse train, and to reduce the level of possible harmonic distortion of the sinewave.

Typically, the converter would have control inputs to provide some or all of the following facilities:

- output frequency control;
- output amplitude control;
- output null offset adjustment;
- mark/space ratio control;
- sinewave distortion control.

These converters have a wide application in the instrumentation field but their use in the control field is limited largely to tracking filters employing Phaselock techniques. However, many modern oscillators will employ the type of circuitry described above but configured to have preset values of output amplitude and frequency: a common application for such an oscillator would be an AC voltage reference source for AC-carrier transducers and other control elements.

10.18 AIR—TO—CURRENT CONVERTERS

The usual purpose of these converters is to enable a 3 to 15 psi (20 to 100 kPa) pneumatic signal source to be interfaced to an electronic process controller. The converter typically generates an output signal in the range of 4 to 20 mA DC.

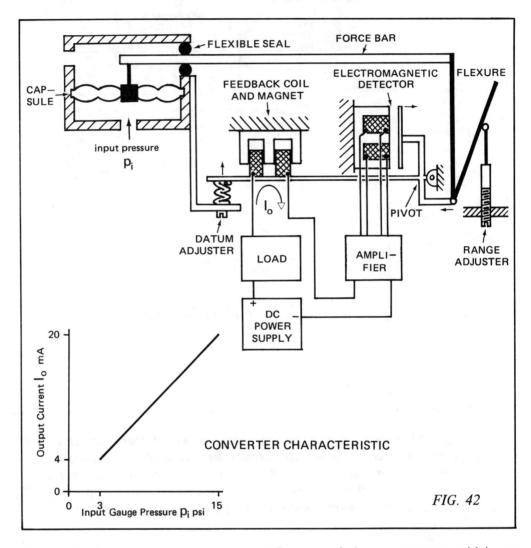

FIG. 42

Figure 42 shows a typical arrangement for one of these converters, which are sometimes referred to as "P/I Converters". It is almost identical in operation to the electronic force balance transmitter described in Section 4.2, the principal difference being that it responds to a single input (pneumatic) pressure: no further explanation should therefore be necessary.

10.19 CURRENT—TO—AIR CONVERTERS

The usual purpose of these converters is either to enable a 4 to 20 mA DC electronic signal source to be interfaced to a pneumatic process controller or to enable an electronic process controller to drive a pneumatically-actuated final control element. One of these converters would enable an electronic function generator to be used as a signal source for testing pneumatic control systems.

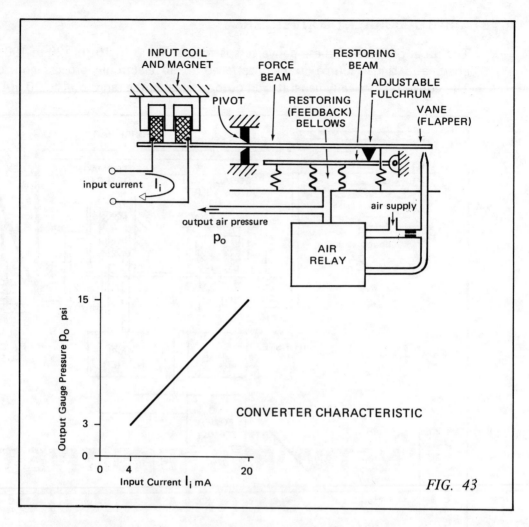

FIG. 43

Figure 43 shows a typical arrangement for one of these converters, which are sometimes referred to as "I/P Converters". It is almost identical in operation to the pneumatic force balance transmitter described in Section 4.2, the principal difference being that it responds to a force established by an applied DC input current: no further explanation should therefore be necessary.

11

NETWORKS SENSITIVE TO SIGNAL AMPLITUDE

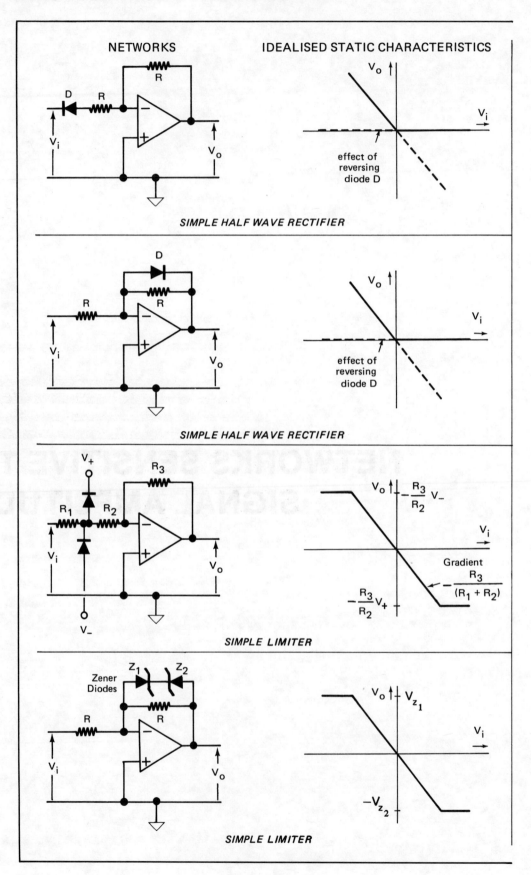

NETWORKS   IDEALISED STATIC CHARACTERISTICS

SIMPLE HALF WAVE RECTIFIER

SIMPLE HALF WAVE RECTIFIER

SIMPLE LIMITER

SIMPLE LIMITER

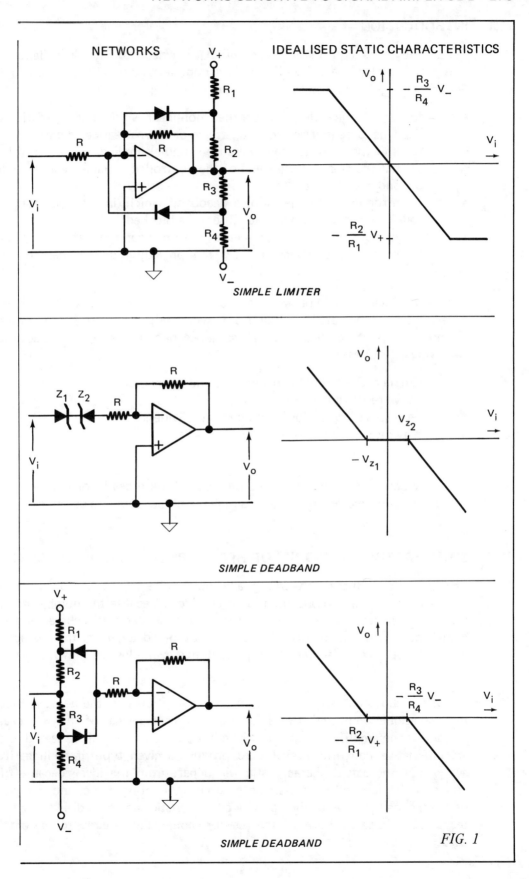

FIG. 1

11.1 INTRODUCTION

Occasionally, the control engineer will have a need to introduce deliberately, into a control loop, a network having a nonlinear static characteristic. Typical reasons for requiring to do this include the following:

- to cancel the effect of another nonlinear static characteristic which happens to be inherent in an upstream or downstream element;
- to limit the demand (the reference variable) applied to the control loop, so that the steady state value of the controlled variable cannot be driven beyond preset limits;
- to introduce, into the loop, a deadband which, in the steady state, will cause the passage of parasitic noise to be blocked;
- to introduce a variable dynamic performance, the nature of which is arranged to be determined by the prevailing operational conditions.

Passive nonlinear shaping networks are relatively uncommon, so that consideration here will be concentrated upon active networks: that is, those incorporating one or more stages of amplification. These active networks can be divided into the following categories:

- simple active networks of resistors and signal diodes;
- active resistive ladder networks;
- networks using analog multipliers and dividers;
- networks using logarithmic amplifiers.

The only passive networks to be considered will be those involving special types of servo potentiometer. In addition, a digital technique will be described.

11.2 SIMPLE ACTIVE NETWORKS OF RESISTORS AND SIGNAL DIODES

The simplest of these networks make no precise allowance for the forward volt drop across each diode used, as it conducts. Because the number of diodes used in each network is small, the resulting nonlinear static characteristic will approximate a small number of straight lines joined together: the characteristic is said to be "piecewise-linear". Representative examples are shown in Figure 1.

All of the above networks operate on the assumption that the negative input of the operational amplifier always functions as a virtual earth: this will cease to be valid if the amplifier output is driven into saturation. It will be seen that there are alternative networks available to produce a given type of nonlinearity. In every case, the actual characteristic will depart from the ideal, because of the effect of the forward characteristic of each conducting diode, and the gradient of the inclined portion of the network characteristic can be modified by changing the value of one or both of the resistors connected directly to the amplifier negative input.

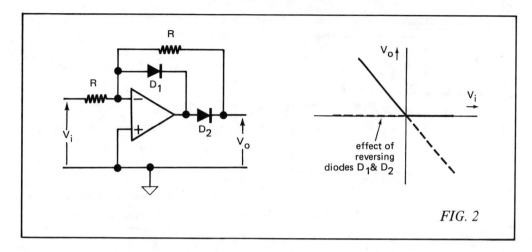

FIG. 2

Figure 2 shows a network in which a diode D_2 has been placed within the feedback loop with the result that, whenever D_2 is conducting, V_o will be precisely equal and opposite in value to V_i (provided that the resistor values are carefully matched): in this case, conduction always occurs whenever V_i is negative. Diode D_1 is included in order to prevent the amplifier from saturating negatively whenever V_i is positive. During the conducting half cycle, the forward volt drop across D_2 has no influence on the relationship between V_o and V_i, so that the actual static characteristic approaches the ideal. More complex precision piecewise-linear nonlinearities can be constructed using this precision half wave rectifier network as a basis, and examples are given in Figure 4.

Many other networks of this type, together with variations which can operate at frequencies much higher than those normally pertaining to control systems, are described elsewhere in the literature.

11.3 ACTIVE RESISTIVE LADDER NETWORKS

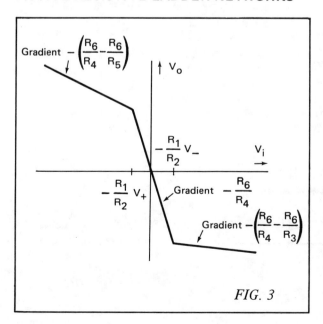

FIG. 3

If, in the last example in Figure 4, resistors R_3, R_4 and R_5 had deliberately been made unequal in value, the type of piecewise-linear characteristic shown in Figure 3 would have resulted: this is seen to consist of three linear segments, each having a variable gradient. Obviously, many more linear segments could be added to the characteristic, if more parallel channels of half wave rectifiers were to be added to the network.

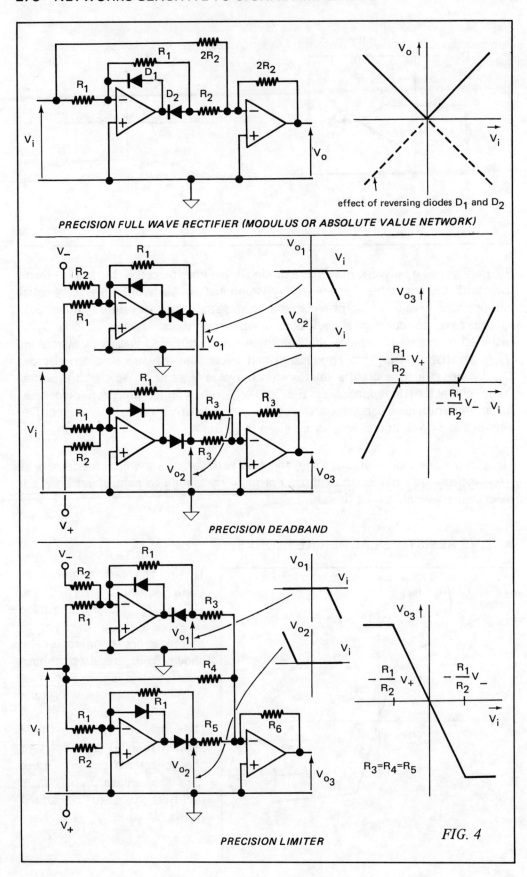

PRECISION FULL WAVE RECTIFIER (MODULUS OR ABSOLUTE VALUE NETWORK)

PRECISION DEADBAND

PRECISION LIMITER

FIG. 4

An alternative technique would be to create multiple parallel channels of analog comparators and solid state digitally-controlled analog switches, as shown in Figure 5.

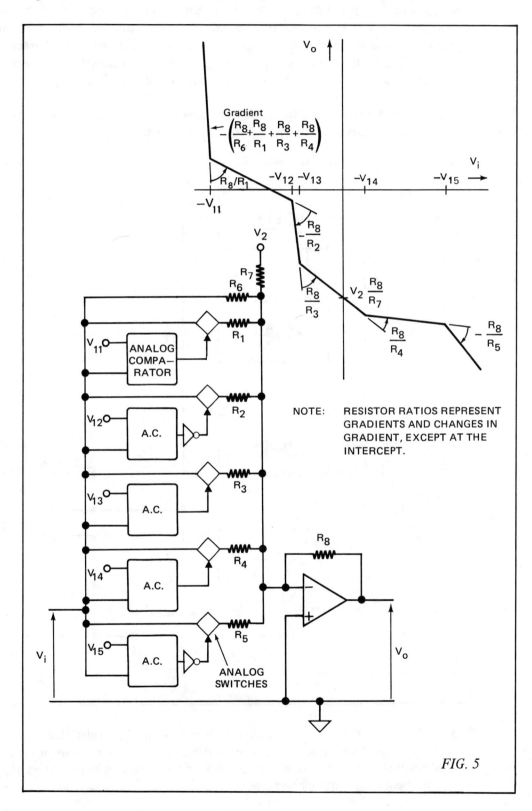

NOTE: RESISTOR RATIOS REPRESENT GRADIENTS AND CHANGES IN GRADIENT, EXCEPT AT THE INTERCEPT.

FIG. 5

For the configuration shown, input breakpoint voltages V_{11}, ..., V_{15} can be preset at any positive or negative value, within the range of V_i, and need not be distributed evenly. Changes in gradient may be positive or negative, depending on whether a particular comparator, when it changes state, turns on or off the analog switch to which it is connected. The value of each gradient may be modified by changing the value of the resistor R_1, ..., R_5 concerned. The characteristic may be raised or lowered bodily, by changing the magnitude (and, if necessary, the polarity) of V_2 and/or by changing the value of resistor R_7.

Variations on the above configuration have been built using active ladder networks of diodes and resistors, as shown in outline in Figure 6.

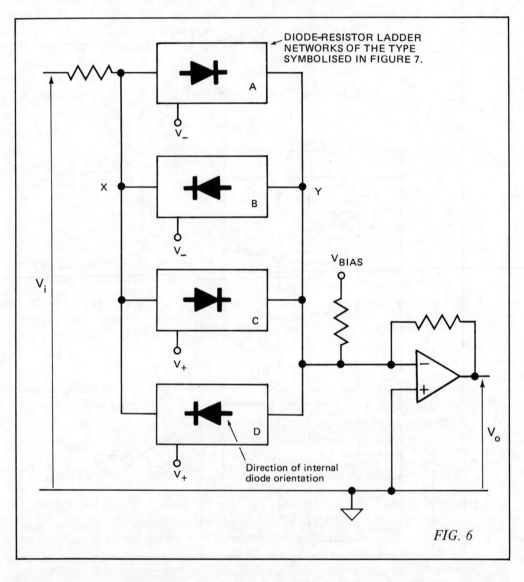

FIG. 6

Blocks A and B operate for positive-going values of V_i, whilst blocks C and D operate for negative values. Whenever a diode conducts, it causes a reduction in the effective resistance between points X and Y, resulting in a negative increase in the gradient of the static characteristics.

The detail of the ladder network for block A is shown in Figure 7. The number of "rungs" shown in the ladder is not necessarily representative of a practical network: a much greater number of rungs would be more commonplace.

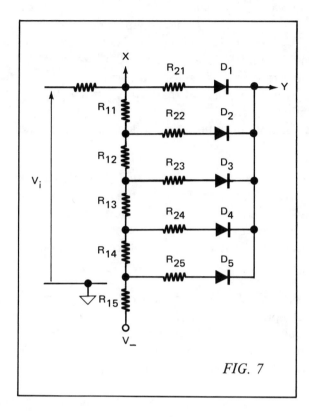

FIG. 7

Diodes D_1, ..., D_5 are connected in the reverse direction for blocks B and D. The V_- supply is replaced by V_+ for blocks C and D.

Changing the values of resistors R_{11}, ..., R_{15} will modify the breakpoint values.

Changing the values of resistors R_{21}, ..., R_{25} will modify the changes in gradient occurring at the breakpoints.

A diode will conduct, or cease to conduct, when V_i is driven through a value of potential such that the diode becomes, or ceases to become, forward biassed, bearing in mind that node Y will behave as a virtual earth, if the amplifier output is unsaturated.

Ladder networks such as the one described are difficult to design with precision, because of the effect of the actual voltage dropped across each conducting diode. However, diode-resistor networks can be significantly cheaper than networks employing analog comparators and analog switches.

11.4 NETWORKS USING ANALOG MULTIPLIERS AND DIVIDERS

Analog multipliers can be used to form the basis of nonlinear shaping networks which are not piecewise-linear. This possible advantage must be weighed against the fact that the choice of nonlinear law is rather limited. In addition to this application, multipliers may also be used, in control systems, in their fundamental role of multiplying together two analog signals, in such elements as Ratio Controllers (see Section 8.3.2) and analog adaptive controllers: in the latter case, provision may be made for enabling, for example, a DC voltage signal to vary a gain constant or time constant in the control law of a feedback controller. Analog dividers, whilst being less common than multipliers, can be used to perform similar tasks.

11.4.1 Multiplier and Divider Characteristics

Analog multipliers normally mechanise a relationship having the form $V_o = KV_x V_y$, where V_x and V_y are two input voltages, V_o is an output voltage, and K is a proportionality constant. Typically, 1/K would have a value of 10 V, so that $V_o = 10$ V when $V_x = V_y = 10$ V. Analog dividers normally mechanise a law of the form $V_o = KV_x/V_z$, where V_x and V_z are now the two input voltages and, in this case, K typically would have a value of 10 V, so that $V_o = 10$ V when $V_x = V_z = 10$ V. A more rare type of device is the analog multiplier/divider, mentioned in Section 10.13, which has a law of the form $V_o = KV_x V_y/V_z$:   in this case, the proportionality constant K normally would be unity. Modern devices in these categories usually are either encapsulated circuits or monolithic integrated circuits.

The combinations of polarities of V_x, V_y, and V_z which a particular device can handle determine the alternative "quadrants" in which the device can be operated: the choice normally is between either one, two, or four quadrant operation. Where division (by V_z) is involved, it will be commonplace for V_z to be restricted to positive values, with the lower limit being that which will cause V_o just to saturate.

A number of techniques (for example, "Quarter-Squares", variable-transconductance, Hall-effect, pulse width-pulse height, and log-antilog) have been employed for multiplying together analog signals. By far the most common method used in encapsulated and monolithic multipliers employs the variable-transconductance phenomenon applied to current signals passing through P-N junctions.

Considerations to be taken into account, when selecting one of these devices, include:

- number of quadrants;
- accuracy;
- input and output signal ranges;
- input and output null offsets;
- bandwidth.

11.4.2 External Circuitry Required with Analog Multipliers

Encapsulated and monolithic multipliers usually require a significant number of external components before they can perform their specified role. Typically, these components perform such tasks as null offset adjustment, scale factor setting, input range setting, and output voltage level shifting. Figure 8 shows typical external circuitry required by a representative monolithic multiplier.

It is most important, for stable and consistent operation of such a network, that the DC supply rail voltages V_+ and V_- possess long term stability: otherwise, there may be significant drift in the offset and scale factor values. Some resistors may be required to have values which are very precise and stable and not in the preferred-value range.

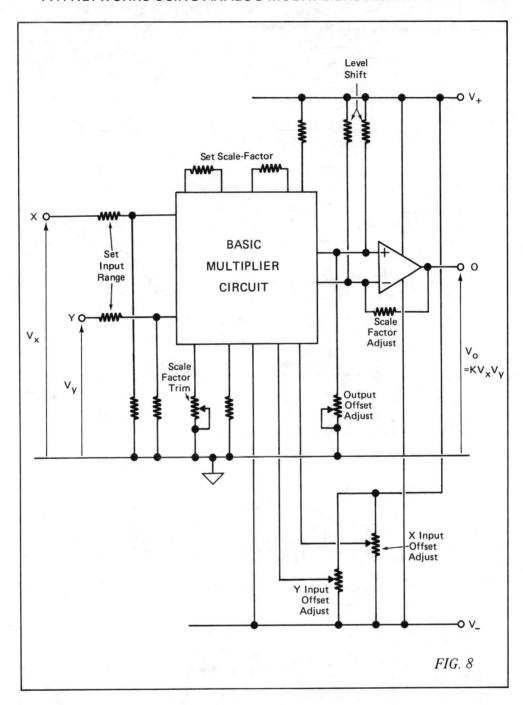

FIG. 8

By making specified changes in the external circuitry, sometimes it is possible to change the function of a given encapsulated or monolithic device from multiplication to other roles such as division, squaring, square–rooting, etc.: manufacturer's data sheets will provide the necessary information.

11.4.3 Generation of Power Laws

The analog multiplier may be connected in a number of alternative ways, in order to generate power laws. Figure 9 shows some typical examples.

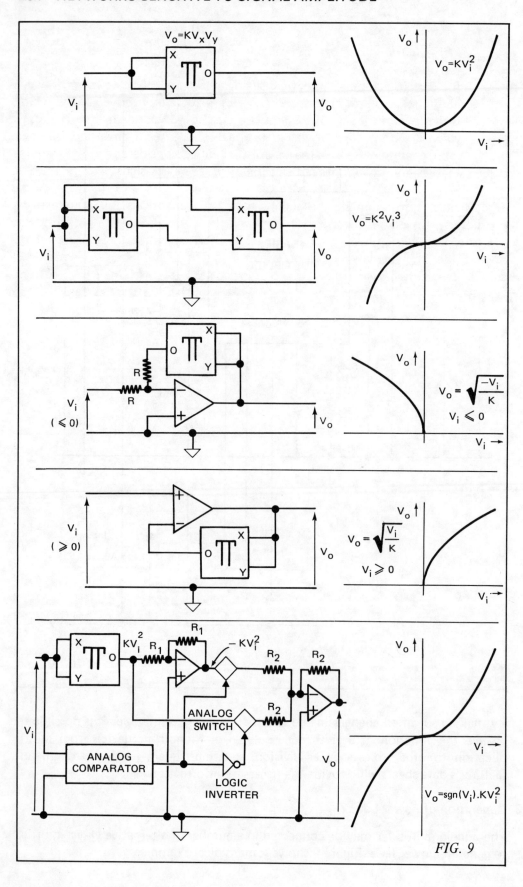

FIG. 9

It is shown readily that:

- increasing the number of cascaded multipliers increases the index of the power law;
- for certain combinations of cascaded multipliers, the output may always be unipolar, unless circuitry which will invert the output sign, and which is sensitive to the sign of the input voltage, is incorporated;
- when a multiplier is placed in the feedback path of an otherwise open loop operational amplifier network, stability considerations will require that the multiplier does not sign-invert the feedback signal.

A particular application of the square–root law network is the Square–Root Extractor. This element is used for removing the square law relating differential pressure to flowrate, which is inherent in those flowrate transducers which involve the insertion of a fixed obstruction in a pipeline: refer to Section 4.5 for details of these. Since the extractor typically will be concerned with current signals in the 4 to 20 mA range, the actual law required for this device will be of the form

$$I_o = 4 + 16 \sqrt{\frac{(I_i - 4)}{16}} = 4 \left[1 + \sqrt{(I_i - 4)} \right] \quad \text{mA}.$$

Figure 10 shows how a square–root extractor may be created, using networks discussed above and in Chapter 10.

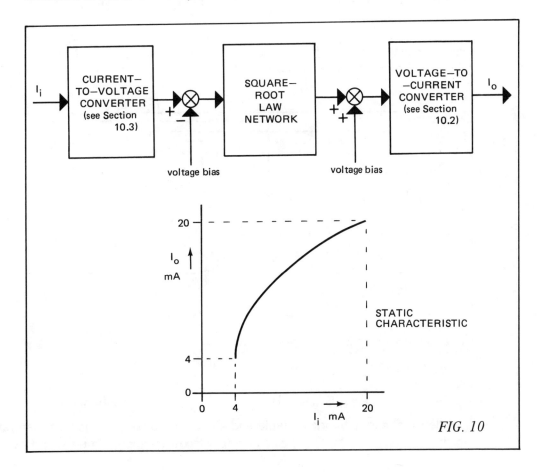

FIG. 10

11.4.4 Other Applications of Analog Multipliers

Figure 11 shows how an analog multiplier may be used for division.

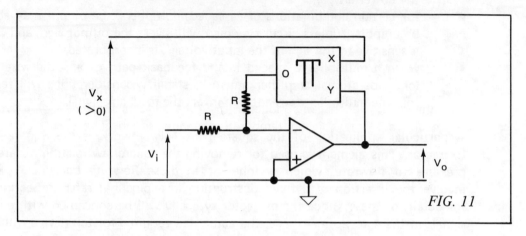

FIG. 11

It is shown readily that, provided the operational amplifier is stable and unsaturated,

$$V_o = - \frac{1}{K} \frac{V_i}{V_x} .$$

In fact, the network will be stable only for negative feedback, so that only positive values are acceptable for V_x. In addition, the amplifier will saturate if V_x is much less than V_i in value, so that the voltages V_i and V_x must be scaled carefully before the network can be applied successfully.

Another application for analog multipliers is in adaptive analog filters, which may be used, for example, to implement control laws in adaptive analog controllers. An example of an adaptive simple phase-lag network (see Section 12.3) is shown in Figure 12.

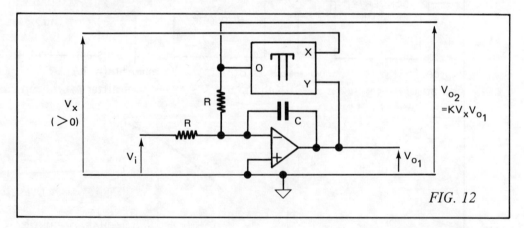

FIG. 12

For this network, it is shown readily that

$$\frac{V_{o_1}}{V_i}(s) = - \frac{1/KV_x}{1 + s\,(CR/KV_x)} \quad \text{and} \quad \frac{V_{o_2}}{V_i}(s) = - \frac{1}{1 + s\,(CR/KV_x)}$$

provided that the network is stable and the operational amplifier is unsaturated, which requires that V_x be positive and places an upper limit on V_i/KV_x. In this event, the network behaves as a simple phase-lag with a voltage-controlled −3dB break frequency of $KV_x/2\pi CR$ Hz.

Another common application of analog multipliers is in modulators for use in AC-Carrier control systems and this topic is covered in **Section 10.4**.

11.5   NETWORKS USING LOGARITHMIC AMPLIFIERS

Modern monolithic logarithmic amplifiers use the logarithmic properties which are inherent in silicon semiconductor junctions, and which afford a wide dynamic range and are amenable to temperature compensation. The circuit commonly used is based upon a transistor placed in the feedback path around an operational amplifier, as shown in Figure 13.

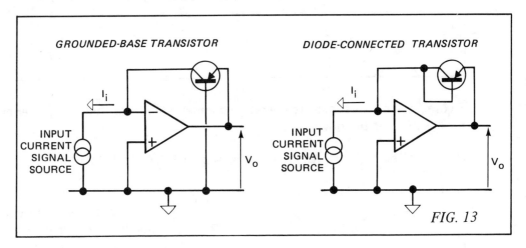

FIG. 13

It can be shown that, for the first network, $V_o \cong \dfrac{kT}{q} \ln (I_i/I_{ES})$ and that this

expression is approximately true also for the second network, provided that the transistor used has a very high value for h_{FE}. In this expression, q is unit charge (= 1.602×10^{-19}C), k is Boltzmann's constant (= 1.38×10^{-23}J/K), T is absolute temperature in Kelvin, and I_{ES} is the emitter saturation current.

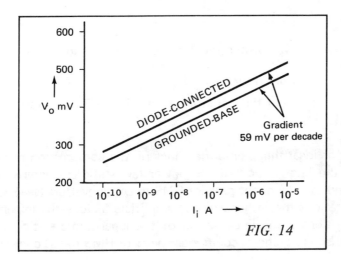

FIG. 14

Figure 14 shows typical characteristics for the two types of configuration. In each case, the characteristic is highly linear over at least five decades, with a gradient of 59mV per decade. Only one polarity of input signal can be accommodated by each network, but the alternative input polarity can be handled by comparable networks using NPN instead of PNP transistors.

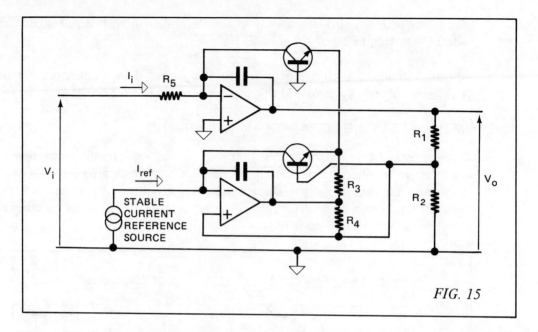

FIG. 15

Figure 15 shows a typical temperature compensated logarithmic amplifier circuit, for which it can be shown that

$$V_o = - K \log_{10} (V_i/R_5 I_{ref}), \text{ where } K = [1 + R_1/R_2]\frac{kT}{q} \ln 10.$$

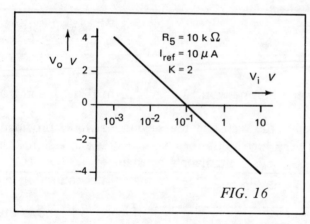

FIG. 16

The capacitors are provided for stabilisation purposes and the presence of the $R_3 - R_4$ resistor combination permits extension of operation to cover up to six decades of values for I_i. A typical transfer characteristic is shown in Figure 16.

Figure 17 shows a minor circuit rearrangement which, in fact, produces an antilogarithmic amplifier with a law given by $V_o = R_5 I_{ref} 10^{-V_i/K}$ This is brought about by virtue of the fact that the potential divider $R_1 - R_2$ and resistor R_5 have, in effect, been interchanged.

Typical applications for logarithmic amplifiers include the compression of wide-range analog signals, the linearisation of the power law static characteristics of certain transducers, and as component parts of RMS-to-DC converters (see Section 10.13). Typical applications for antilogarithmic amplifiers include the expansion of compressed analog signals, the linearisation of the logarithmic static characteristics of certain transducers, and as component parts of RMS-to-DC converters.

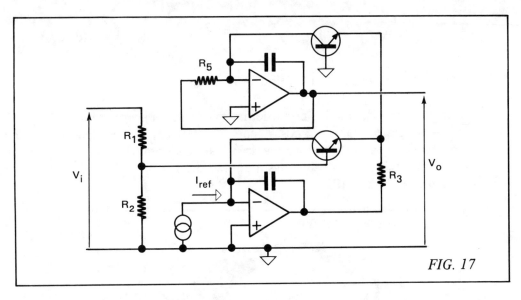

FIG. 17

11.6 SPECIAL–PURPOSE SERVO POTENTIOMETERS

Commercially available is a limited range of servo potentiometers having defined nonlinear laws relating brush voltage to shaft displacement. These may have a wirewound or composition track, and the nonlinear function usually is built in by graduating the cross-sectional area of the track.

Figure 18 shows a hypothetical nonlinear function $f(\theta)$, for a wirewound potentiometer, relating length-of-turn I to shaft displacement θ. Assuming the other properties (resistivity, etc.) of the winding to be constant, it follows that the resistance between the brush and the datum of the track will be given by

$$K_1 \int_0^\theta f(\theta)\, d\theta,$$

where K_1 is a constant in ohm/mm (for example), and the unloaded output voltage V_o will be related to the applied voltage V_s by the law

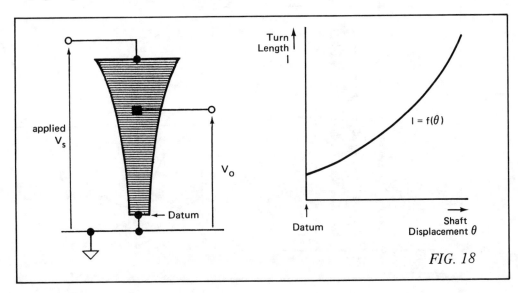

FIG. 18

$$V_o = V_s \int_0^\theta f(\theta)\, d\theta \bigg/ \int_0^{\theta\,max} f(\theta)\, d\theta = K_2 \int_0^\theta f(\theta)\, d\theta,$$

where K_2 is a constant in V/mm (for example).

Typical laws available for potentiometers of this type would include $V_o = V_s \sin\theta$, $V_o = V_s \cos\theta$, and $V_o = V_s \log(A\theta + B)$, where A and B are constants. The sine and cosine laws can be obtained by using a continuous toroidal track with two brushes mounted on axes at right angles to one another, as shown in Figure 19.

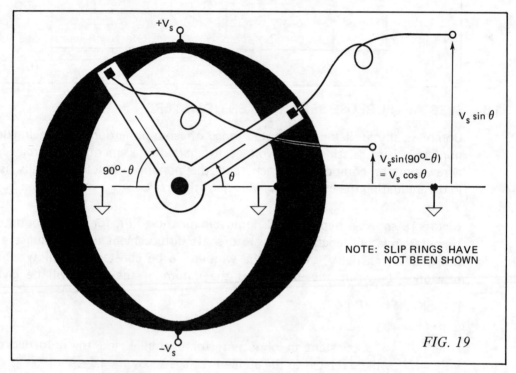

FIG. 19

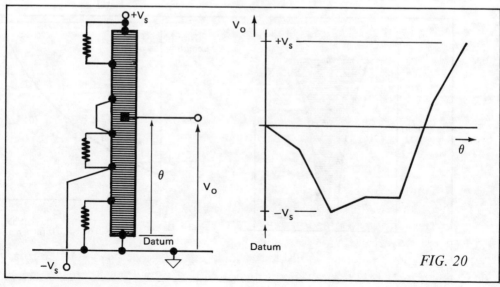

FIG. 20

Piecewise-linear characteristics can be imposed upon nominally linear servo potentiometers, if they are provided with a suitable set of tappings along the track. Sections of the track are shunted with appropriate fixed resistance values, and the potentiometer is then said to be "padded". Figure 20 shows one possible arrangement for a potentiometer with five tappings and external padding.

The advantage with this latter technique is that the law may be modified at will by the user, but offset against this are the limitation on the maximum number of tappings which can be accommodated and the fact that only straight line segments will result, for the static characteristic.

When driven by a linear servosystem but not used as the displacement feedback transducer of that system, these special potentiometers will enable one variable to be multiplied by a nonlinear function of a second variable, as shown in Figure 21. Obvious shortcomings of this technique are the low bandwidth of the servosystem and the limited life and high breakaway torque of the potentiometer.

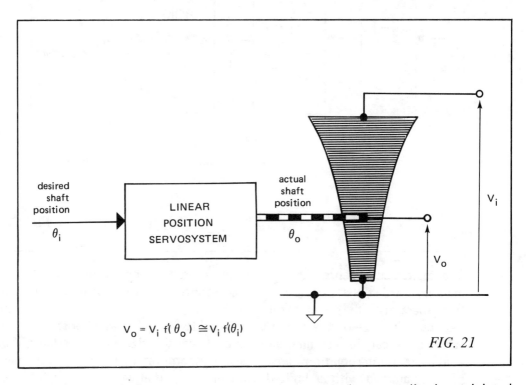

$$V_o = V_i \ f(\theta_o) \cong V_i \ f(\theta_i)$$

FIG. 21

V_i need not be a DC voltage but could be, for example, an amplitude-modulated AC-carrier. The law $f(\theta_i)$ will always become distorted if the load circuit being driven by V_o draws significant current levels from the potentiometer.

A similar effect can be achieved with a linear potentiometer, if it is configured to be driven, from the servo output shaft, through an interposed cam and cam-follower. This technique will permit special nonlinear functions to be obtained, including curved functions, but imposing certain constraints: for example, the requirement for a sudden discontinuity in the law could necessitate the follower being required to jump a radial face of the cam — an impossible undertaking.

11.7 DIGITALLY—SYNTHESISED AMPLITUDE SENSITIVE NETWORKS

An extremely powerful and relatively fast technique is an extension of the code-conversion application of semiconductor read-only memory (ROM) discussed in Section 10.15. Figure 22 indicates how the hardware would need to be organised.

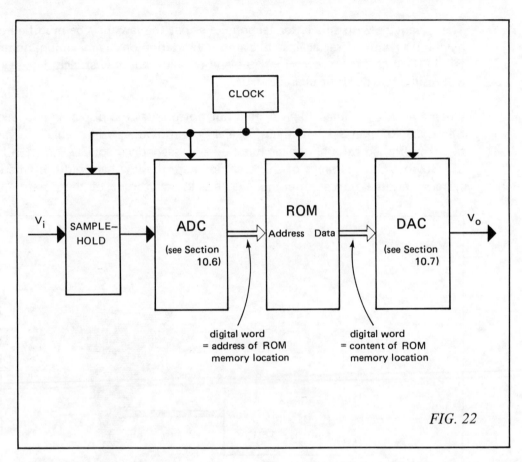

FIG. 22

The digital code representing V_i is interpreted as the address of a location in memory, whilst the (previously stored) content of that location will represent V_o: therefore, the relationship of V_o to V_i will be the nonlinear function required. The size of the memory will need to be such that all possible alternative values of V_i can be accommodated, except that this size may be reduced if special digital data interpolation networks are incorporated. Memories are marketed pre-programmed with a limited number of alternative functions: for example, sine and cosine laws.

The obvious versatility of the technique means that the nonlinear function could incorporate curvature, discontinuity, and four-quadrant operation. Against this must be weighed the complexity and cost of the hardware, together with the possible disadvantage of introducing sampling and quantisation processes into the control system into which the network is introduced. For maximum resolution, the input voltage V_i and output voltage V_o should each be scaled so that maximum use is made of the available voltage excursion of the ADC and DAC, respectively.

12

NETWORKS SENSITIVE TO SIGNAL FREQUENCY

12.1   INTRODUCTION

In many control systems, the need arises for the deliberate introduction, into the loop, of networks which exhibit gain magnitude and phase shift variations as functions of signal frequency. Such networks normally are linear, in the sense that the values of these variations are independent of input signal amplitude except that, in practice, all active networks will exhibit saturation, if this amplitude becomes excessive.

In control systems, frequency-dependent networks are introduced normally for one or more of the following reasons:

- to establish and/or improve closed loop system stability;
- to optimise closed loop dynamic performance;
- to filter out (that is, to suppress) parasitic noise components in system signals and power supplies;
- to correct parasitic phase shifts in the carrier components in AC-Carrier control systems.

Networks which perform the first two functions listed here often are referred to as "compensation networks" or "compensators".

The passive components normally used in analog filters are either resistors or capacitors. This is because these components can be manufactured to very close tolerances and usually exhibit long term stability: for example, $\pm$ 1% tolerance or better is obtained readily in resistor values over the range 5Ω to $1M\Omega$ and in capacitor values over the range 10nF to 10μF. For certain noise filters, electrolytic capacitors can be obtained with values up to the mF range, but the fact that they are polarised usually restricts their use to applications in which the voltages are of single polarity; however, tantalum electrolytic capacitors have occasionally been used in back-to-back pairs (that is, connected in series opposition) in bipolar applications. Inductors do not appear very frequently in these networks: only air-cored inductors can be made to close-tolerance specifications and have an inductance which is independent of signal level. Air-cored inductors having more than a small inductance value must be large physically and the inherent resistance value may be excessive for the particular application. Inductors cored with soft iron laminations, encapsulated iron dust, or ferrite can achieve a high inductance/volume ratio, but then the inductance invariably becomes variable as a function of signal level: for this reason, the application of such inductors usually is restricted to filters for DC power supplies.

The design of frequency-dependent networks covers a considerable field, so that the space available here permits only a brief survey of the techniques used. Most filters are designed using the transfer function as a basis, so that familiarity with the use of the Laplace operator is essential; the design of filters for DC power supplies is a possible exception, this often being undertaken using standard graphs and algebraic formulae.

When using the transfer function as the basis for design, often it is insufficient to design for a nominal transfer function: that is, using nominal values for the parameters (gain constant, time constants, etc.) of the transfer function. Quite frequently, it is necessary to compute the sensitivities of these parameters to changes, from component nominal values, arising from such factors as manufacturing tolerances, ageing, operating conditions, etc.

As far as compensators are concerned, the advent of digital techniques has established a very valuable alternative to the traditional analog networks. Digital synthesis of filters provides high precision, considerable versatility, and long term stability, but some potential disadvantages may be present and these will be discussed in Section 12.7.

12.2 PASSIVE R–C NETWORKS

The advantage with using a passive network is the absence of the need for an amplifier. However, if the load applied to the network is significantly large, then the network transfer function for the loaded case may become markedly different from that for the unloaded case. It is the loaded version which is relevant, when the network is introduced into the control system. If the load is changing, during normal operation of the system, then the loaded case transfer function will be changing also, with the result that the nature of the dynamic performance of the system will be variable. This situation can be resolved by interposing a buffer amplifier between the passive network and its load, so that the relevant transfer function now becomes the (stationary) unloaded version: however, this then tends to destroy any advantage which might have arisen from using a passive network, so that an equivalent active network might be a preferable alternative to the passive network-buffer amplifier combination.

Passive R-C networks can only attenuate the input signal, so that signal amplification cannot be achieved by the network itself. This is in contrast to the situation with passive R-L-C networks, in which tuned circuits can be used to amplify voltages or currents at signal frequencies in the region of the natural frequencies of the tuned circuits.

Passive R-C circuits can assume an almost infinite variety of configurations, and the properties of these have been tabulated in many of the literature references. The unloaded transfer functions can be determined using normal mesh-nodal network analysis techniques, and often they are classified in terms of the properties of the corresponding frequency responses: typically, either the sequence of asymptote gradients on the Bode magnitude plot and/or the sequence of sign changes (that is, lag-lead, lead-lag, etc.) on the Bode phase plot.

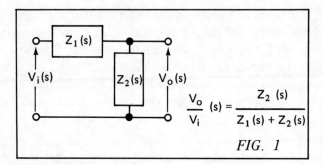

$$\frac{V_o}{V_i}(s) = \frac{Z_2(s)}{Z_1(s) + Z_2(s)}$$

FIG. 1

Frequently, the simpler networks are based on an inverted-L arrangement of simple combinations of resistors and capacitors, as shown in Figure 1. Examples of these R-C combinations have been tabulated in Figure 2, although this list is far from exhaustive.

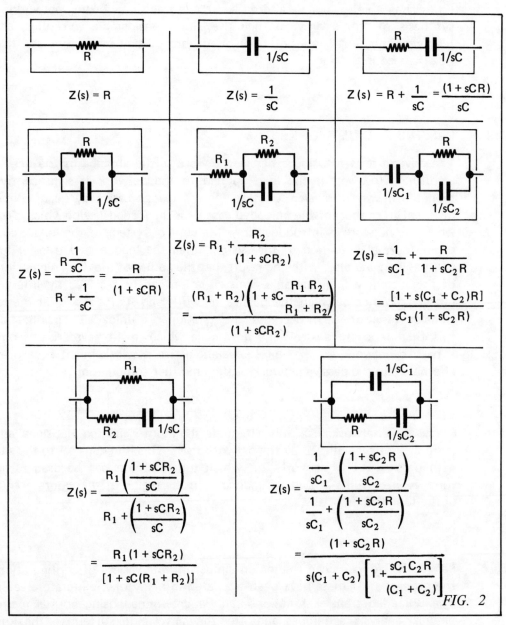

FIG. 2

More complex networks may be constructed using the ladder, bridged-Tee, and parallel-Tee types of configuration shown in Figure 3, using R-C combinations such as those in Figure 2 to create the complex impedances.

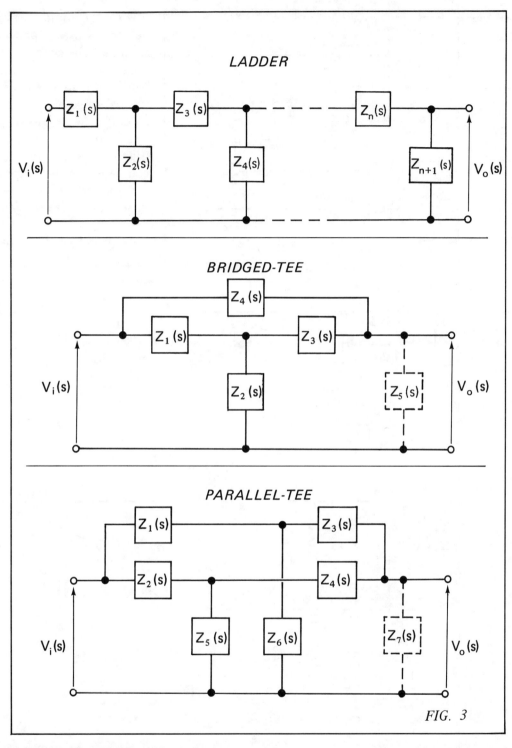

FIG. 3

The simple networks of Figure 2 are referred to as "two-terminal networks" or "one-port networks" because each requires only two external connections. By similar reasoning, the networks of Figures 1 and 3 are called "three-terminal networks" or "two-port networks", because, although the diagrams show four terminals, in fact the input signal source and the output load share an electrically common terminal.

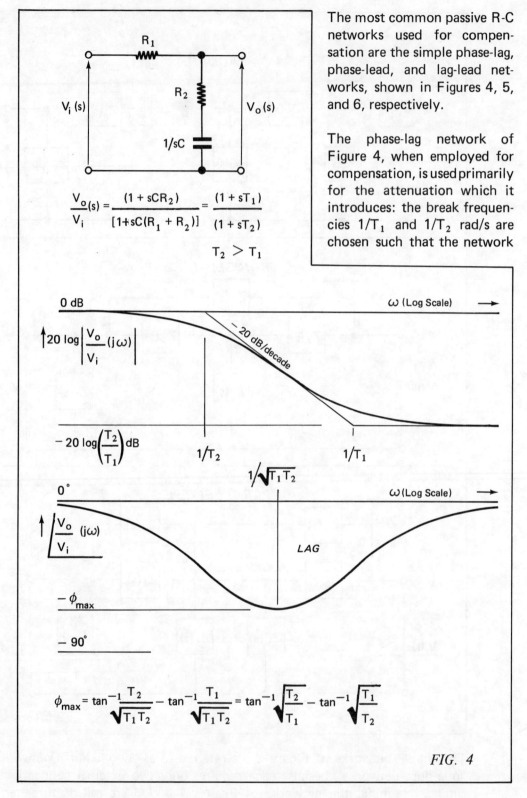

$$\frac{V_o(s)}{V_i} = \frac{(1 + sCR_2)}{[1+sC(R_1 + R_2)]} = \frac{(1 + sT_1)}{(1 + sT_2)}$$

$$T_2 > T_1$$

The most common passive R-C networks used for compensation are the simple phase-lag, phase-lead, and lag-lead networks, shown in Figures 4, 5, and 6, respectively.

The phase-lag network of Figure 4, when employed for compensation, is used primarily for the attenuation which it introduces: the break frequencies $1/T_1$ and $1/T_2$ rad/s are chosen such that the network

$$\phi_{max} = \tan^{-1}\frac{T_2}{\sqrt{T_1 T_2}} - \tan^{-1}\frac{T_1}{\sqrt{T_1 T_2}} = \tan^{-1}\sqrt{\frac{T_2}{T_1}} - \tan^{-1}\sqrt{\frac{T_1}{T_2}}$$

FIG. 4

will reduce the system gain crossover frequency by a greater margin than the accompanying reduction in phase crossover frequency, in order to improve the system stability margins, as discussed in Chapter 15.

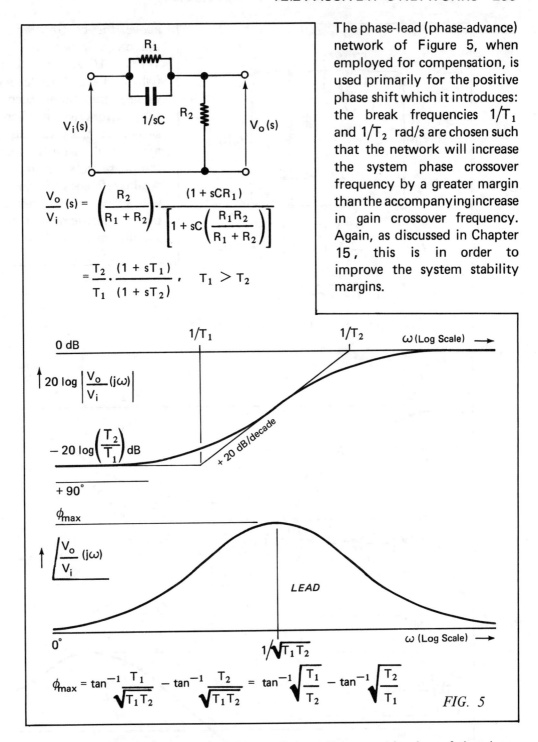

The phase-lead (phase-advance) network of Figure 5, when employed for compensation, is used primarily for the positive phase shift which it introduces: the break frequencies $1/T_1$ and $1/T_2$ rad/s are chosen such that the network will increase the system phase crossover frequency by a greater margin than the accompanying increase in gain crossover frequency. Again, as discussed in Chapter 15, this is in order to improve the system stability margins.

$$\frac{V_o}{V_i}(s) = \left(\frac{R_2}{R_1 + R_2}\right) \cdot \frac{(1 + sCR_1)}{\left[1 + sC\left(\frac{R_1 R_2}{R_1 + R_2}\right)\right]}$$

$$= \frac{T_2}{T_1} \cdot \frac{(1 + sT_1)}{(1 + sT_2)}, \quad T_1 > T_2$$

$$\phi_{max} = \tan^{-1}\frac{T_1}{\sqrt{T_1 T_2}} - \tan^{-1}\frac{T_2}{\sqrt{T_1 T_2}} = \tan^{-1}\sqrt{\frac{T_1}{T_2}} - \tan^{-1}\sqrt{\frac{T_2}{T_1}}$$

FIG. 5

The lag-lead (notch) network of Figure 6 is really a combination of the phase-lag network of Figure 4 and the phase-lead network of Figure 5. The phase response has odd-symmetry about the centre frequency $1/\sqrt{T_{11}T_{12}} = 1/\sqrt{T_{21}T_{22}}$ rad/s and the value of the maximum phase shift increases as the depth of the notch is increased: that is, by enlarging the ratio $T_{21}/T_{11} = T_{12}/T_{22}$. The network, when employed for compensation, is used primarily for its attenuation in the region of the centre frequency, in combination with positive phase shift

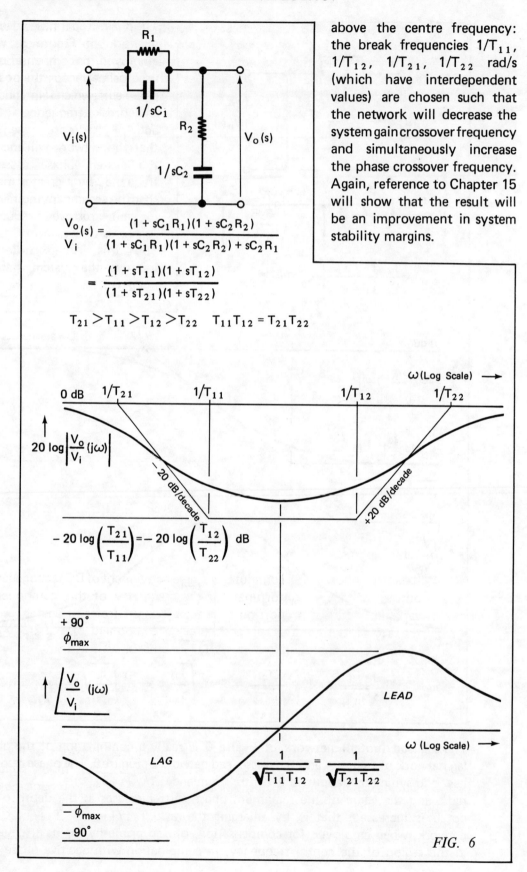

above the centre frequency: the break frequencies $1/T_{11}$, $1/T_{12}$, $1/T_{21}$, $1/T_{22}$ rad/s (which have interdependent values) are chosen such that the network will decrease the system gain crossover frequency and simultaneously increase the phase crossover frequency. Again, reference to Chapter 15 will show that the result will be an improvement in system stability margins.

$$\frac{V_o}{V_i}(s) = \frac{(1 + sC_1R_1)(1 + sC_2R_2)}{(1 + sC_1R_1)(1 + sC_2R_2) + sC_2R_1}$$

$$= \frac{(1 + sT_{11})(1 + sT_{12})}{(1 + sT_{21})(1 + sT_{22})}$$

$$T_{21} > T_{11} > T_{12} > T_{22} \quad T_{11}T_{12} = T_{21}T_{22}$$

$$-20\log\left(\frac{T_{21}}{T_{11}}\right) = -20\log\left(\frac{T_{12}}{T_{22}}\right) \text{ dB}$$

$$\frac{1}{\sqrt{T_{11}T_{12}}} = \frac{1}{\sqrt{T_{21}T_{22}}}$$

FIG. 6

The network of Figure 7 is the simplest of the range of "low-pass filters", which are used frequently as noise filters and which are passive in most instances. When employed for noise filtering, the network is used primarily for the attenuation which it introduces at the higher frequencies, which are characteristic of most noise signals: this attenuation and the accompanying negative phase shift often are deleterious to system performance (but have to be tolerated), if the filter is

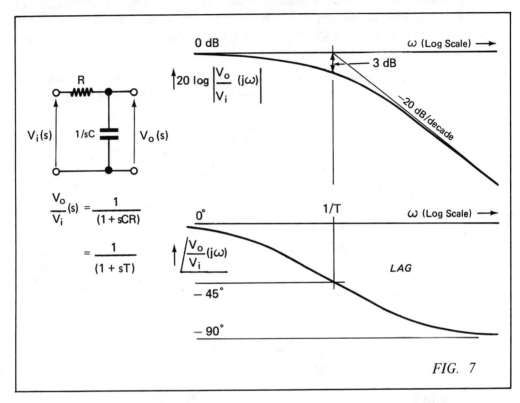

$$\frac{V_o}{V_i}(s) = \frac{1}{(1 + sCR)}$$

$$= \frac{1}{(1 + sT)}$$

FIG. 7

connected within the loop of a closed loop system. Typical applications for noise filters include:

- the attenuation of the commutator ripple component of DC tachogenerator output voltage — unfortunately, the frequency of this component is variable, in direct proportion to the shaft speed (refer to Section 2.4.1);
- the attenuation of the carrier frequency component of the DC output voltage from demodulators in AC-Carrier control systems (refer to Section 10.5);
- the attenuation of the AC component in the output voltage from RMS-to-DC and frequency-voltage converters (refer to Sections 10.13 and 10.16 respectively).

Note that compensation networks such as the phase-lead network of Figure 5, which introduce at low frequencies an attenuation which is much higher in value than that at high frequencies, will tend to have an effect on parasitic noise components which is the reverse of the effect of noise filters. Thus, phase-lead compensation networks will tend to worsen signal/noise ratios and, for this reason, it is preferable to avoid their use in those systems in which a high level of parasitic noise is present.

12.3   ACTIVE R–C NETWORKS

For all of the passive R-C networks, discussed in the previous section, there are active network counterparts. In addition, the active nature of these latter networks enables them to provide amplification as well as attenuation, and ensures that the transfer function being synthesised is independent of the loading of the network output. Active configurations of this type normally are constructed around operational amplifiers, with most single-stage configurations being sign-inverting: however, Figure 8 shows general arrangements for both sign-inverting and non-inverting configurations.

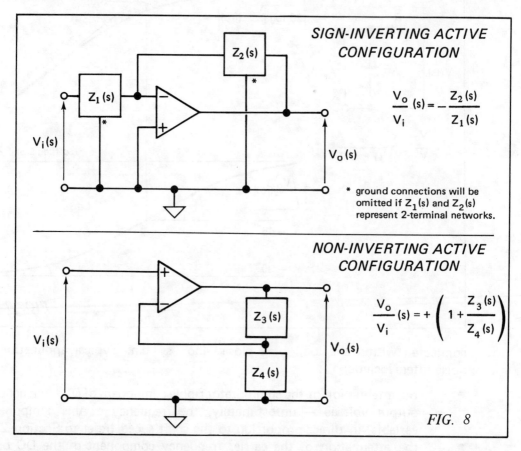

FIG. 8

Typically, the networks implied by blocks $Z_1(s)$ .... $Z_4(s)$ would be two-terminal passive R-C networks of the type indicated in Figure 2 or, less commonly, $Z_1(s)$ and/or $Z_2(s)$ might be three-terminal passive R-C networks of the kind outlined in Figure 3.

In the case of three-terminal networks in active configurations, complex impedances $Z_1(s)$ and $Z_2(s)$ need to be defined as "short-circuit transfer impedances": such an impedance relates, to the applied input voltage, the current flowing from the network output, when the output is imagined to be short-circuited to signal common. This is because, during normal operation, the negative input terminal of the operational amplifier will be at signal common potential; in addition, the operation of the configuration will be such that there will be zero current entering this terminal.

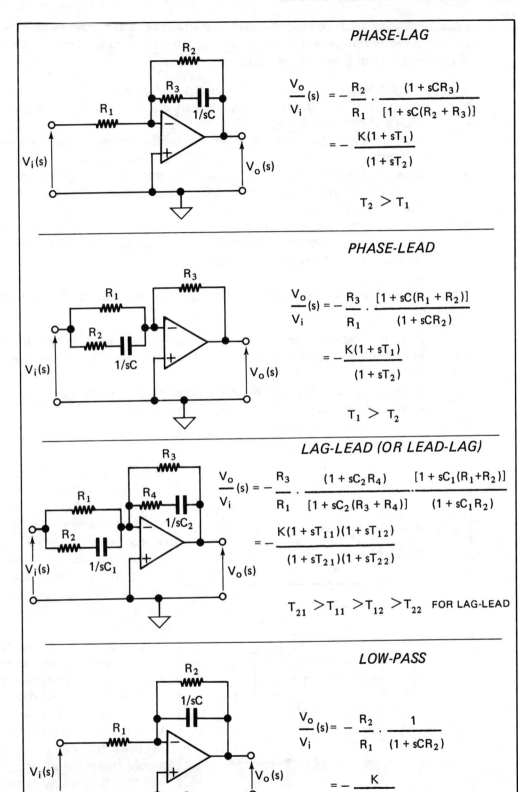

PHASE-LAG

$$\frac{V_o}{V_i}(s) = -\frac{R_2}{R_1} \cdot \frac{(1 + sCR_3)}{[1 + sC(R_2 + R_3)]}$$

$$= -\frac{K(1 + sT_1)}{(1 + sT_2)}$$

$$T_2 > T_1$$

PHASE-LEAD

$$\frac{V_o}{V_i}(s) = -\frac{R_3}{R_1} \cdot \frac{[1 + sC(R_1 + R_2)]}{(1 + sCR_2)}$$

$$= -\frac{K(1 + sT_1)}{(1 + sT_2)}$$

$$T_1 > T_2$$

LAG-LEAD (OR LEAD-LAG)

$$\frac{V_o}{V_i}(s) = -\frac{R_3}{R_1} \cdot \frac{(1 + sC_2R_4)}{[1 + sC_2(R_3 + R_4)]} \cdot \frac{[1 + sC_1(R_1 + R_2)]}{(1 + sC_1R_2)}$$

$$= -\frac{K(1 + sT_{11})(1 + sT_{12})}{(1 + sT_{21})(1 + sT_{22})}$$

$$T_{21} > T_{11} > T_{12} > T_{22} \quad \text{FOR LAG-LEAD}$$

LOW-PASS

$$\frac{V_o}{V_i}(s) = -\frac{R_2}{R_1} \cdot \frac{1}{(1 + sCR_2)}$$

$$= -\frac{K}{(1 + sT)}$$

FIG. 9

Figure 9 shows four commonly used sign-inverting active counterparts of the passive networks presented in Figures 4, 5, 6 and 7. These active versions are more versatile than their passive equivalents, because:

- the gain constant K can have a wide range of values;
- the lag-lead configuration may be converted to lead-lag, by a suitable choice of component values;
- the numerator time constants of the lag-lead network can be adjusted independently of one another, as can the denominator time constants;
- with the lag-lead network, the high-frequency gain magnitude can have a value different from that at DC, if the product $(T_{11}T_{12})$ is made unequal to $(T_{21}T_{22})$;
- the transfer functions given for the configurations are unaffected by loading of the network, provided that the output current rating of the operational amplifier is not exceeded.

Integration will always be present in the transfer function of a sign-inverting configuration, if:

(i)   there is a capacitor in the feedback network around the amplifier; and
(ii) the feedback capacitor is not shunted, directly or indirectly, by a resistor; and
(iii) there is no capacitor, in the input network of the configuration, which is not shunted, directly or indirectly, by a resistor.

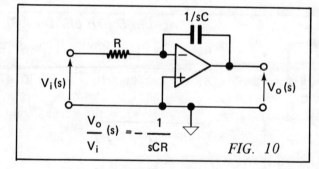

$$\frac{V_o}{V_i}(s) = -\frac{1}{sCR}$$

FIG. 10

Figure 10 shows a sign-inverting integrator for which, incidentally, no precise passive or non-inverting active counterparts exist. A common use for such a compensation network, or more complex alternatives to it, is for increasing the type number of a control system, as discussed in Chapter 15.

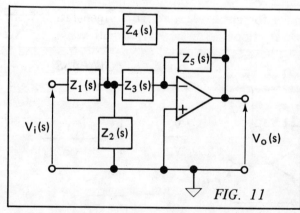

FIG. 11

Yet another variation, sometimes used for sign-inverting configurations, involves the use of "five-impedance" networks, as is shown in Figure 11. Usually, each of the blocks denoted by $Z_1(s)$ .... $Z_5(s)$ would represent either a single resistor or a single capacitor, but this does not preclude the use of other two-terminal or three-terminal networks in these positions. Techniques such as this enable a complex transfer function to be synthesised using a minimum number of operational amplifiers, although this apparent advantage has tended to become of doubtful value, because of the plummetting of the prices of IC operational amplifiers.

The transfer functions given for all active configurations will be invalidated if the input signal level is sufficiently high for the amplifier output to be driven into saturation, either transiently or in the long term. Configurations which give increasing gain magnitude at high frequency will tend to be saturated transiently by discontinuities or other fast changes in input signal.

For all sign-inverting active configurations, it is advisable to avoid the use of any input network which places a capacitor directly between the configuration input terminal and the virtual earth point (the negative input terminal of the operational amplifier): this is because such a capacitor will present transiently, to the input signal source, the equivalent of a short–circuit to signal common, whenever the input signal changes suddenly.

With all active configurations, the precision with which a particular transfer function is synthesised depends not only upon the precision of the resistance and capacitance values but also on the performance specification of the operational amplifier. Amplifier characteristics which can be of particular concern include:

- input bias current;
- input offset voltage;
- small signal bandwidth;
- output voltage slew rate limit.

The input bias current is especially critical in those configurations which synthesise integration. In those networks not synthesising integration, the input offset voltage can particularly affect the DC behaviour, especially when the DC gain is required to be precise. Bandwidth and slew rate limit are significant normally only in high frequency applications, which frequently do not concern the control engineer.

12.4   FILTER NETWORKS FOR DC POWER SUPPLIES

Normally, DC power supplies for electronic circuits are generated, from single phase AC mains, using power diodes configured for half wave, full wave, or bridge operation. The output voltage from the diode network takes the form of a DC level superimposed on which are half sinewaves, and it is the purpose of the filter to reduce the magnitude of this latter, "ripple", component to an acceptable value. A figure will also be specified for the acceptable tolerance on the value of the DC output voltage, which will vary with changes both in load and in AC supply voltage, the effect being related to the cause by "load regulation" and "supply voltage regulation" figures, respectively.

Where close limits are placed upon these regulation figures, it is normal practice to employ a voltage regulator IC between the filter and the load: this regulator will also assist in the attenuation of the ripple component so that, when the regulator is used, less demand is placed upon the filter to provide the necessary attenuation of this component.

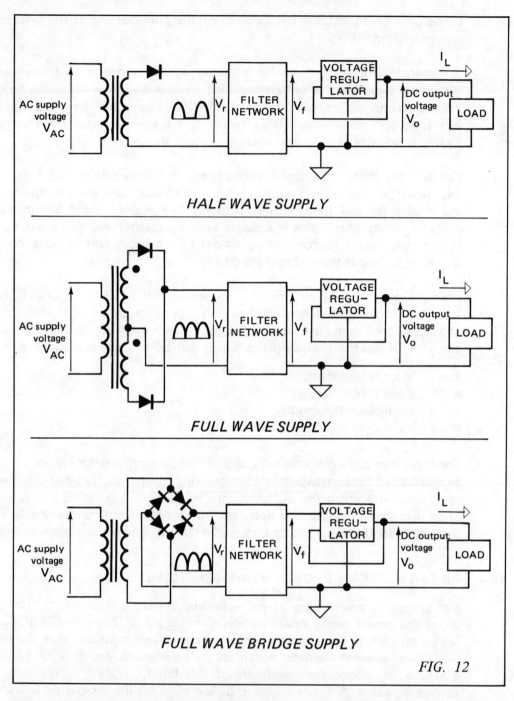

HALF WAVE SUPPLY

FULL WAVE SUPPLY

FULL WAVE BRIDGE SUPPLY

FIG. 12

Figure 12 shows three alternative configurations for voltage regulated DC power supplies: the third arrangement would be the most commonly used, because it does not require a centre-tapped transformer secondary winding, and the full wave rectified waveform is smoothed much more readily than is the corresponding half wave version. The voltage regulator behaves as an output-voltage controlled series resistor, with the resistance automatically varied so as to keep V_o matched to the desired value, which normally is generated internally within the IC regulator: this device is thus a small closed loop (voltage) control system in its own right, with filter voltage V_f and load current I_L being wild variables.

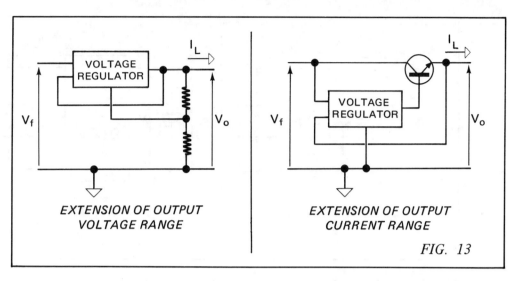

EXTENSION OF OUTPUT VOLTAGE RANGE

EXTENSION OF OUTPUT CURRENT RANGE

FIG. 13

Figure 13 shows how the output voltage and load current ranges of a given regulator IC may be extended, using an output potential divider for the former case and a power transistor for the latter: the two techniques may be combined, should both ranges require simultaneous extension.

Where the power supply is used for digital circuits, it is the usual practice to connect a high value (mF range) electrolytic capacitor across the power supply output: this serves as a bypass for short duration current pulses, which tend to circulate in the supply bus connections of digital circuits and which otherwise could cause spurious switching conditions to occur. An additional effect of this capacitor will be to cause V_o to decay only slowly, after the AC supply has been switched off.

Digital circuits frequently will require the maximum safe value of V_o to be less than the peak value of V_f: one result of this is that, if the voltage regulator should fail to a condition whereby it presents a low series resistance between V_o and V_f, then V_o may jump consequently to a value which could be sufficient to destroy the digital circuits. In this situation, it is imperative that protection circuits, such as "crowbar networks", be provided in order to limit, to a safe level, the maximum value of V_o which can occur under fault conditions.

The design of the filter depends upon:
- the value of the DC component of V_r;
- the nature and magnitude of the ripple component of V_r;
- the value required for the DC component of V_f;
- the value required for the ripple component of V_f;
- the frequency of the supply;
- the maximum value of load current I_L.

Most filters for this type of application would incorporate a choke, which is a ferrous or ferrite cored inductor, and one or more electrolytic capacitors. The two most commonly used types of network are shown in Figure 14, with the first being preferred for applications requiring close voltage regulation.

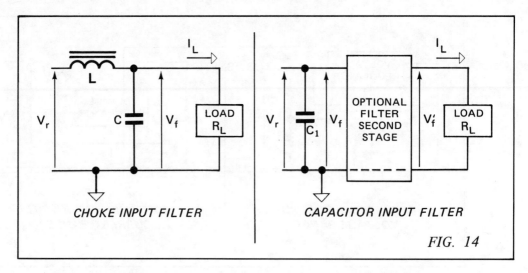

CHOKE INPUT FILTER   CAPACITOR INPUT FILTER

FIG. 14

Choke input filters typically are designed using, for the particular supply frequency, a standard graph of L versus C (each plotted to a logarithmic scale) on which are superimposed contours of constant percentage ripple content in the V_f waveform, and contours of constant load resistance R_L. Capacitor input filters typically are designed in stages: the first stage, which involves C_1, would be designed using, for the particular diode configuration selected, a standard graph of (DC component of V_f)/V_{AC} versus $2\pi f C_1 R_L$ (plotted to linear versus logarithmic scales) on which are superimposed contours of constant value for the function R_L /(average source resistance presented to the filter).

Further stages of filtering may be added to either type of filter, in order to reduce further the ripple content, and typically these would resemble the choke input filter. These stages may be designed either on the basis of transfer functions or by using, for the particular supply frequency, a standard graph of percentage output ripple component versus the LC product, plotted to logarithmic scales, superimposed on which are contours of constant percentage input ripple component. However, the need for these extra stages of filtering will tend to disappear in those applications in which voltage regulators are used.

12.5   COMPENSATION NETWORKS FOR AC–CARRIER SYSTEMS

For any analog control system, the design techniques used will yield a conventional transfer function, which the compensator is required to introduce into the control loop. Sections 12.2 and 12.3 have shown how suitable networks can be created to mechanise the transfer function but, unfortunately, these network designs will be directly applicable only to those systems using DC components in the forward path of the loop. Whenever AC-carrier types of component are used, in the control loop, between the error detection point and the final stages of amplification, the compensation hardware will need to process amplitude-modulated AC-carrier signals, and this requirement will necessitate the application of special techniques.

The problem can be demonstrated by visualising the compensators of equivalent DC and AC-Carrier systems being subjected to frequency response testing, as shown in Figure 15.

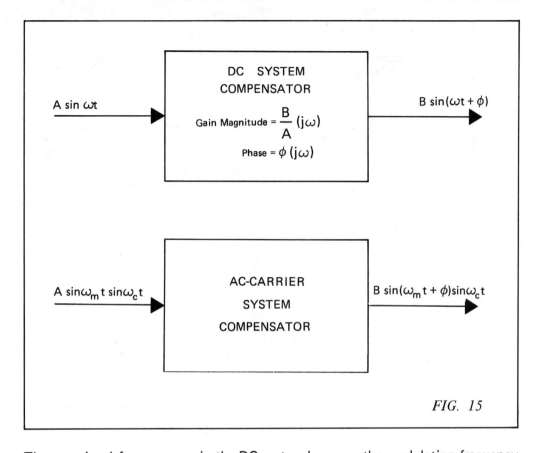

FIG. 15

The test signal frequency ω in the DC system becomes the modulation frequency ω_m in the AC-Carrier system and the input signal to the latter system becomes a sinusoidally amplitude-modulated sinusoidal carrier: the data are represented by the envelope of the waveform (equivalent to $|A \sin \omega_m t|$) and, relative to the carrier reference supply, the phase of the carrier (representing $\text{sgn}(A \sin \omega_m t)$), as described in Section 14.9. For the output signal from the AC-Carrier system to be comparable to that from the DC system, the signal envelope should have been modified, by the compensator, to represent $|B \sin (\omega_m t + \phi)|$ and the phase of the carrier should now represent $\text{sgn}[B \sin (\omega_m t + \phi)]$. Thus, the carrier at the output should always be either precisely inphase or precisely anti-phase with respect to the carrier at the input, assuming the phasing of the input to be exactly correct, relative to carrier phasing at other points within the system.

The input signal to the AC compensator converts to
$\frac{1}{2}A \cos (\omega_c - \omega_m) t - \frac{1}{2} A \cos (\omega_c + \omega_m) t$, whilst the output signal from the compensator becomes $\frac{1}{2} B \cos [(\omega_c - \omega_m) t - \phi] - \frac{1}{2} B \cos [(\omega_c + \omega_m) t + \phi]$. Thus, both signals have components at the sideband frequencies $\omega_c \pm \omega_m$.

The AC compensator is required, therefore, to have a gain magnitude B/A and phase shift $-\phi$ at the lower sideband $(\omega_c - \omega_m)$, and a gain magnitude B/A and phase shift $+\phi$ at the upper sideband $(\omega_c + \omega_m)$. If, for example, the DC compensator is required to have a phase-lead characteristic of the type indicated in Figure 5, then the frequency response of the equivalent AC compensator will need to resemble that shown in Figure 16.

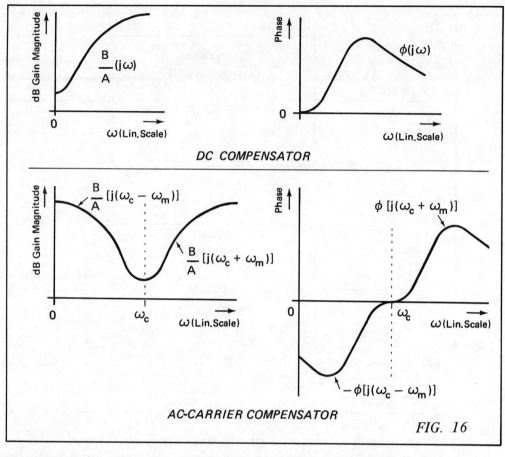

FIG. 16

It is apparent immediately that the gain magnitude plot must possess even symmetry about the carrier frequency ω_c, whilst the phase plot must have odd symmetry about ω_c; moreover, the symmetry is required to be *arithmetic*, not *logarithmic*.

The effect of any departure from symmetry can be demonstrated, for any particular modulation frequency ω_m, by supposing that

gain magnitude = C   and   phase = $-\alpha$ at $\omega = (\omega_c - \omega_m)$, and that
gain magnitude = D   and phase = $+\beta$ at $\omega = (\omega_c + \omega_m)$. The compensator output becomes ½ AC cos [$(\omega_c - \omega_m)$ t $- \alpha$] $-$ ½ AD cos [$(\omega_c + \omega_m)$t $+ \beta$]

= ½ A [sin ω_c t sin ω_m t (C cos α + D cos β)
+ sin ω_c t cos ω_m t (C sin α + D sin β)
+ cos ω_ct sin ω_m t ($-$C sin α + D sin β)
+ cos ω_ct cos ω_m t (C cos α $-$ D cos β)] .

This can be reduced to an expression of the form E sin $(\omega_m t + \theta)$ sin $(\omega_c t + \gamma)$, which is equivalent to the form of the ideal expression B sin $(\omega_m t + \phi)$ sin $\omega_c t$ only when C = D (= B/A) and $\alpha = \beta$ (= ϕ). The effects of distortion of the symmetry of the frequency response of the compensator are therefore threefold:

● the gain magnitude E is incorrect;
● the phase shift θ applied to the modulation is incorrect;
● the carrier is also phase shifted (γ).

The design of an AC compensator which can approach the desired frequency response may require considerable skill, in order to minimise the distortion of the symmetry. The types of network (such as bridged-Tee and parallel-Tee) which can achieve the necessary shape of frequency response may need to be very finely tuned, particularly if the control system bandwidth is considerably less than the carrier frequency, which is often the case. Fine tuning implies that the network components must possess long term stability; it also implies that the method used could be impracticable, if the carrier reference frequency ω_c were to experience long term drift. In any case, precise arithmetic symmetry cannot be obtained for the frequency response of an active or passive R-C network, so that this factor must always remain a source of error, which can be minimised but not eliminated.

One alternative to the use of R-C networks is an approach, sometimes quoted in the literature, which initially involves the design of the equivalent DC compensator. Subsequently, the design of the AC compensator is generated by using the substitutions shown in Figure 17.

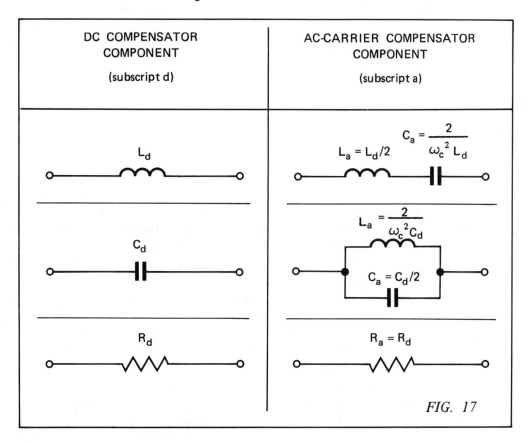

FIG. 17

In practice, this approach may be problematical, because of the following factors:

- the AC compensator must contain inductors, with all of their attendant problems (see Section 12.1), even when the DC compensator does not contain inductors;
- the resulting frequency response possess logarithmic symmetry;
- the technique requires long term stability for the carrier frequency ω_c.

A third approach to the problem is potentially the most expensive but is likely to introduce a minimum number of difficulties: in fact, it can resolve one, as will be seen. This technique involves the conversion of the modulated AC-carrier input signal to an equivalent DC voltage, the processing of this voltage by the equivalent DC compensator, and (if necessary) the conversion of the resultant DC voltage back into an equivalent modulated AC-carrier output signal, as shown by Figure 18.

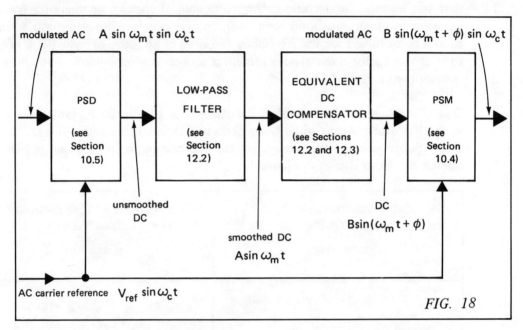

FIG. 18

This method of compensating AC-Carrier systems has the following advantages:

- the operation is insensitive to drift in the carrier frequency ω_c;
- the overall frequency response possesses the required arithmetic symmetry;
- the compensator components are not required to have unreasonable accuracy or long term stability specifications;
- any small parasitic phase shift ϵ (see Section 10.5) in the carrier component of the input signal (so that, now, it becomes $A \sin \omega_m t \sin (\omega_c t + \epsilon)$) is not propagated as a phase shift in the carrier component of the output signal (which now becomes $B' \sin (\omega_m t + \phi) \sin \omega_c t$, with $B' = B \cos \epsilon$) but only slightly reduces the overall gain magnitude: thus, the ability to eliminate parasitic carrier phase shifts is a bonus arising from the compensation method;
- a simple active or passive R-C network could well be adequate for the DC compensator, so that this would easily be designed and implemented;
- in some applications, it might become preferable to use DC components downstream of the compensation, in which case the modulator would not be required.

A potential problem arises from the transfer function of the low-pass smoothing filter: the attendant time constants should either be small, in comparison to those associated with the DC compensator, or the transfer function terms to which they relate should be included, in the design calculations, as part of the compensator transfer function. Moreover, it is desirable that the DC compensator should not be a phase-lead type, because the associated high-frequency amplification could well cancel out the smoothing effect of the low-pass filter, with the result that the regenerated harmonics of ω_c could saturate the DC compensator (if it is the active variety) and/or the modulator.

Because of the complexity of AC compensation design, it is quite commonplace, at least with AC-Carrier servosystems, to compromise by using a rate transducer (in other words, an AC tachogenerator) to provide a damping signal, in lieu of a compensation network. Problems can still arise, mainly from parasitic phase shifts in the carrier component of the tachogenerator output, with these shifts being variable as a function of shaft speed, in the case of some commercial products. The degree of damping is adjusted readily, by attenuating the tachogenerator signal, but the compensation achieved may result in the system dynamic performance, although stable, being far from optimal.

12.6   PHASELOCKED LOOPS

In essence, a "Phaselocked Loop", at least in its usual locked mode state, is a phase control system. In a control engineering context, these loops may be used as tracking filters but the technology is interesting because it can also be used as the basis of frequency control and synchronisation control systems for alternators and oscillators.

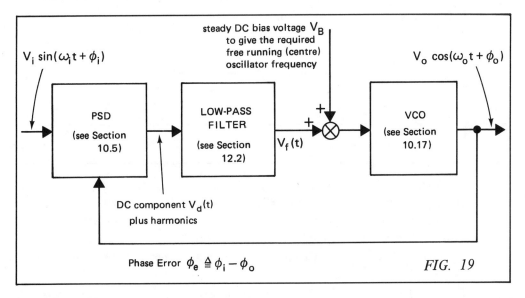

FIG. 19

Figure 19 shows the principal components of a simple phaselocked loop. The quiescent operating condition occurs when the oscillator is running at frequency ω_o which is equal in value to the input frequency ω_i which, at this stage, is assumed to be constant. The output waveform from the demodulator will contain harmonics of ω_o ($= \omega_i$), together with a DC component which is proportional to $\sin\phi_e$, and therefore approximately proportional to ϕ_e for small values of ϕ_e. (The cosine law of the PSD has been converted to a sine law, by shifting by 90° the datum from which ϕ_e is measured: this is implicit in the definition of the VCO output as a cosinewave, rather than a sinewave).

It is assumed that the low-pass filter attenuates to insignificance the harmonic components in the PSD output waveform, leaving a DC component V_f which is related to the DC component V_d of the PSD output by the transfer function of the filter. This signal then augments the steady DC bias voltage V_B, to yield that value of nett DC voltage necessary to make the oscillator run at frequency ω_o (= ω_i).

Typically, the relevant formulae are:

PSD $\quad : \quad V_d(s) = K_d V_i V_o \sin\phi_e \cong K_d V_i V_o \phi_e = K_d' \phi_e(s) , \quad K_d' = K_d V_i V_o$

FILTER $\quad : \quad V_f(s) = K_f G_f(s) V_d(s)$

VCO $\quad : \quad \phi_e(s) = \dfrac{K_o}{s} \left[\dfrac{V_B}{s} + V_f(s) \right]$

The K s are steady state sensitivities (gain constants) and $K_f G_f(s)$ is the filter transfer function. The formulae can be represented by the small-signal block diagram of Figure 20.

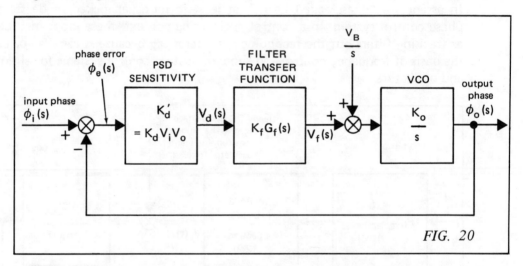

FIG. 20

Normally, V_o will have a constant value (for the peak of the oscillator output waveform) but V_i may be a variable, in which case the loop gain will vary in proportion to input signal strength, because of the dependence of K_d' on V_i. This problem can be resolved by preconditioning the input waveform, by first converting it to a squarewave having a constant peak-to-peak magnitude.

There are many variations on the basic configuration described here, and these can involve more sophisticated types of demodulator and oscillators generating waveforms which are non-sinusoidal.

Phaselocked loops can be designed to have a very narrow closed loop bandwidth, so that only relatively slow variations in $\phi_i(t)$ are propagated as variations in $\phi_o(t)$. Since frequency is the rate of change in phase, a constant component of input frequency $\omega_i(t)$ will be equivalent to a ramp in input phase $\phi_i(t)$. If $G_f(s)$ is designed to include an integration term, then $\lim_{t \to \infty} \phi_e(t) \to 0$ for a ramping $\phi_i(t)$, as is explained in Chapter 15, in connection with Type 2 systems. In this situation, the output phase $\phi_o(t)$ will also ramp and therefore the output frequency $\omega_o(t)$ will, in the steady state, have a constant component equal in value to the constant component of input frequency $\omega_i(t)$.

To summarise, the oscillator output will tend to have an undistorted waveform synchronised with and having a frequency equal to that of the fundamental component of any periodic input waveform, which may be heavily corrupted with noise. This fundamental property of the loop will be consistent for any value of input frequency ω_i occurring within a specified range: the upper practical limit will be set by the maximum frequency at which the oscillator is designed to run; the practical lower limit will be that for which the residual high frequency components in $V_f(t)$ are just insufficiently large to drive the oscillator input voltage intermittently negative. This last limitation arises due to the fact that VCOs are designed to respond only to one polarity of input voltage, because negative frequency is meaningless, in practical terms.

12.7 DIGITAL COMPENSATORS

As has been stated in the introduction to this chapter, the use of digital techniques to synthesise compensation transfer functions represents an extremely powerful addition to the range of techniques available to the control engineer. The design of digital filters is a very large topic, so that available space can permit only a brief introduction to the subject.

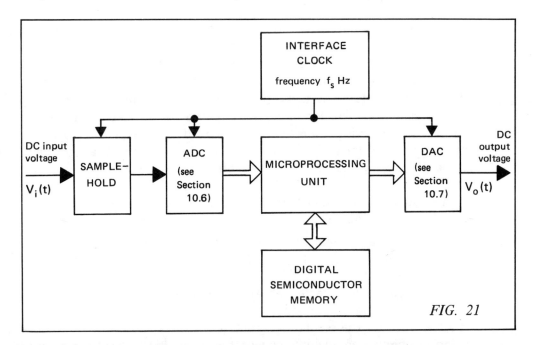

FIG. 21

Figure 21 shows how a microprocessor, memory, and interface hardware would be configured in order to generate a digital compensator. If the clock frequency f_s Hz is chosen to be several orders of magnitude greater than the bandwidth of the system into which the compensator is to be inserted, then the variations in $V_o(t)$ will resemble a smooth waveform and the digital compensator will resemble an analog compensator. However, such an approach could be inefficient economic-ally, because it could preclude the hardware from being time-shared between a set of control loops, thus losing one of the potential advantages of this type of hardware arrangement. If the sampling frequency is chosen to be significantly lower in value, then the variations in $V_o(t)$ will resemble a staircase waveform, with the steps occurring synchronously with the clock pulses, so that the digital compensator now tends to lose its resemblence to an analog compensator.

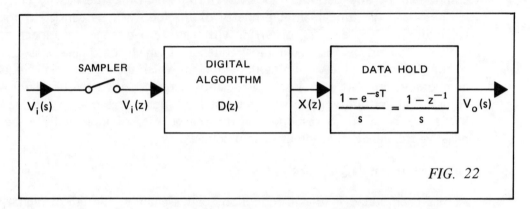

FIG. 22

Figure 22 shows a block diagram to represent mathematically the digital compen-sation hardware. A new operator z has to be introduced, in order to handle the mathematical processes, and this is defined as $z \triangleq e^{sT}$, where s is the Laplace operator and sampling interval, $T = 1/f_s$.

$V_i(z)$ is the Laplace transform of $V_i(t)$ after it has been subjected to the sampling process, with z replacing each e^{sT}. Note that Laplace transforms of pulse trains, or of sequences of numerical values, yield expressions which are functions of e^{sT}. $V_i(z)$ also represents the Laplace transform of the sequence of numerical values which, in coded form, is to be processed by the digital algorithm embodied in the processor program. Similarly, $X(z)$ represents the Laplace transform of the sequence of numerical values which, in coded form, is generated as a result of the application of the digital algorithm. This algorithm may therefore be modelled mathematically by a "pulse transfer function" $D(z) \triangleq X(z)/V_i(z)$.

The first stage of the design procedure would be to choose a value for the sampling frequency, f_s, bearing in mind:

- the probable bandwidth of the final control system design;
- the requirement (if any) for time sharing, and thus multiplexing, of equipment;
- the conversion time of the ADC and settling time of the DAC.

One approach for the second design stage would be to devise, using conventional design techniques, an analog compensator $G_c(s)$ $\left(= \dfrac{V_o}{V_i}(s)\right)$ for the control loop,

and then to use appropriate transformations to arrive at an expression for an equivalent pulse transfer function $D(z)$: this approach only yields an approx-imately equivalent function, and the approximation becomes worse as the sampling frequency is lowered towards the bandwidth of the ultimate closed loop system.

Note that, for any given $G_c(s)$, there is no physically realizable $D(z)$ which will exhibit a frequency response which is identical to that of $G_c(s)$ at all frequencies: the choice of $D(z)$ therefore must be subject to compromise. Many different transformations have been proposed, some of which are tabulated below in Table 1, which assumes that $G_c(s)$ has been expressed as the ratio of two polynomials in the variable $(1/s)$.

TABLE 1. ALTERNATIVE TRANSFORMATIONS FROM $G_c(s)$ TO $D(z)$

METHOD	SUBSTITUTION FOR:		
	s	s^2	s^3
First Difference	$\dfrac{(1 - z^{-1})}{T}$	$\left(\dfrac{1 - z^{-1}}{T}\right)^2$	$\left(\dfrac{1 - z^{-1}}{T}\right)^3$
z Transform	$\dfrac{(1 - z^{-1})}{T}$	$\dfrac{(1 - z^{-1})^2}{T^2\,z^{-1}}$	$\dfrac{2}{T^3}\dfrac{(1 - z^{-1})^3}{z^{-1}(1 + z^{-1})}$
Tustin	$\dfrac{2}{T}\left(\dfrac{1 - z^{-1}}{1 + z^{-1}}\right)$	$\left(\dfrac{2}{T}\right)^2\left(\dfrac{1 - z^{-1}}{1 + z^{-1}}\right)^2$	$\left(\dfrac{2}{T}\right)^3\left(\dfrac{1 - z^{-1}}{1 + z^{-1}}\right)^3$
Boxer-Thaler	$\dfrac{2}{T}\left(\dfrac{1 - z^{-1}}{1 + z^{-1}}\right)$	$\dfrac{12}{T^2}\cdot\dfrac{(1 - z^{-1})^2}{(1 + 10 z^{-1} + z^{-2})}$	$\dfrac{2}{T^3}\cdot\dfrac{(1 - z^{-1})^3}{z^{-1}(1 + z^{-1})}$
Madwed-Truxal	$\dfrac{2}{T}\left(\dfrac{1 - z^{-1}}{1 + z^{-1}}\right)$	$\dfrac{6}{T^2}\cdot\dfrac{(1 - z^{-1})^2}{(1 + 4z^{-1} + z^{-2})}$	$\dfrac{24}{T^3}\cdot\dfrac{(1 - z^{-1})^3}{(1 + 11z^{-1} + 11z^{-2} + z^{-3})}$

In any situation, the choice of the "best" transformation will depend upon the likely nature of the variations in $V_i(t)$ to be expected. A transformation which is effective for one type of variation (for example, a ramp in $V_i(t)$) may prove to be poor for a second type of variation (for example, a sinusoidal variation in $V_i(t)$).

The alternative approach for the second stage in the design process, would be to design the system as a complete entity, using the z operator as a basis, to optimise that design, and finally to ascertain the expression for $D(z)$ needed to implement that optimisation. This is a much more precise approach to the problem, but it requires the engineer to have a sound working knowledge of sampled data system design techniques.

The third stage of the design process is to convert the pulse transfer function $D(z)$, however obtained, into an equivalent "finite difference equation", which is a formula relating the sequence of numerical values, generated by the digital algorithm, to the sequence of numerical values being supplied to the algorithm. This can best be demonstrated by means of an example.

Suppose we require $D(z) \triangleq \dfrac{X(z)}{V_i(z)} = \dfrac{20(z - 0.2)}{(z + 0.7)} = \dfrac{20 - 4z^{-1}}{1 + 0.7z^{-1}}$

Cross-multiplying yields $\quad X(z) + 0.7z^{-1} X(z) = 20 V_i(z) - 4z^{-1} V_i(z)$

so that $\qquad\qquad\qquad X(z) = 20V_i(z) - 4z^{-1} V_i(z) - 0.7z^{-1} X(z).$

In the time domain, this transforms to a finite difference equation:

$$x_n = 20\, v_{i_n} - 4\, v_{i_{n-1}} - 0.7 x_{n-1}$$

for which

x_n = current value, of the algorithm output, to be computed

x_{n-1} = previous value, of the algorithm output; previously computed and stored, for use at the current time

v_{i_n} = current value of the input to the algorithm

$v_{i_{n-1}}$ = previous value of the input to the algorithm, stored for use at the current time.

The difference equation would then be rewritten as a set of program statements (using machine language, assembly language, or a high level language such as BASIC, FORTRAN, PASCAL, etc.) which would be stored in the program area of the semiconductor memory.

The advantages with using digital compensators include the following:

- The wide range of types of algorithm which can be implemented; (there are even some realisable digital algorithms which do not have a physically realisable analog compensator counterpart).
- The ability to incorporate amplitude sensitive algorithms as well, along lines comparable to those described in Section 11.7.
- The ability to make the algorithms adaptive, by using program statements to cause the values of the difference equation coefficients to be varied.

The potential disadvantages would be:

- The complexity and cost of the hardware, although, in some installations, this can largely be offset by timesharing the hardware between many control loops.
- The deleterious effects arising from the introduction of sampling and quantisation processes into the control system : the effects of sampling can be minimised by maximising the sampling frequency, whilst resolution can be maximised by scaling the input and output DC voltages to use fully the available voltage excursions of the ADC and DAC.

13

DEVELOPMENT OF COMPLETE SYSTEMS AND THE CONSTRUCTION OF SCHEMATIC DIAGRAMS

13.1 DEVELOPMENT OF COMPLETE SYSTEMS

Experience shows that the control engineer is rarely consulted in the initial development stages, when a new plant is under construction. Thus, he usually is presented with a completed plant design, as a *fait accompli,* and is requested to control it.

Obviously, a pre-requisite for the control engineer is that he should have a reasonable knowledge of the operating principles and the technical details of the plant, before he can attempt to control it with an adequate level of performance.

His first task is to identify those properties (the controlled variables) of the plant which ultimately are to be controlled. Having done so, he can formulate a specification for the degree of precision to which each variable is to be controlled, both in a dynamic sense and in a steady state sense, taking into account the parasitic disturbances to which the plant is likely to be subjected and the acceptance limits on the quality of whatever product is being produced by the plant.

His next task is to identify those properties (the manipulated variables) of the plant which are going to be manipulated, by the final control elements, in order that the variations in the controlled variables shall remain within specification. Usually, the choice of manipulated variables is limited and, moreover, obvious.

Having identified the controlled variables, these must be instrumented with appropriate feedback transducers. Ideally, each controlled variable would be measured directly, by means of its allotted transducer. In rare instances, no suitable transducer may exist or the variable may be inaccessible (due, for example, to a harsh environment), in which case it will be necessary to transduce related variables and to infer, from the signals generated, the value of the controlled variable of interest, using appropriate computing hardware.

The sorts of factor which could be relevant to the selection of a feedback transducer have been listed in Section 1.6, but will be repeated here for completeness:

- cost
- availability
- ruggedness, in respect to the plant environment
- range
- accuracy
- linearity
- repeatability
- speed of response
- reliability
- maintainability
- life
- power supply requirements
- physical compatibility with the plant
- signal compatibility with the controller
- signal-to-noise ratio.

Having identified the manipulated variables, it becomes necessary to select final control elements, in order to provide the necessary manipulation. In most cases, these will be either control valves, heaters, pumps, actuators, or motors and the factors relevant to motor selection (for example) were listed in Section 1.6 and are repeated here:

- cost
- availability
- ruggedness, in respect to the plant environment
- load details: inertia, friction constants, torque loadings
- maximum and minimum velocity
- maximum acceleration
- duty cycle
- reliability
- maintainability
- life
- mounting and coupling requirements
- power supply requirements
- input signal characteristics.

The feedback transducer and final control element in each loop are physically connected to the plant, and therefore have to be selected to cope with the plant environment. The remaining components in each control loop are not physically coupled to the plant, being linked to the feedback transducer and final control element usually by means of electrical, pneumatic or hydraulic connections, and may even be sited quite remotely from the plant: often, these remaining elements will be situated in a control room, which usually will have a much more benign environment than that of the plant.

The remaining elements which normally would constitute each loop perform the following functions:

- signal and power amplification of the error signal, in order to drive the final control element;
- means for generating a reference input signal, normally to be manually set by the operator;
- hardware for generating the error signal from the reference and feedback signals;
- hardware (for example, active R-C filters) for modifying the dynamic and steady state behaviour of the loop, in order to satisfy the performance specification.

In the case of process loops, all of these functions can be provided by the general purpose process controller which normally is used in such cases. In other instances, it often is necessary for the control engineer to custom design a controller to perform these tasks.

In many cases, ancillary equipment may be required to perform one or more of the following tasks:

- incorporation of additional feedback or feedforward signals from additional transducers or controllers;
- signal conversion and/or conditioning;
- alarm indication when system performance exceeds preset limits;
- limitation of the reference variable values, in terms of (say) magnitude and/or rate of change;
- limitation of the controller output or final control element output action, to prevent (for example) unnecessary stressing of the plant;
- noise filtering;
- automatic detection and indication of equipment failure;
- sequence control, for scheduling the sequence of operating levels and modes of the control loop.

As a final stage of commissioning the hardware of each control loop, it is necessary usually to adjust (that is, "fine tune") the compensation elements, in order to optimise the dynamic and steady state performance. When general purpose process controllers are being used, there is a range of alternative procedures available for tuning the numerical values of the terms in the control law, and these usually are based upon simple tests and routine adjustment procedures. When a controller is being custom designed, a much more elaborate procedure is necessary: this often involves identifying (characterising) the dynamic and steady state properties of the plant process, between the input to the final control element and the output from the feedback transducer, and then designing the optimum control law, using one or more of a number of alternative design techniques; finally, the completed system must be tested in order to demonstrate that it complies with the performance specification. Refer to Chapters 14 and 15 for detailed information on these topics.

13.2   CONSTRUCTION OF SCHEMATIC DIAGRAMS

The diagrammatic representation of a complete control system often is made in terms of what is generally known as a "schematic diagram". However, there is no specific definition of exactly what constitutes such a diagram. Certainly, a schematic diagram is distinguishable from a block diagram: in the latter case arrowed interconnections indicate data flow and each block represents a mathematical relationship between output data and input data.

The following comments would apply generally to schematic diagrams:

- all physical interconnections (including signal common connections, in electrical cases) which transmit signals representing system data transfer would be shown;
- power supplies and power supply connections usually would not be shown;
- terminal identifiers often would be added for the signal interconnectors, as an aid to fault finding;

- high power level circuits (electrical, hydraulic and pneumatic) usually would be shown in detail;
- mechanical elements (gears, clutches, couplings, etc.) would be shown and represented by appropriate pictorial symbols;
- the plant process would be included and represented by appropriate pictorial symbols;
- complex low power level circuits (for example, electronic amplifiers, electronic or pneumatic logic networks, etc.) often would be represented by a simple pictorial symbol, with the details supplied elsewhere on other diagrams;
- transducers would be represented by appropriate pictorial symbols;
- the hardware involved in signal combination (addition and subtraction) typically would be shown in detail.

The completed schematic diagram thus yields a wealth of information about the physical interrelationships between the different system elements which constitute each control loop. Such a diagram can be regarded as a stage in the process of analysing system behaviour, because usually the block diagram for the loop can be developed readily from the schematic diagram, certainly in terms of the configuration of the block diagram: the schematic diagram will yield little information about the transfer functions and static characteristics, required for the block diagram, except that their general form may be implied.

13.3 EXAMPLE OF THE DEVELOPMENT OF A CONTROL SYSTEM AND ITS SCHEMATIC DIAGRAM

The evolution of this system will follow a natural sequence:

1. Formulation of the requirements, in qualitative terms.
2. Specification of the ultimate performance in qualitative terms.
3. Selection of system hardware.
4. Development of a schematic diagram.
5. Design, construction and commissioning of the system.
6. Identification of the dynamic and steady state characteristics of the system hardware.
7. Fine tuning of the control laws.
8. Demonstration that performance meets specification.

The example to be presented is hypothetical, so that only stages 1, 3 and 4 in the above procedure will be described in detail.

13.3.1 Requirements for the Example System

The requirements are for a precision linear position control system for a machine tool. The degree of accuracy and resolution is to be in the order of 0.001 mm over a total travel of (say) 1 metre, which amounts to 1 part in 10^6. The system is to have a very fast dynamic response and is to be capable of slewing at rates up to (say) 50 mm/second. There must be no relative motion between the workpiece and cutting tool whilst cutting is taking place, so that the system is required to generate high holding forces in order that the cutting reaction does not generate significant displacement errors.

The above requirements to a large extent are qualitative and have been expressed in fairly general terms. In practice, a detailed performance specification in quantitative terms now would have to be formulated.

13.3.2 Selection of the Feedback Transducer

To obtain the degree of accuracy and resolution required, the selection of a feedback transducer would have to be limited to the following alternatives:

- optical diffraction grating or equivalent;
- Inductosyn, in a coarse-fine measuring system;
- multi-turn shaft encoder containing two encoding discs geared together internally;
- multiple synchro chains geared together, to produce a coarse-fine measuring system.

Let us suppose that, having applied the factors listed for transducer selection, in Section 13.1, to commercially available devices, it has been decided to use an optical diffraction grating. This device with its integral electronics will generate pulses, to indicate increments in displacement, together with signal(s) representing the direction of motion. These signals must be input to a reversible up/down counter, which will generate a count representing the displacement of the machine tool slide from an arbitrary datum. Means must be included to enable the counter to be reset manually to zero, at the requirement of the operator.

13.3.3 Reference and Error Data Generation

The count size will be available as a set of logic signals, in a suitable binary code, representing controlled variable data. Because it is not practicable to generate analog signals to an accuracy approaching 1 part in 10^6, it is necessary to set up the desired position (the reference data) as a compatible digital word. The error data can then be computed digitally, using the reference and feedback words, by means of hardware to effect binary subtraction (or addition, by suitable manipulation). The error data can then be converted to a simple analog electrical signal, to drive the power amplifiers, by means of a suitable digital-analog converter.

13.3.4 Selection of the Final Control Element

To obtain the velocity, acceleration, and holding force levels required, it is almost certain that a hydraulic drive can satisfy the requirements. The final control element could be a rotary hydraulic piston motor, with the rotary motion being converted to rectilinear by means of a leadscrew and nut: the backlash that could be introduced between the screw and nut would degrade system performance, but this could be minimised by using (say) a recirculating ball-bearing type of arrangement, which is expensive but possesses considerably diminished backlash levels.

An alternative would be to generate rectilinear motion directly, by virtue of using a hydraulic cylinder as the final control element: backlash would not arise but the length of travel might be excessive for commercially available cylinders; in addition, a cylinder is likely to give a slower response than would a piston motor.

Let us suppose that, having applied the factors listed for final control element selection, in Section 13.1, to commercially available motors and cylinders, it has been decided to use a hydraulic piston motor, in conjunction with a recirculating ball leadscrew and nut. This motor then will need to be controlled, by means of manipulation of the flow of high pressure hydraulic fluid into, and out of, the motor.

13.3.5 Selection of the Amplifiers

The performance specification for this type of system will necessitate a very high level of loop gain, and the bulk of this loop gain must be provided by appropriate levels of amplification in the forward path of the loop. In addition, the requirements of the motor would necessitate a relatively high level of power amplification. Therefore, a series of cascaded amplifier stages would almost certainly be required, the combination of which would provide the levels of signal and power amplification necessary.

A typical arrangement for the type of system under consideration would be a hydraulic spool type of servovalve to control the motor flow, with the spool being displaced by the hydraulic pressure controlled by a flapper-nozzle type of hydraulic amplifier; in turn, the flapper of the latter would be displaced by a solenoid-armature-linkage arrangement and the excitation of the solenoid would be controlled by a transistor power amplifier. Finally, the first stage would be a transistor or I C signal amplifier, driven by the analog error voltage from the digital-analog converter and driving the input to the power amplifier.

13.3.6 Development of the Schematic Diagram

Bearing in mind the comments outlined in Section 13.2, a schematic diagram can be constructed for the system as described so far: each system element selected can be represented by either a block or a pictorial symbol, as appropriate, and all interconnections (electrical, hydraulic, mechanical, etc.) can be incorporated to show how the elements are interlinked. In a real-world situation, terminal identifiers would be added to the diagram. Figure 1 gives an indication of the type of diagram (without identifiers) which would result.

In a practical situation, waveforms, voltage and current levels, hydraulic supply pressures, etc. might also be added to the diagram.

Not shown in Figure 1 are means for modifying and tuning the dynamic behaviour of the complete system. Typically, an active R-C network might be incorporated into the I C preamplifier; alternatively, a tachogenerator might be coupled mechanically to the leadscrew and its output combined with the

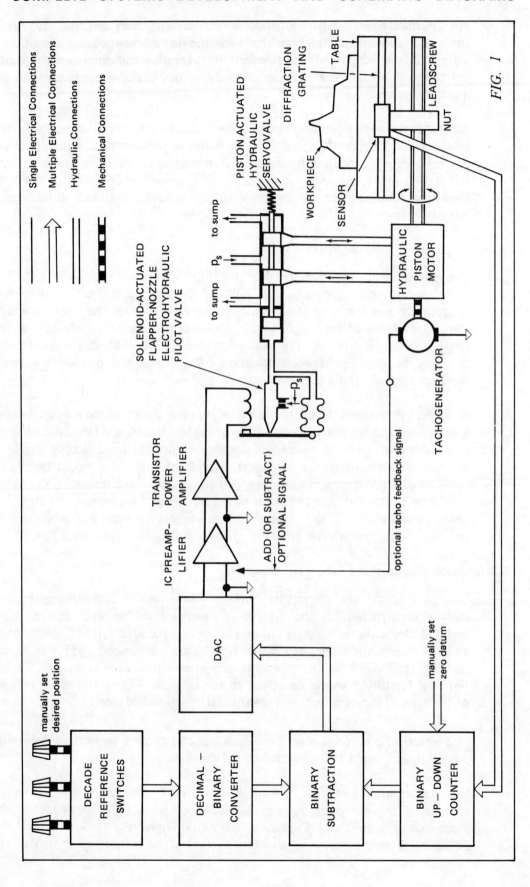

FIG. 1

error voltage (from the digital-analog converter), using the I C preamplifier in a signal combining configuration. Fine tuning typically would be implemented by adjusting the R and/or C values in the R-C filter or, in the alternative arrangement, by adjusting a potentiometer to manipulate the proportion of tachogenerator feedback voltage combined with the position error voltage.

Having created a schematic diagram, the control engineer then would proceed through development stages 5 to 8 as listed in Section 13.3. Refer to Chapters 14 and 15 for detailed information, of a general nature, on these topics.

The particular example chosen represents a relatively complex and sophisticated type of control system. It was selected because it demonstrates a combination of a wide range of types of system element. Of course, it will be appreciated that the majority of control systems are relatively simple and have a less demanding performance specification than the example which has been presented.

13.4 FURTHER EXAMPLES OF POSITION CONTROL SYSTEMS

The position control system described in Section 13.3 was elaborate, mainly as a result of the high level of performance required. In this next section, some of the systems described are assumed to have a somewhat less stringent performance specification. Unless otherwise stated, the power level requirements are assumed to be relatively low, and, in these situations, electric servomotors will be suitable as the final control elements: otherwise comparable position control systems having a high output power level requirement may, for example, either use these servomotors as torque motors for electrohydraulic drives or replace these motors with high power "conventional" electric motors.

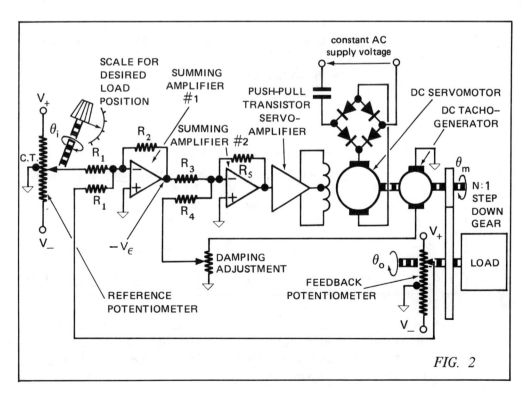

FIG. 2

13.4.1 Typical DC Position Control System

The control system to be described here would be typical of the types used, for example, in recording instruments. Figure 2 shows a common arrangement, which assumes that the nature of the load necessitates rotary motion.

In this example, the tachogenerator provides a rate signal, which is used to modify the degree of damping of the position response. Although two summing amplifier configurations have been used, they are providing differencing action by virtue of suitable connection of the tachogenerator and output potentiometer for an appropriate sense for the velocity and displacement feedback data. Figure 3 shows one possible version for the small signal block diagram for the system, and this assumes that the motor characteristics have been linearised.

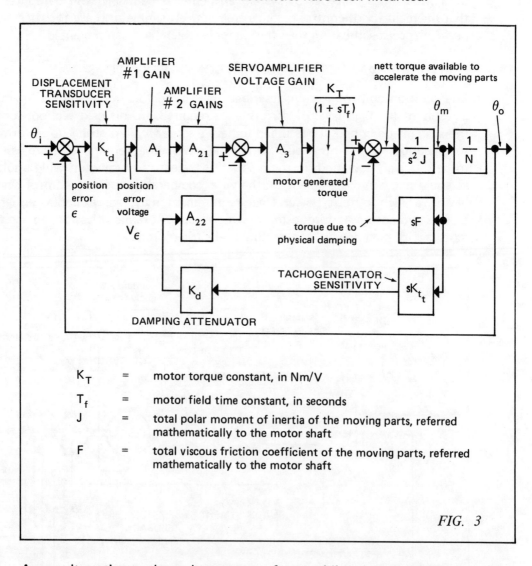

$$K_T \quad = \quad \text{motor torque constant, in Nm/V}$$

$$T_f \quad = \quad \text{motor field time constant, in seconds}$$

$$J \quad = \quad \text{total polar moment of inertia of the moving parts, referred mathematically to the motor shaft}$$

$$F \quad = \quad \text{total viscous friction coefficient of the moving parts, referred mathematically to the motor shaft}$$

FIG. 3

As an alternative to the tachogenerator, for providing damping action, an active R-C compensation network could be incorporated into the operational amplifier networks. Armature control of the servomotor would be a potential alternative to the field control arrangement shown.

13.4.2 Typical AC-Carrier Position Control Systems

Figure 4 shows an AC-carrier counterpart to the DC servosystem of Figure 3.

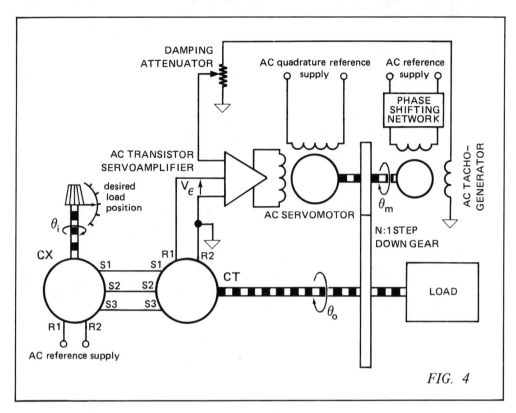

FIG. 4

The AC-Carrier system will be different from the DC system in the following respects:

- there will be no discontinuity in the measuring system, because the synchro law is re-entrant;

- the synchro system imposes a sine law upon the V_ϵ vs ϵ characteristic;

- the servomotor torque vs speed characteristic synthesises an additional component of viscous friction, at the motor shaft.

The block diagram for this system will be similar in form to Figure 3, except that the displacement transducer sensitivity will be dependent upon a law of the form $V_\epsilon = K_{t_d} \sin \epsilon$, and the first amplifier is no longer present.

As an alternative to the tachogenerator for providing damping action, an active compensation network (refer to Section 12.5) could be incorporated into the channel between the synchro control transformer and the servoamplifier.

The AC transducers of this system could also provide the measuring system for a DC motor drive, with a phase-sensitive demodulator inserted in the forward path between the signal combination point and a (DC) servoamplifier. Any compensation network now could be either an AC-carrier of a DC type, depending upon whether it is inserted upstream of downstream of the demodulator, respectively.

The system of Figure 4 can be developed further, by incorporating an additional synchro chain to provide considerably improved accuracy and resolution. The system to be described represents a specific application of the coarse-fine measuring techniques discussed in Section 2.2.9. The complete system is presented in Figure 5 and would have application in the areas of precision machine tools, astronomical telescopes, etc.

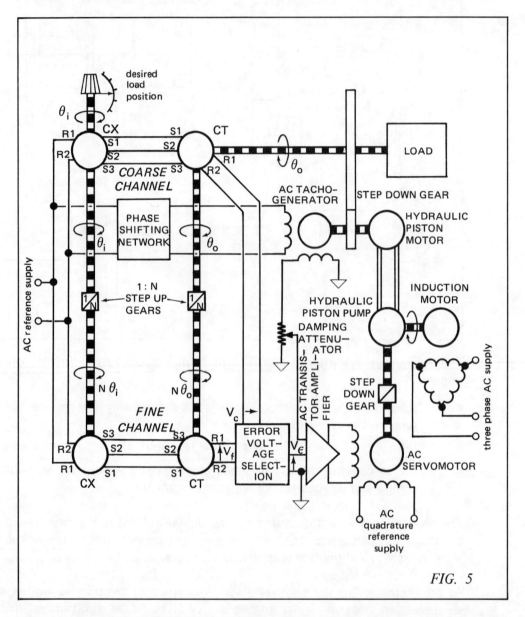

FIG. 5

Figure 6 shows the characteristics of the coarse and fine channel error voltages, plotted to a base of error ϵ (= $\theta_i - \theta_o$). For ease of representation, a much smaller value has been chosen for the gear ratio N than would be used in a practical system. Also shown is one possible characteristic for the error voltage selection, although several alternatives are possible. This characteristic will emerge in the displacement transducer sensitivity block of any large signal block diagram for the system, indicating that this will be a highly nonlinear system.

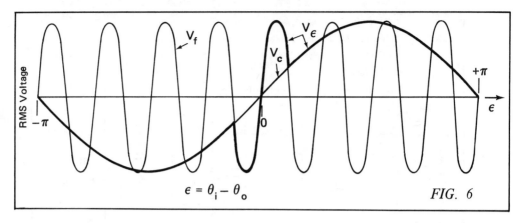

$$\epsilon = \theta_i - \theta_o$$

FIG. 6

Figure 7 shows another coarse-fine system, in which the fine feedback transducer now is a rectilinear Inductosyn. In this case, the reference voltages are assumed to be synthesised and selected by decade switches, using one of the types of network discussed in Section 2.3.3.

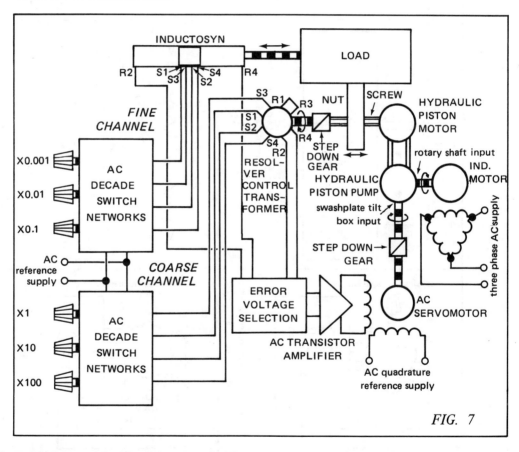

FIG. 7

13.4.3 Typical Numerical Position Control Systems

When digital hardware (and sometimes software) is used to synthesise reference and feedback transducers, error generators, signal combiners, compensation networks, amplifiers, etc., the number of alternative combinations possible becomes extremely large, and Figures 8 to 11, inclusive, illustrate some of these alternatives.

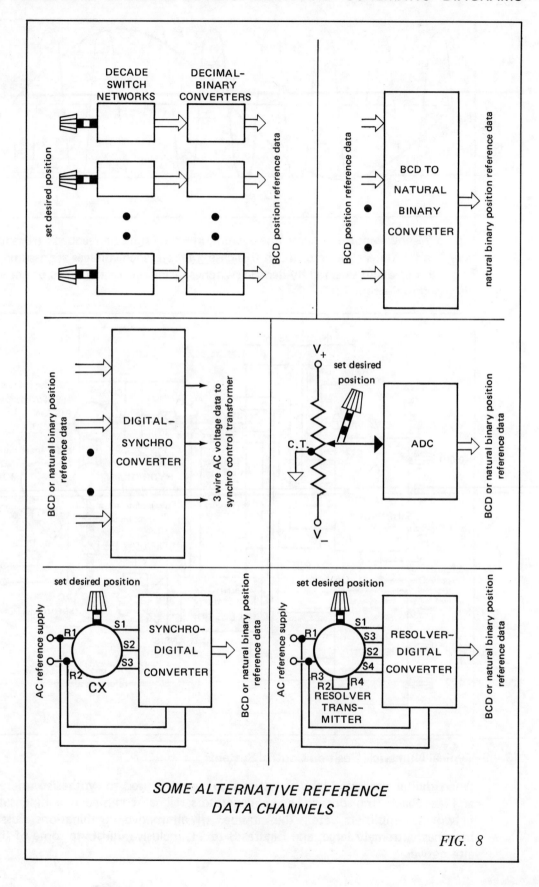

SOME ALTERNATIVE REFERENCE
DATA CHANNELS

FIG. 8

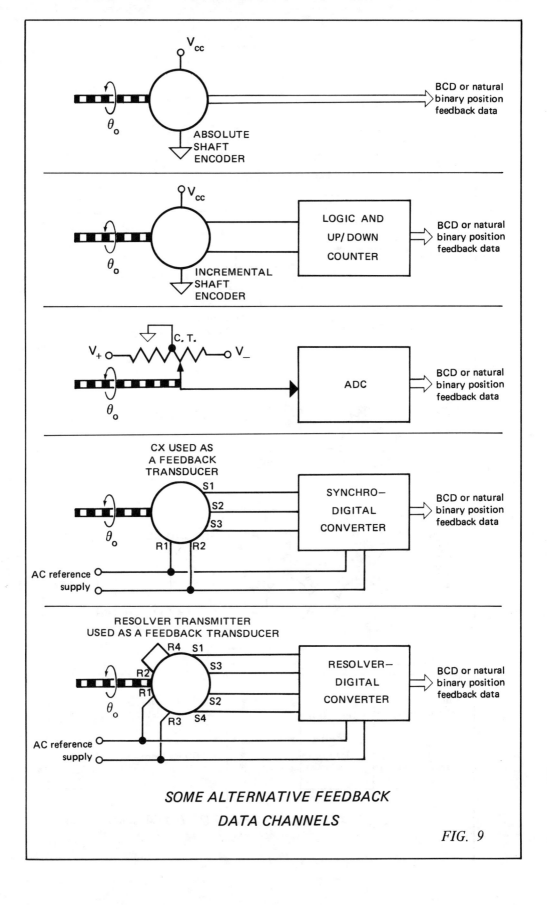

SOME ALTERNATIVE FEEDBACK

DATA CHANNELS

FIG. 9

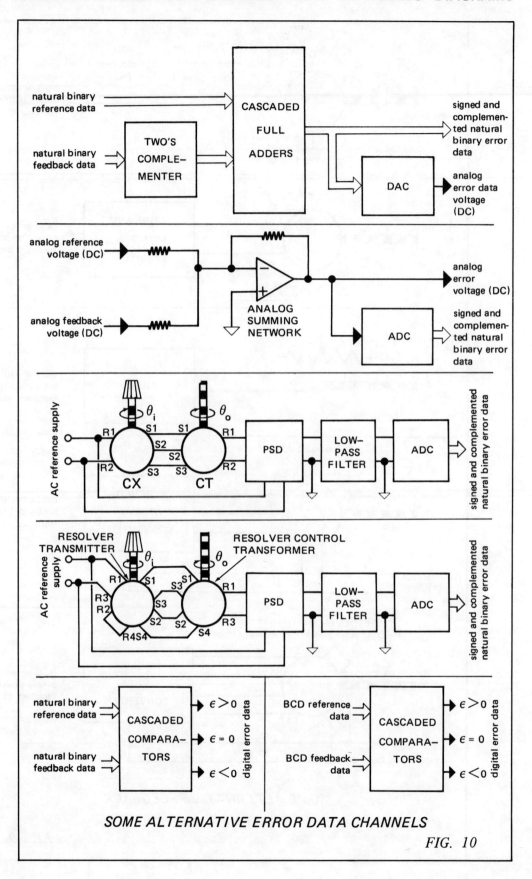

SOME ALTERNATIVE ERROR DATA CHANNELS

FIG. 10

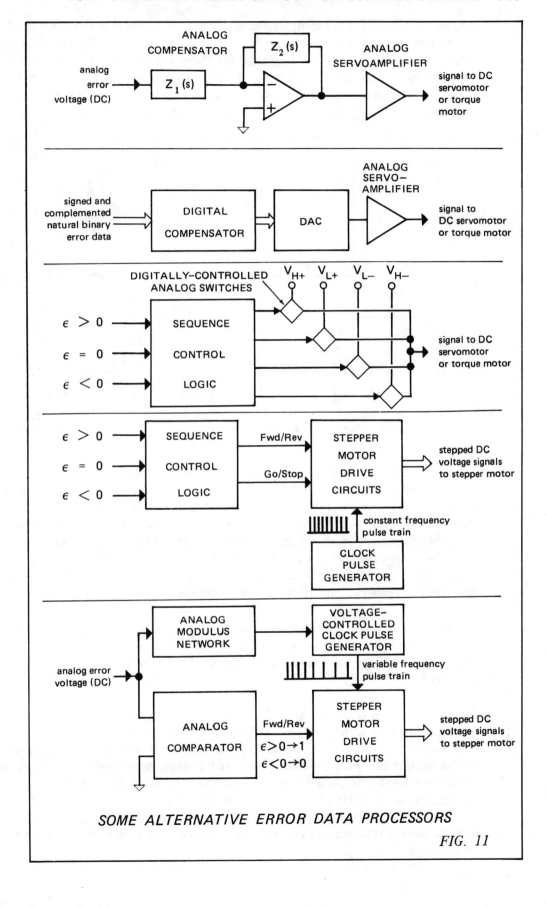

SOME ALTERNATIVE ERROR DATA PROCESSORS

FIG. 11

Where, in some of the examples shown in Figure 8, the digital reference signals are shown to have been generated by manually set decade switches, a computer could be used as an alternative source for these signals, with the computer then performing a supervisory type of role. Other digital networks shown in Figures 8 to 11 could well be synthesised using a programmable digital processor, with the functions being configured by means of appropriate program statements.

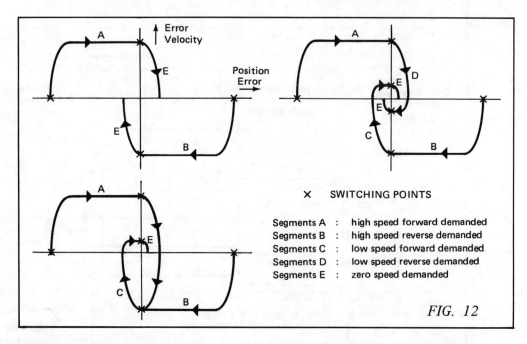

X		SWITCHING POINTS
Segments A	:	high speed forward demanded
Segments B	:	high speed reverse demanded
Segments C	:	low speed forward demanded
Segments D	:	low speed reverse demanded
Segments E	:	zero speed demanded

FIG. 12

In those configurations in Figure 11 in which only sign of error and null error data are provided, the control logic must be configured so that the position error is driven towards zero at sequentially stepped speeds. Representative "phase portraits" of error velocity vs position error are shown in Figure 12, to illustrate some possible positioning routines: these routines would only be usable provided that the position reference value is stationary during the positioning sequences. This distinction results in these systems sometimes being called "point-to-point positioning systems", in contrast to "continuous path positioning systems".

As an alternative to switching the motor to drive at various fixed speeds, it would be possible to use the signals to engage and disengage clutches in a clutch-gear system, driven by a single-speed motor, of the type shown in Figure 20 of Chapter 9.

Obviously, if the drive is brought to rest from a fairly low speed condition, the ultimate position error will be small but the positioning time may be large. If the sequence results in final stopping always from the same direction, irrespective of the sign of the initial position error, then the ultimate position error should be more consistent than would otherwise be the case, especially when the values of the friction and inertia of the moving parts are consistent. When the initial value of position error is small, the sequence controller should be arranged so that full speed always is attained during the positioning cycle, in order to achieve consistency of stopping.

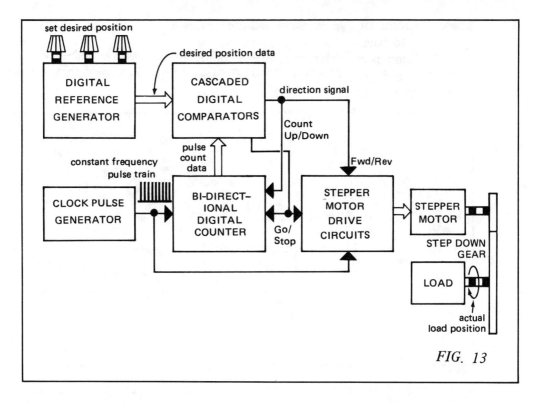

FIG. 13

Figure 13 shows one possible system in which a stepper motor can be used for open loop position control, and this is one of the few cases where open loop control of position is practicable. The motor is driven in such a manner that the current output count from the bidirectional counter always is driven towards that value represented by the desired position data, the difference being sensed by the cascaded digital comparators. This arrangement will produce faulty positioning in the event that the load should prevent the motor from responding to demanded steps: no measurement of load position is fed back to indicate, to the controller, that such an event has occurred.

13.5 EXAMPLES OF SPEED CONTROL SYSTEMS

In Sections 8.4.1 and 8.4.2, commercially available speed controllers for conventional DC and AC motors were described. In the event that these should be unsuitable for a particular application, it becomes necessary to custom design a speed controller. Whilst almost any closed loop speed control system will still function, after a fashion, as an open loop speed control system, if the feedback is disconnected, accurate speed control rarely will eventuate in this situation.

At low output power levels, servomotors may be used to provide drives for instrument types of application. At higher levels of output power, these servomotors can be used as torque motors to actuate hydraulic servovalves or pumps which, in turn, would manipulate hydraulic rotary actuators, cylinders, motors, etc. Alternatively, speed controllers using the same principles as commercial types may be custom designed, to operate with electric motors. A few examples of low power configurations will be described, in Sections 13.5.1, 13.5.2, and 13.5.3.

13.5.1 Speed Control of a Typical Small DC Motor Drive

Figure 14 shows a typical DC instrument velocity servosystem. It will be seen to be similar to the position servosystem of Figure 2, except that the position feedback of the latter now is absent.

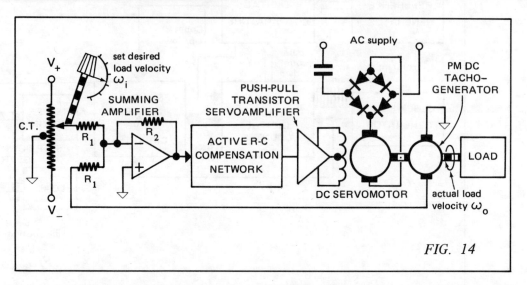

FIG. 14

The summing amplifier provides a differencing action, by virtue of suitable connection of the tachogenerator for appropriate sense for the velocity feedback data. In the absence of any suitable (minor) feedback transducer for compensation use, compensation normally would be provided by an active or passive R-C network in the forward path. Armature control of the servomotor would be a potential alternative to the field control arrangement shown.

For the selection of preset speed references, a potentiometric reference network of the type described in Section 2.3.1 would be used to replace the reference potentiometer shown in Figure 14. The supply to the reference transducer need only be unipolar if the drive is to be unidirectional.

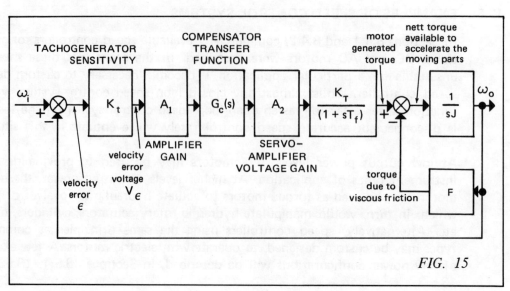

FIG. 15

Figure 15 shows one possible version of the small signal block diagram for the system of Figure 14.

13.5.2 Speed Control of a Typical Small AC Motor Drive

Figure 16 shows a typical AC instrument velocity servosystem. It will be seen to be very similar to its DC counterpart of Figure 14.

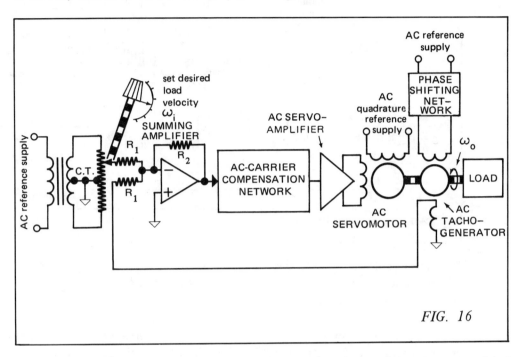

FIG. 16

The transformer connected to the reference potentiometer has been provided in order to establish a supply symmetrically balanced about signal common, on the assumption that the motor drive is to be bidirectional: this transformer is redundant for unidirectional drives. An alternative, and potentially superior, reference transducer would be an auto-transformer, with either a continuously variable wiper output or switched output tappings. The summing amplifier provides a differencing action, by virtue of suitable connection of the tacho-generator for appropriate sense for the velocity feedback data. In the absence of any suitable (minor) feedback transducer for compensation use, compensation normally would be provided by an AC-carrier compensation network in the forward path.

The small signal block diagram for this system would resemble that shown in Figure 15.

13.5.3 Speed Control of Stepper Motors

Provided that a stepper motor can develop sufficient torque to drive the load for which it has been chosen, its speed can be controlled accurately without the need for velocity feedback. Because the stepping rate will be proportional to the frequency of the pulse train supplied to the drive circuits, a speed controller for this type of motor will be required to establish a precisely varied pulse frequency.

In Section 8.4.3, some types of stepper motor speed controllers were described: in these, the pulse train was developed by a voltage-controlled oscillator, with the applied DC control voltage determining the pulse frequency. An alternative technique is to use digital means to manipulate the frequency, and an example is shown in Figure 17.

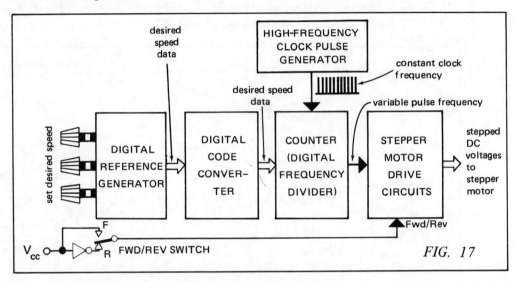

FIG. 17

The counter could be arranged so that the frequency of the pulse train supplied to the stepper motor drive circuits is equal to the clock pulse frequency divided by the output word from the digital code converter, so that the latter will need to be representative of the reciprocal of the desired load speed. The drive could be made bidirectional by causing a Forward/Reverse switch on the set point station to reverse the sense in which the DC output voltages are circulated around the motor windings.

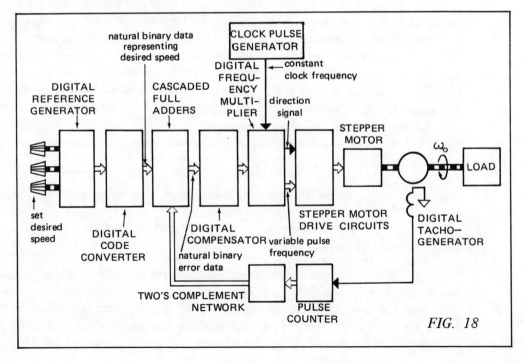

FIG. 18

When closed loop control using numerical means is required, this may be undertaken using a scheme like that of Figure 18. The algorithm of the digital compensator should include a synthesis of integration, so that the value of pulse frequency necessary to drive the load at the desired speed can be sustained even when the speed error has been reduced to zero. The digital frequency multiplication is best implemented by reciprocating the data from the compensator and then using a pulse counter as a frequency divider. The system shown is best used for unidirectional drives, although conceivably it could be adapted for bidirectional action, possibly by using the Forward/Reverse arrangement on the open loop system of Figure 17.

13.6   EXAMPLES OF ELECTROHYDRAULIC DRIVES

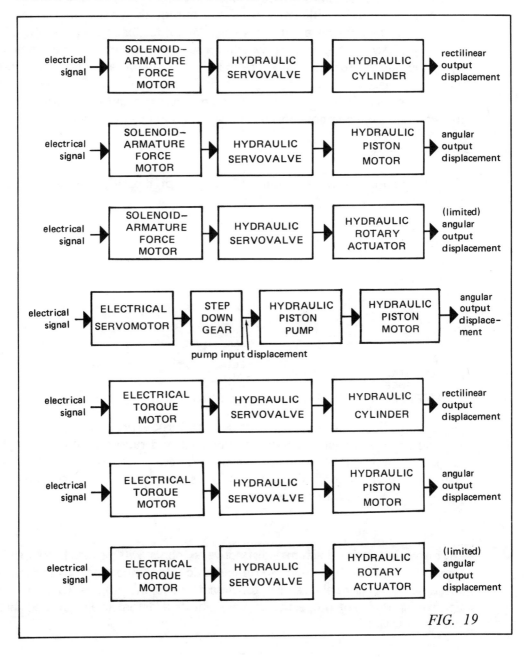

FIG. 19

In those servosystems in which the drive is required to develop high power levels, it becomes necessary to use either large conventional electric motors or hydraulic drives. In the latter case, the error signal of the control system usually will be electrical and, after suitable amplification and compensation, this must be used to manipulate the upstream component in the hydraulic drive. Figure 19 illustrates some alternative arrangements.

In the absence of any minor feedback loop, the transfer function relating output displacement to electrical actuating signal usually will contain two integrations, which often must then be reduced in quantity, by the use of negative feedback. In the case of rectilinear drives, minor feedback may be implemented using mechanical linkages, connected from the output shaft back to the servovalve, which may incorporate an inner sleeve. Minor feedback may also be effected electrically, using transducers which sense the pressure of the manipulated hydraulic supply to the motor, cylinder, or actuator and feed back into the amplifier which is developing the electrical actuating signal. Feedback also will have a linearising effect upon the static characteristic and will modify the speed of response of the components around which it has been connected.

The servomotor shown in Figure 19 may be of the DC, AC, or stepper type, which may be used as a torque motor.

13.7   EXAMPLES OF PROCESS CONTROL SYSTEMS

In Section 8.3, it was explained that general purpose process controllers could be configured as feedback, cascade, feedforward, and ratio controllers, each having an appropriate control law. In this section, a few examples will be described, to demonstrate their application. Figure 20 shows some typical symbols used in schematic diagrams for process loops.

In many industrial diagrams, distinctive symbols will be used, to distinguish between electrical, hydraulic, and pneumatic interconnections. In process mimic diagrams, it is normal practice to allocate different colours to process loops controlling different properties of the plant or different chemicals and materials within the plant.

TRANSMITTERS

xT

TT	temperature transmitter
PT	pressure transmitter
FT	flow transmitter
LT	level transmitter
DT	density transmitter
pHT	pH transmitter
CT	composition transmitter

CONTROLLERS

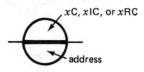

xC, xIC, or xRC

address

xC	controller, with no indication or recording
xIC	indicating controller
xRC	recording controller
TxC	temperature controller
PxC	pressure controller
FxC	flow controller
LxC	level controller
DxC	density controller
pHxC	pH controller
CxC	composition controller
FFC	feedforward controller
RC	ratio controller

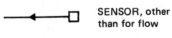

SENSOR, other than for flow

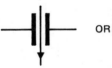

ORIFICE PLATE

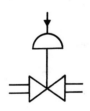

FLOW CONTROL VALVE WITHOUT POSITIONER

SQUARE-ROOT EXTRACTOR

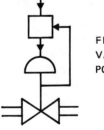

FLOW CONTROL VALVE WITH POSITIONER

FIG. 20

13.7.1 Typical Process Loop using a Feedback Controller

A very simple example of the use of a feedback controller would be for the control of the level of liquid in a storage tank, by manipulating the inflow rate, with outflow rate being a wild variable. Such a system is illustrated in Figure 21.

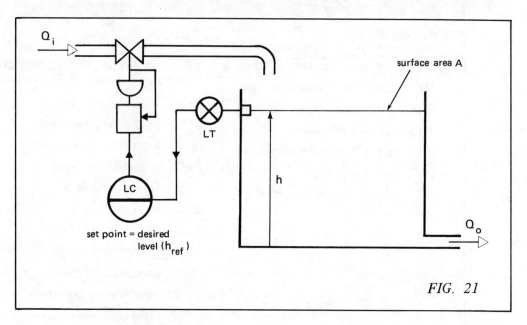

FIG. 21

A small signal block diagram for this type of configuration would take the form shown in Figure 22.

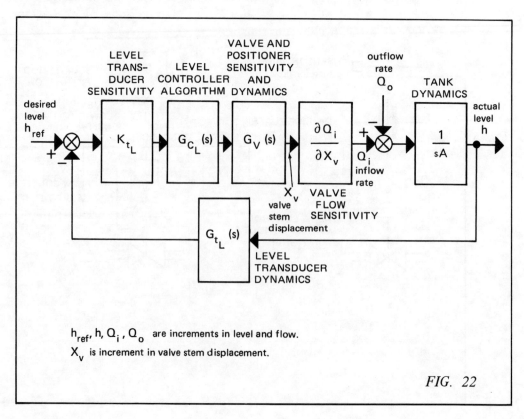

h_{ref}, h, Q_i, Q_o are increments in level and flow.

X_v is increment in valve stem displacement.

FIG. 22

13.7.2 Typical Use of a Cascade Controller

In the previous example, the nonlinearity of the control valve flow characteristic and possible slowness in the valve speed of response can both be alleviated by the introduction of a minor feedback loop, in which the inflow rate is measured and fed to a flow controller. Figure 23 illustrates this modified system.

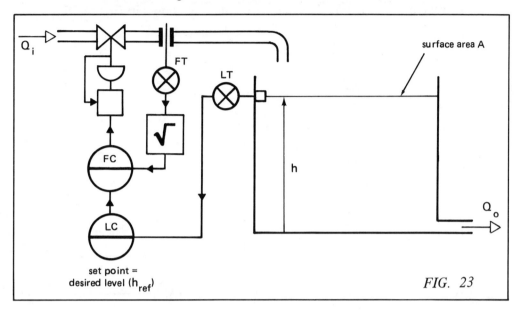

FIG. 23

In this arrangement, the level controller performs the role of a feedback controller and its output becomes the (remote) set point for the flow controller, which acts as a cascade controller. Figure 24 illustrates the small signal block diagram, and it can be seen that the level loop is the outermost (major) loop, with greater authority than the flow loop, which is the inner, minor, loop.

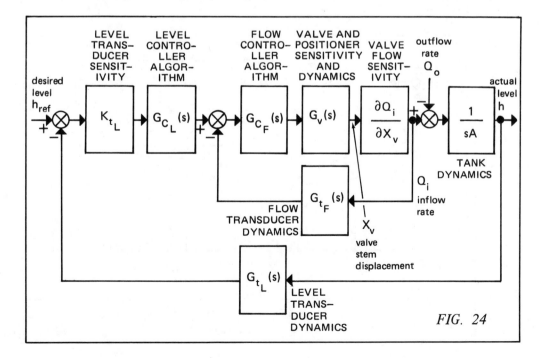

FIG. 24

13.7.3 Typical Use of a Feedforward Controller

In the example of Figure 21, the feedback controller has to attempt to hold the liquid level at the set point value, despite changes in the wild variable, the outflow rate Q_o. If, in a practical case, the controller cannot achieve the desired accuracy, then the situation can be relieved by instrumenting the wild variable and incorporating a feedforward controller, as shown in Figure 25.

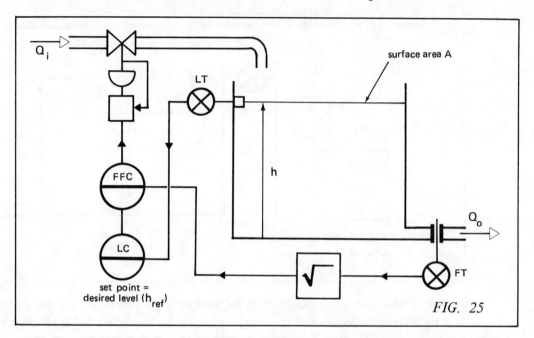

FIG. 25

Reference to the small signal block diagram of Figure 26 shows that the new controller does not provide additional feedback action, because it does not create a new closed loop, but it enables compensation to be effected for fluctuations in Q_o.

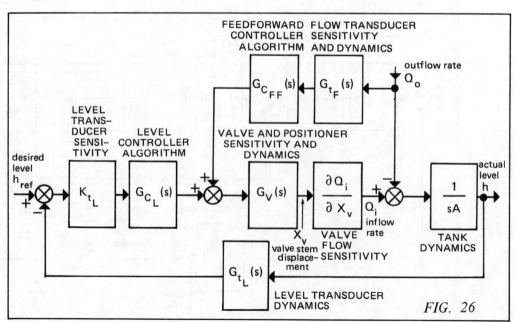

FIG. 26

With the plant under discussion, both feedforward and cascade controllers conceivably could be incorporated with the feedback controller, in the one system.

13.7.4 Typical Process Loop using a Ratio Controller

In this example, inflows of two different liquids are mixed in a hold up vessel and the flow rate of one is to be manipulated in order to maintain the composition of the mixture in the vessel at a desired consistency. The inflow rate of the other liquid is not controlled by this process and therefore is regarded as being wild.

One approach is to measure the composition of the mixture with a suitable composition transducer and to incorporate this with a composition controller, as shown in Figure 27.

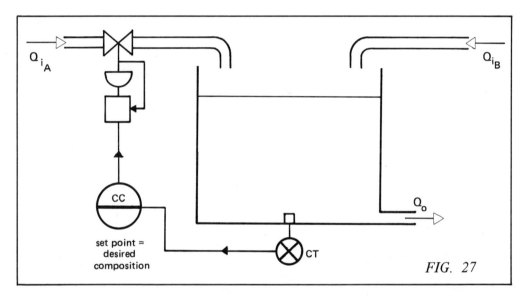

FIG. 27

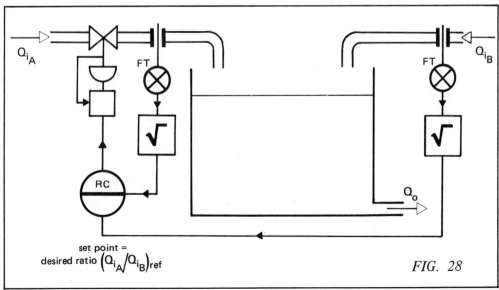

FIG. 28

If a suitable composition transducer cannot be obtained, for whatever reason, then ratio control can be used as a possible alternative, with the two inflow rates being measured and their (controlled) ratio being used to infer the current composition of the mixture: such a scheme is shown in Figure 28.

It will be seen that any long term error in the actual value achieved for the ratio may result in a significant error in the composition of the mixture, and there is no instrumentation to directly indicate that this situation has arisen.

14

EXPERIMENTAL TESTING OF PLANT, SYSTEM ELEMENTS, AND SYSTEMS

14.1   THE NEED FOR CHARACTERISATION

The design of a closed loop system cannot be completed rigorously until the properties of every element in the loop can be specified mathematically. The steady state sensitivity and time– and frequency– dependent characteristics are normally specified in terms of a linear transfer function, and the departure of the steady state sensitivity from a straight line output/input relationship is normally specified in terms of a static characteristic.

Characterisation (or Identification) is the name given to the set of alternative experimental procedures available for determining the unknown dynamic and steady state properties of a system element. In particular, the techniques would be applied to the testing of plant, final control elements, and feedback transducers, although this does not preclude their application from the testing of controllers and of completed closed loop systems, in order to verify the design procedures which have subsequently been adopted. Sections 14.2 to 14.8 provide descriptions which assume that DC electrical systems are being tested, whilst Sections 14.9 to 14.11 indicate how the techniques could be modified for AC-Carrier, digital, and pneumatic systems.

14.2   EXPERIMENTAL   PROCEDURES   FOR   OBTAINING   STATIC   CHAR-ACTERISTICS

Figure 1 shows a typical arrangement for establishing the static characteristic of a final control element – plant process – transducer combination. If the signal generator is set up to inject a steady signal into the control element, and the value of this signal is measured by meter A, then the steady state value of the transducer output signal will be measured by meter B, after sufficient time has been allowed to elapse for transient components of response behaviour to decay

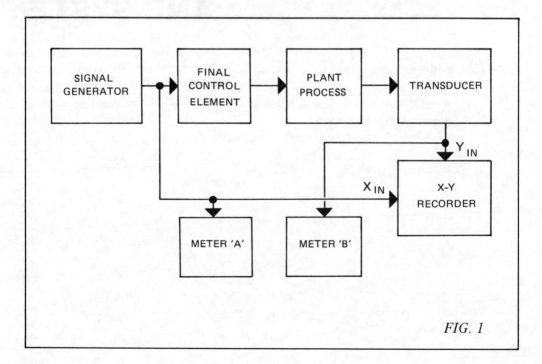

FIG. 1

to zero. A graphical plot of the reading of meter B to a base of the reading of meter A will represent the static characteristic, if the procedure is repeated for a sufficient number of different levels of steady input signal: the steady state sensitivity will be the gradient of this characteristic.

An alternative approach is to sweep the input signal, through an appropriate range of values, by causing the signal generator to inject (say) a triangular wave into the control element. The output/input relationship can now best be recorded on either an X–Y plotter or a storage oscilloscope operated in the X–Y mode.

With either technique, the signal should be stepped or swept in each direction, alternately, if there is any possibility of hysteresis being present in the characteristic being plotted. With the latter technique, the presence of dynamic lags can artificially create a resemblance to hysteresis in the experimental plot, if the sweep rate is too high; this can be verified by repeating the experimental procedure at a lower rate of sweep: if there is no difference between the two plots, then there is no significant contamination arising from dynamic lags. In any case, it will always be necessary to make sweep rates extremely small: for example, several minutes might be required for sweeping through the full excursion.

Once the form of the static characteristic is known, a suitable procedure for undertaking dynamic testing can then be determined. If the static characteristic is a simple straight line relationship, then the plant being tested can normally be regarded as linear, which will mean that dynamic testing will yield the same form of response, irrespective of the size of the applied disturbance: that is, the magnitude of the test signal applied during the dynamic test is not critical. (An exception to this occurs in plant possessing the phenomenon of rate limiting: with such a system, the static characteristic may well be linear but the dynamic response for a large disturbance would differ from that for a small disturbance, due to the finite limit on output slew rate occurring in the former case).

On the other hand, if the static characteristic is nonlinear, then the input signal conditions for the dynamic testing can be critical: an approximation to a linear transfer function may be obtained by applying a small signal disturbance super-imposed on a known quiescent signal level, and the relevant sensitivity will be the gradient of the static characteristic, measured at that quiescent level; this amounts to "small signal testing", and the situation is demonstrated by Figure 2. Repeating the dynamic test at a different quiescent level will normally yield different experimental data.

Large signal disturbances can also be applied when characterising nonlinear plant; in these cases, the disturbances would normally be sinusoidal, so that operation is in the frequency domain. With test equipment capable of rejecting harmonic signal components, it is possible to measure experimentally the "Describing Function", which is used to relate the fundamental component of the periodic output waveform (after sufficient time has been allowed to elapse for transient components to decay to zero) to the applied sinusoidal input waveform.

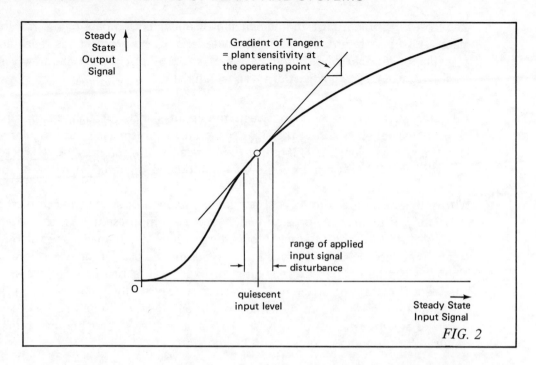

FIG. 2

There is one type of process for which the static characteristic cannot be measured by the alternative techniques so far described, and this occurs when the plant contains an integration process. (An example is when the transducer is measuring liquid level and this is being controlled by the manipulation of liquid inflow, or outflow, rate by the final control element: flow rate is proportional to the time rate of change of level, so that level is proportional to the time integral of flow rate). In this type of case, the output will not attain a steady state (in fact, it eventually ramps) when a steady input is applied, so that this will not readily yield data for the static characteristic. One solution is either to record the output ramp, using a Y–T plotter, and to measure the gradient from this, or to record the output rate of change experimentally, by attempting to use hardware to generate the time derivative of the output signal; a second alternative is to add a suitable transducer to the plant, in order to measure the rate of change of the output variable: only very rarely will this technique be practicable. Unfortunately, because it is ramping, the slewing output may well arrive at the limit of available excursion before any meaningful data have been collected! An often better alternative is to test the hardware in a closed loop configuration, in which output ramping will not occur under conditions of steady applied input signal: this type of testing will be dealt with more fully later, in Section 14.6.3.

14.3 EXPERIMENTAL PROCEDURES FOR MEASURING BASIC PLANT PARAMETERS

In a limited number of instances, the form of the transfer function of the plant will not only be known in advance, but the relationships between the parameters of the transfer function (typically, the time constants) and certain basic parameter of the plant will be known as well. If these basic parameters can be measured, then the transfer function (and possibly the static characteristic and the describing function) can be calculated.

The types of basic parameter which are amenable to this approach include the following:

mechanics — mass, moment of inertia, viscous friction, coulomb friction, static friction, gear backlash;

electric drives — magnetic saturation level, torque constant, back-emf constant, armature reaction, armature and field resistance and inductance;

hydraulic drives — degree of lap in valves, orifice flow coefficients, physical dimensions of cylinders, pistons, etc., oil density and viscosity.

This list is by no means complete. As a general rule, parameters such as those listed can be measured using relatively simple experimental equipment and the measurement procedures need not be dealt with, here.

On rare occasions, manufacturers of final control elements and feedback transducers may supply sufficient information to enable transfer functions and static characteristics to be formulated quantitatively: a possible hazard is the wide (and possibly unspecified) tolerances which may apply to the quoted parameters.

14.4   CHARACTERISATION BY STEP RESPONSE TESTING

14.4.1 Experimental Techniques for Obtaining Step Responses

Step response testing represents the most simple experimental technique for recording dynamic behaviour, since the signals required can be generated simply, either by making and breaking a steady supply or by stepping between two steady signal levels. It therefore requires a minimal complement of test equipment.

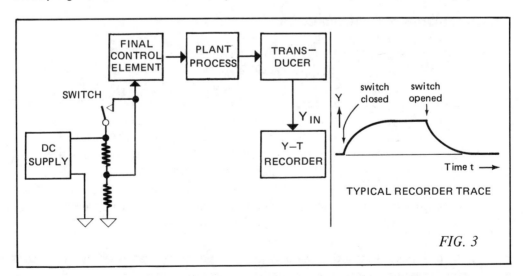

FIG. 3

Figure 3 shows a simple method for manually stepping an input signal between two steady levels: this generates a step superimposed on a quiescent level. The transducer response would be recorded to a base of time, on the Y–T recorder or a storage CRO in its Y–T mode.

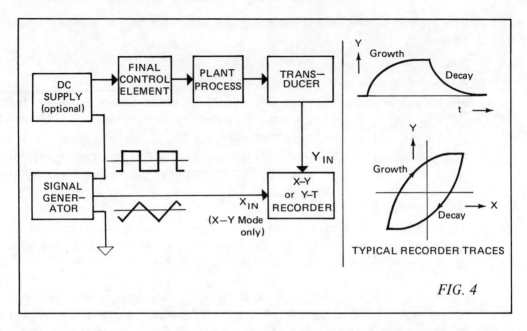

TYPICAL RECORDER TRACES

FIG. 4

Figure 4 shows a technique for obtaining repeated step responses, for both directions of applied step, by injecting into the plant a suitable squarewave, superimposed if necessary on a steady quiescent level. The half-period of the squarewave must be greater than the settling time of the step response, in order that adjacent responses shall not interfere with one another. The sequence of responses may be recorded to a base of time; alternatively, if the signal generator incorporates a suitable, synchronous, triangularwave auxiliary output, then this output may be used to synthesise a synchronous time base, to be used in conjunction with an X–Y recorder or a storage CRO in its X–Y mode: the resulting trace consists of a set of superimposed pairs of step responses.

14.4.2 The Order of the Response

The degree of ease or difficulty encountered in interpreting experimental step responses (and also impulse responses) depends on the Order (or Degree) of the plant being tested. Once any dead time and steady state offset in a linear step response are allowed for, the remaining data can usually be decomposed into an additive set of simple time dependent terms, equal in number to the set of terms in the corresponding linear transfer function. The number of such terms is the order of the system and it can readily be shown that, as the order of the system increases, so it becomes increasingly difficult to graphically decompose the response into its constituent parts (which, in effect, represent terms in a partial-fraction expansion): if these components cannot be determined, then the transfer function cannot be computed quantitatively.

In practice, first and second order responses are easily analysed, provided that the transfer function contains no numerator terms in the Laplace operator s. Third and higher responses are difficult or impossible to decompose, especially when the transfer function contains numerator terms in s. In the latter event, only frequency response testing will yield data amenable to analysis approaching a reasonable degree of reliability.

14.4.3 Examples of Simple First Order Step Responses

Figure 5 shows typical first order growth and decay responses, with and without dead time, which might be obtained experimentally. Dead time can be measured directly, as indicated, provided that the instant of application of the step disturbance is also recorded; time constant is most accurately measured by taking the time for the response to grow to 63% of its final excursion, or to decay to 37% of its initial value, as the case may be. In the case of all the transient responses being discussed in this chapter, the output is assumed to be stationary when the input step is applied. The presence of numerator terms in s in the transfer function will always result in curves which are more complex than those shown here, and these will necessarily be more difficult to interpret.

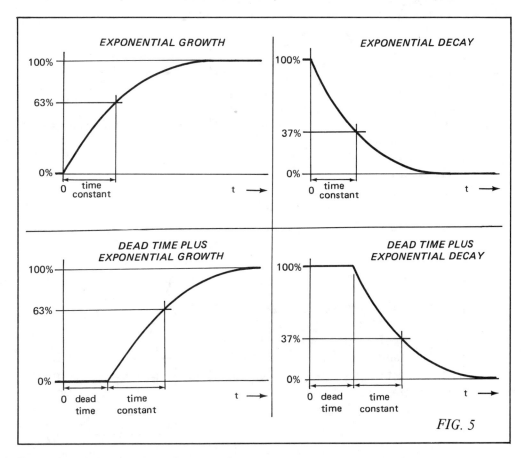

FIG. 5

14.4.4 Examples of Simple Second Order Step Responses

The approach to the interpretation of second order responses depends upon the degree of damping present, bearing in mind that lightly damped responses are those exhibiting a relatively large number of significant oscillations before the response settles.

In the case of light and medium damping, the damped natural frequency ω_t can be computed by measuring the period of the oscillation, as shown in Figures 6 and 8: thus, $\omega_t = 2\pi/\text{period}$, rad/s. Figures 7 and 9 give alternative techniques for computing damping factor ζ, for light and medium damping cases, respectively.

Figure 7 involves plotting the natural logarithm of each overshoot and undershoot, to a base of the numerical position in the series of overshoots/undershoots, whereas Figure 9 represents a standard curve of peak overshoot versus damping factor, which is most appropriately used in mid-range. Once ζ is known, then the undamped natural frequency ω_n can be computed from the formula

$$\omega_n = \omega_t \big/ \sqrt{1-\zeta^2} \; ; \text{ this will then yield the transfer function}$$

$$\omega_n^2 \big/ \left(s^2 + s2\zeta\omega_n + \omega_n^2\right).$$

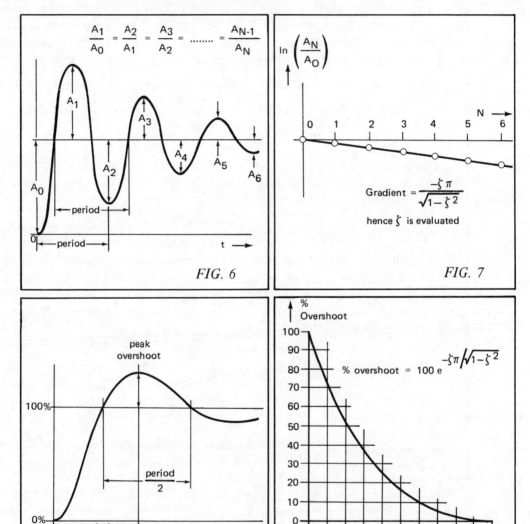

FIG. 6

FIG. 7

FIG. 8

FIG. 9

In the case of heavy damping, the most accurate technique involves constructing a tangent to the point of inflexion, as shown in Figure 10: the orientation of this tangent can be matched to the corresponding tangent for each of a set of standard quadratic response curves, which are freely available in the literature. Figure 11 represents one such set of standard curves. Using interpolation where necessary, the values of ω_n and ζ can be obtained from the curve representing the best match.

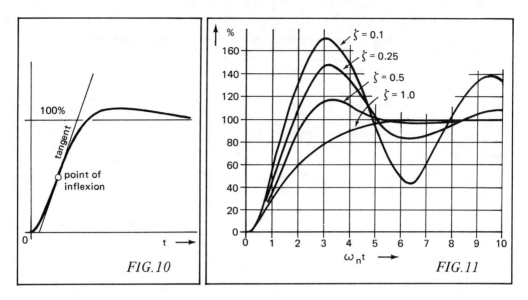

FIG.10

FIG.11

As with the case of first order responses, the presence of numerator terms in s in second order transfer functions will always result in curves which are more complex than those which have been described.

14.4.5 Treatment of Third Order Step Responses

In the absence of numerator terms in s in the transfer function numerator, a third order step response can be decomposed into a constant term (that is, the steady state level) together with either three first order exponential decays or one first order exponential decay plus an under-damped second order oscillatory decay. Identification of the parameter values and form for the transfer function involves identification of the component parts of the experimentally-obtained composite response curve. Figure 12 is an example of a third order response which fairly readily can be decomposed graphically into three terms, which are amenable to being quantified, whereas Figure 13 is an example of a third order response for which graphical decomposition is virtually impossible.

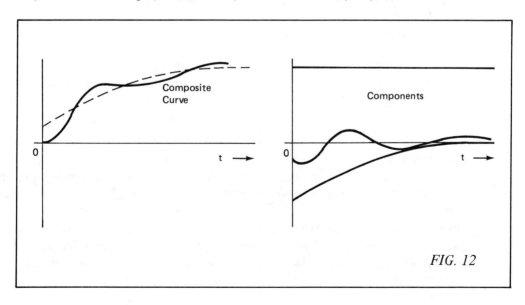

FIG. 12

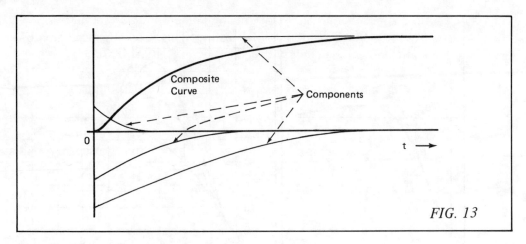

FIG. 13

14.4.6   Limitations of Step Response Testing

It can be seen that graphical interpretation of third and higher order step responses, plus those responses influenced by transfer function numerator terms in s, may be either extremely unreliable or impossible. With appropriate software, it may be possible, using numerical analysis and curve fitting, to use a digital computer to identify the transfer function; a more commonly used alternative is to abandon step response testing in favour of frequency response testing, which is much more versatile.

14.5   CHARACTERISTISATION FROM THE IMPULSE RESPONSE

The other class of time domain responses which are sometimes obtained experimentally is the class of responses which would be obtained following the application of an impulsive disturbance. (In addition, ramp responses are sometimes generated, usually in repetitive form, by injecting a suitable triangularwave disturbance). Since the application of an impulse containing a sufficient amount of energy, to obtain a significant response, would be difficult to generate and control and might be destructive to the plant being characterised, the usual procedure is to synthesise the effect of an impulsive disturbance.

14.5.1   Experimental Techniques for Obtaining Impulsive Responses

The first technique is suitable when data representing the rate of change of the output variable are available. This comes about from the mathematical relationship

$$\frac{d}{dt}\left\{ \mathcal{L}^{-1}\left[\frac{1}{s}\, G(s) \right] \right\} = \mathcal{L}^{-1}\left[G(s) \right] \text{, where } G(s) \text{ is}$$

the transfer function being identified. This means that the impulse response must be identical to the rate of change of the step response. Data could be obtained by graphical differentiation of step response data but, of course, if the step response data are already to hand, there will be little point in not characterising directly from the step response. However, in those cases where the plant includes a rate of change transducer (such as a tachogenerator in a position servosystem), this transducer will generate the response of interest when a step disturbance is applied to the plant.

Impulse response analysis is of much greater practical application when the plant is subjected to random signal testing. This is an advanced area of analysis and testing, and will be dealt with separately in Section 14.7.

14.5.2 Examples of Simple First and Second Order Impulse Responses

Figures 14, 15, and 16 are examples of simple first and second order impulse responses. The techniques used for quantitative interpretation are similar to those employed on comparable step responses, so that no separate explanation is required.

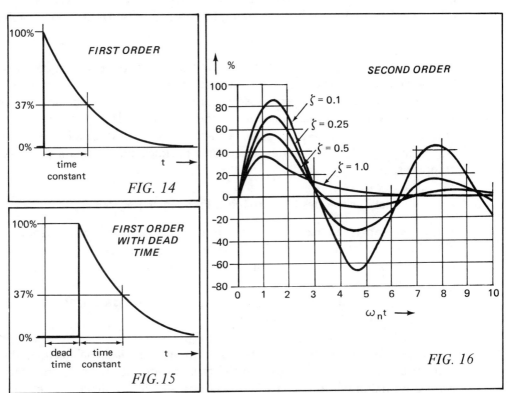

FIG. 14

FIG.15

FIG. 16

14.6 CHARACTERISATION FROM THE FREQUENCY RESPONSE

Frequency response techniques have the merit that their application is not restricted to low order transfer functions. Moreover, the effects of numerator terms are as readily distinguished as are those of denominator terms of the transfer function. Dead time and the presence of negative numerator terms are also amenable to identification using these techniques. The experimental method involves the application of suitable test sinewaves of known magnitude and computation of gain magnitude and phase shift between the output signal and either the applied input signal or a second output signal. The measuring equipment should be capable of operating down to very low frequencies (sometimes lower than 1mHz) and should preferably be frequency selective, in order to reject harmonics. These requirements tend to make the testing procedures very time consuming and also require a much greater expenditure on test equipment, especially if good harmonic rejection is required; this last property is essential for the measurement of describing functions.

Note that equipment normally used for frequency response testing in the audio frequency range is usually useless for control systems, because it has a lower frequency limit typically in the region of 10Hz, which is beyond the bandwidth of most control systems.

All practical frequency responses roll off at higher frequencies, so that output signal levels diminish at the higher end of the spectrum, as the frequency is swept upwards. Since all experimental signals will be corrupted by parasitic noise, to a greater or lesser extent, it is to be expected that the experimental data may become increasingly erroneous as the frequency is progressively increased: the effect can be minimised by employing test equipment having good noise rejection capability.

Frequency response analysis methods may also be applied to frequency response data which have been computed from time domain data obtained experimentally. This is particularly useful in those cases where the time domain responses are too complex for graphical decomposition. In these cases, the generation of the frequency domain data is undertaken either by a dedicated Fourier Transform Analyser or by a Fast Fourier Transform package on a general purpose digital computer.

14.6.1 Experimental Techniques for Obtaining Frequency Responses

Figure 17 shows an experimental set up for measuring a frequency response experimentally. The output signal from the transducer is displayed on the Y channel of a recorder or a suitable (preferably storage) CRO. It must be borne in mind that, because the frequencies involved are normally very low in value, all connections must be DC coupled and the recording instrument must be capable of recording very slowly varying signals.

When the DC offset provision is included, for small signal testing, the offset will, of course, be adjusted to give the required quiescent level; only the steady state alternating components of the output and input signals are of interest, as far as the data display is concerned. The amplitude of the output sinewave is given by the height of the displayed curve. Phase may be measured by any of the following four alternative techniques:

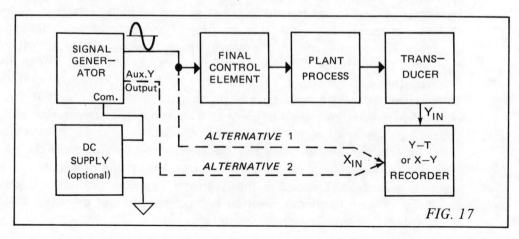

FIG. 17

A.   Record output and input to a base of time, on a two-channel Y–T recorder: phase measurement is based on Figure 18.

B.   Record output and input, plotted against each other, on an X–Y recorder: phase measurement is based on Figure 19.

C.   If available, use an auxiliary quadrature triangularwave output from the signal generator, in conjunction with an X–Y recorder: the triangularwave forms a synchronous timebase and phase measurement is based on Figure 20.

D.   If available, use an auxiliary variable-phase sinewave output from the signal generator, in conjunction with an X–Y display. Adjust the variable phase until the displayed ellipse collapses to a straight line: the phase measurement is read directly from the phase shift calibration.

Proprietary Transfer Function Analysers (sometimes called Frequency Response Analysers) are available, although they are expensive. Typically, they compute gain magnitude and phase data, usually using a correlation technique (discussed in Section 14.8), and thereby can provide a high degree of rejection of harmonics, noise, and DC offsets; often, they are also autoranging. Usually, the signal generator is incorporated into the analyser, with the sinusoidal output signal being synthesised digitally. The more expensive instruments will permit automatic stepping or sweeping of the signal frequency and enable gain magnitude and phase to be measured between two signal output points, neither of which need be the test input signal point. Because of their harmonic rejection property, they can also be used for measuring describing function data.

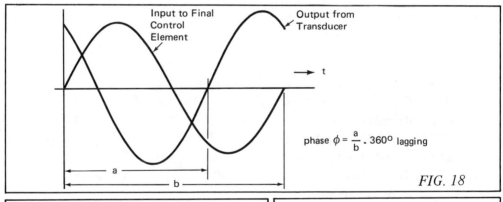

phase $\phi = \dfrac{a}{b} \cdot 360°$ lagging

FIG. 18

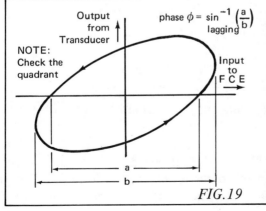

phase $\phi = \sin^{-1}\left(\dfrac{a}{b}\right)$ lagging

FIG.19

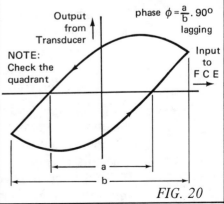

phase $\phi = \dfrac{a}{b} \cdot 90°$ lagging

FIG. 20

By whatever technique the frequency response data are gathered, it is the normal practice to graph the data as Bode gain magnitude and phase plots.

14.6.2 Interpretation of Experimental Bode Plots

The bulk of the information for identification is contained in the magnitude plot. The phase plot serves as a cross check, and can be shown to be entirely predictable (assuming linear behaviour) from the magnitude plot, except when dead time (which is best identified by time domain testing) and negative numerator terms in the transfer function are present. Negative denominator terms cannot arise, because they result in an unstable system incapable of converging to a steady state condition, following the application of a sinusoidal (or any other) disturbance: frequency domain identification is not possible, in this situation, without the application of very special techniques.

The objective is to obtain a best fit, for a suitable set of asymptotes, to the experimental magnitude plot, bearing in mind that:

- Asymptote gradients can only assume values which are whole number multiples of $\pm$ 20dB/decade; i.e. +40, +20, 0, −20, −40, −60 etc. dB/decade. For this reason, designers often construct templates, resembling set-squares, having the appropriate gradients for their hypoteneuses.

- At each of the intersections of the fitted asymptotes, the vertical dB separation between the asymptote intersection and the experimental curve must equal the predictable figure.

- Where asymptote gradients change by +40 or −40 dB/decade at an intersection, the separation between the asymptotes and the experimental curve may be matched to one of a standard set of quadratic lag frequency response curves (these may be inverted as required, for quadratic lead), as presented in Figure 21.

It will be appreciated that some degree of skill and experience are necessary, to obtain good asymptote fitting. The transfer function can then be written down by inspecting the asymptote sequence (bearing in mind that the phase plot should be cross-checked for the rare anomalous cases), as follows:

- Note the dB gain at which the low frequency asymptote (projected if necessary) crosses 1 rad/s (0.16Hz): this is the transfer function gain constant (in dB).

- The number of integrations in the transfer function will relate to the gradient of the low-frequency asymptote, as follows:

      zero integrations   — zero gradient
      one integration   — −20dB/decade gradient
      two integrations   — −40dB/decade gradient.

- Note the break (corner) frequencies at which the asymptotes intersect. Where the gradients change by +20 or −20 dB/decade, the break frequency ω_B yields the value of a time constant T, for $T = 1/\omega_B$. Where the gradients change by +40 or −40 dB/decade, the break frequency ω_B yields the undamped natural frequency ω_n for the corresponding quadratic term, the damping factor ζ for which can be obtained by use of Figure 21.

- For increasing frequency, if the asymptote gradient changes at an inter-section by

  +20 dB/decade, the corresponding transfer function term is $(1 + sT)$

  −20 dB/decade, the corresponding transfer function term is $1/(1 + sT)$

  +40 dB/decade, the corresponding   term is $\left(\dfrac{s^2}{\omega_n{}^2} + \dfrac{s2\zeta}{\omega_n} + 1\right)$

  −40 dB/decade, the corresponding   term is $1\Big/\left(\dfrac{s^2}{\omega_n{}^2} + \dfrac{s2\zeta}{\omega_n} + 1\right)$

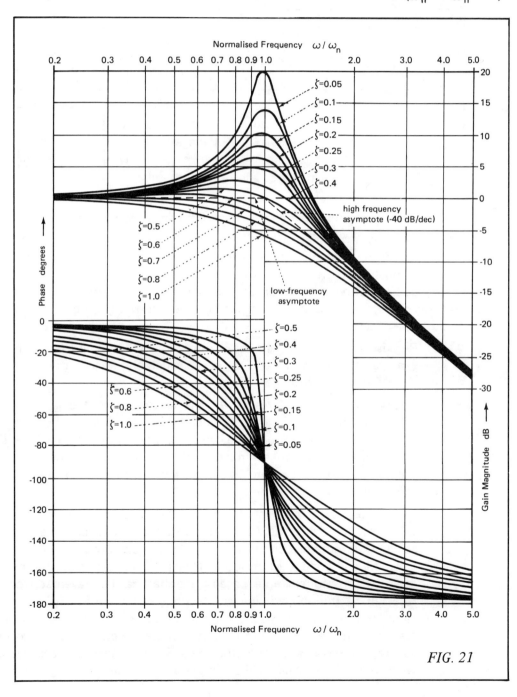

FIG. 21

Thus, anomalous terms apart, the transfer function can be written down, from inspection of the asymptote sequence, as the product of sets of first and second order factors. Where break frequencies (i.e. asymptote intersections) appear to be close to one another, it may be found that alternative sets of asymptotes may be fitted in this region, with equal accuracy, to the experimental curve: in this case, either sequence may be regarded as valid, so that either set of corresponding transfer function terms is also equally valid.

14.6.3 Open Loop versus Closed Loop Testing, for Characterisation

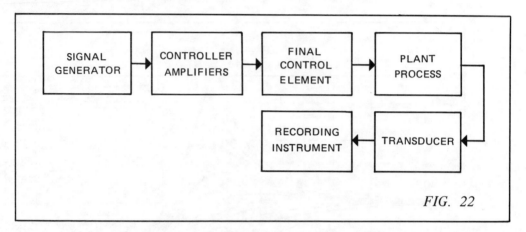

FIG. 22

Figure 22 shows a testing configuration for characterising the complete forward path of a control system, the feedback path not being connected. This testing will yield open loop frequency response data, which subsequently can be used in the compensation design for the control law, which will be added to the controller amplifiers. Generally speaking, the following properties will apply to this type of test:

- Because of the high gain often present in the forward path, the input test signal often will need to be considerably smaller than the output signal from the transducer.

- If any integration is present (in the controller or the plant) then an offset, in any of the elements upstream of the site of the integration, will be integrated to produce a ramp component in the transducer signal: test equipment cannot eliminate this ramp and, moreover, the plant process may reach the end of its available excursion before useful data can be obtained.

- In the absence of a physical limit to the travel of the system output, a DC offset can deliberately be added to the signal generator output signal so that, in suitable circumstances, the system output can be given a constant component of motion. This is useful when open loop testing servosystems, for example, because the shaft can be prevented from being reversed by the applied sinewave, with the result that any backlash and static friction in the mechanics can be prevented from corrupting the test data; however, in this case it will be necessary to record output velocity, using a tachogenerator, because the output displacement signal will not usually be amenable to simple interpretation.

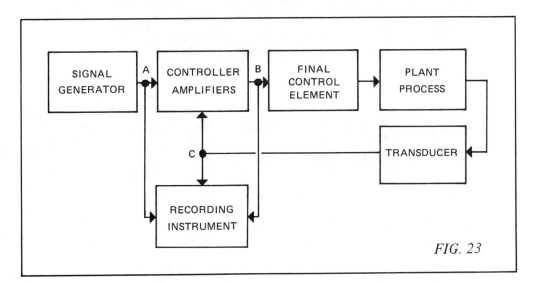

FIG. 23

Figure 23 shows a testing configuration for characterising a complete closed loop system. It is assumed that the characterisation is being undertaken before the compensation has been designed, so that the controller is not yet implementing the final control law; however, the system must be stable before useful tests can be undertaken.

Fortunately, most practical systems can be made stable if the controller is temporarily arranged to provide simply a reduced degree of gain, together with its signal-mixing function. The system performance will obviously not be optimum at this stage, because the compensation has not been designed or implemented. The following properties apply to this type of test:

- The input test signal will be in the same order of magnitude as the transducer output signal, for frequencies within the system bandwidth.

- Closed loop data can be measured by comparing signal C with signal A, and open loop data can be measured (despite the fact that the loop is closed) by comparing signal C with signal B.

- Open loop data can also be predicted from closed loop data, using a Nichols chart in reverse: the experimental data are plotted on the M and α contours and the corresponding open loop data can be read off the scales of the diagram axes. (This is not particularly accurate for low frequencies because of the high resolution of the top right hand corner of the chart, as can be seen from Figure 24). The technique is particularly useful with nonlinear processes, because the linearising effect of the negative feedback, in conjunction with the graphical technique, can yield a notional linearised open loop transfer function.

- Because the configuration is closed loop, offsets cannot generate a ramp component at the output.

- The sinusoidal input signal will cause reversals of the output: this can be disadvantageous in servosystems, for example, because any resulting backlash and static friction in the mechanics will degrade the output data.

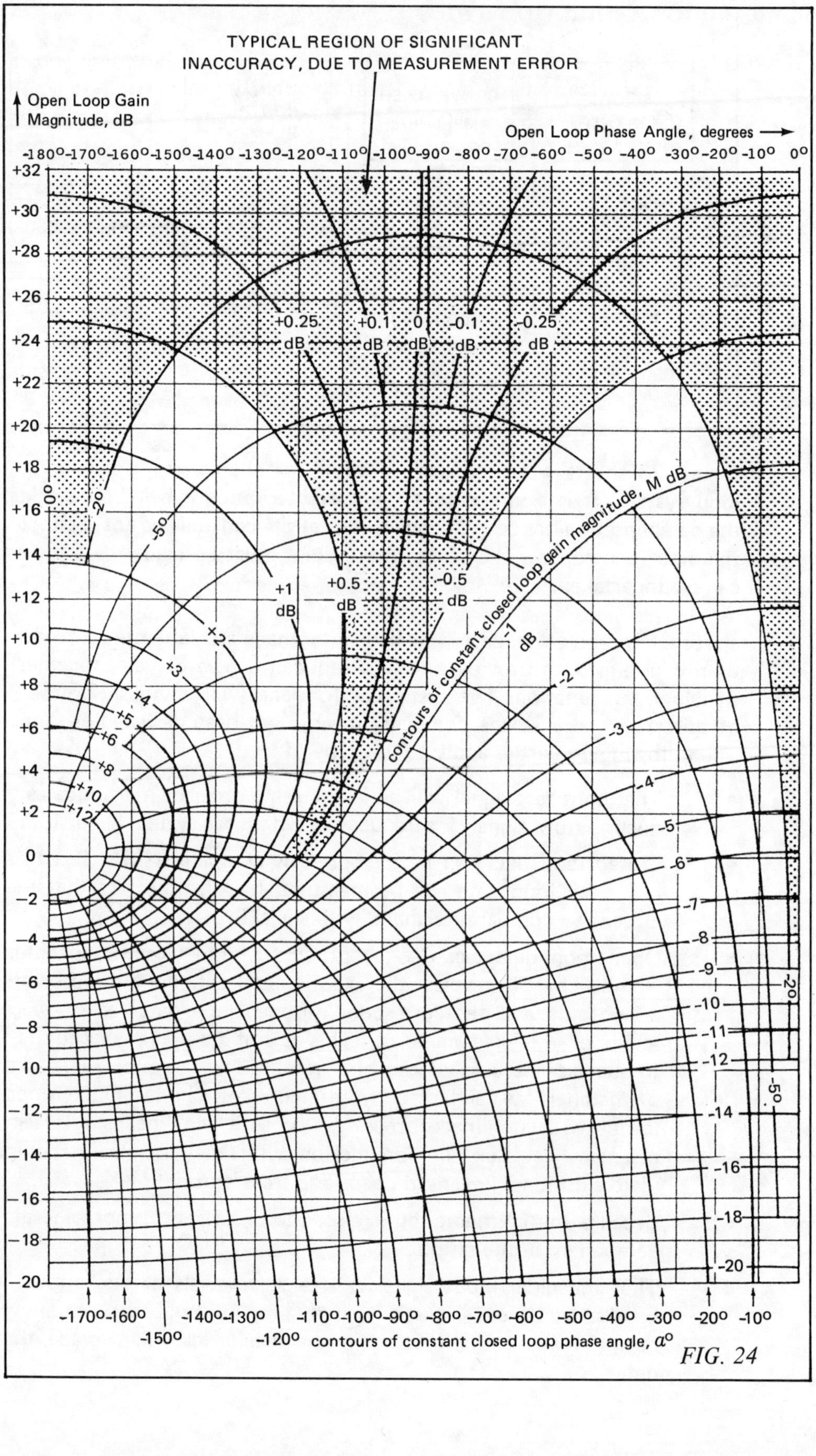
TYPICAL REGION OF SIGNIFICANT
INACCURACY, DUE TO MEASUREMENT ERROR
Open Loop Gain
Magnitude, dB
Open Loop Phase Angle, degrees
-180° -170° -160° -150° -140° -130° -120° -110° -100° -90° -80° -70° -60° -50° -40° -30° -20° -10° 0°
+32 +30 +28 +26 +24 +22 +20 +18 +16 +14 +12 +10 +8 +6 +4 +2 0 −2 −4 −6 −8 −10 −12 −14 −16 −18 −20
+0.25 dB
+0.1 dB
0 dB
-0.1 dB
-0.25 dB
+1 dB
+0.5 dB
-0.5 dB
-1 dB
+2 +3 +4 +5 +6 +8 +10 +12
-2 -3 -4 -5 -6 -7 -8 -9 -10 -11 -12 -14 -16 -18 -20
contours of constant closed loop gain magnitude, M dB
0° -2° -5°
-170° -160° -150° -140° -130° -120° -110° -100° -90° -80° -70° -60° -50° -40° -30° -20° -10°
contours of constant closed loop phase angle, α°

FIG. 24

14.7   CHARACTERISATION BY RANDOM SIGNAL TESTING

All the characterisation techniques so far described assume that the test input signal is sufficiently large for the resulting output signal strength to be discernible from the ambient noise often present. This will usually mean that a significantly large disturbance must be applied, to the extent that it may be unacceptable if the plant is in service. The alternatives to this are to employ techniques which either make use of the signal variations which occur naturally in normal plant operation, or use a suitable test signal which is too small to significantly disturb the plant operation.

In either case, the techniques adopted involve the use of random signals, and it is then the relationships between the statistical properties of those signals which yield the data for identifying transfer functions. Care is needed, when interpreting the data, for processes possessing significant nonlinearities.

14.7.1   The Correlation Function and Power Spectral Density Function

Figure 25 shows a computation process known as Correlation. A signal x is delayed by a time τ and subsequently multiplied by another signal y: the product is averaged over a significantly long period of time to yield an average value $R_{xy}(\tau)$, which is called the "Correlation Function at delay τ". The procedure can be repeated for different values of τ, and the resulting variations in $R_{xy}(\tau)$ indicate the relative dependence of the two signals on one another.

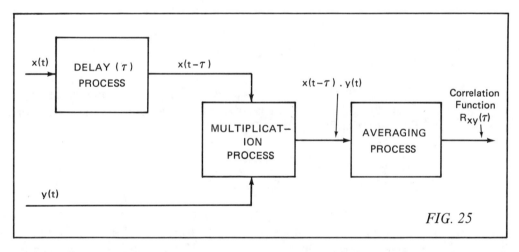

FIG. 25

When x and y are different signals, R_{xy} is called the "Cross Correlation Function", and when x and y are the same signal, $R_{xx}(\tau)$ is called the "Auto Correlation Function". If the function is subsequently Fourier transformed, using either a dedicated or a general purpose digital computer, then $R_{xy}(\tau)$ transforms to $S_{xy}(j\omega)$, the "Cross Power Spectral Density", and $R_{xx}(\tau)$ transforms to $S_{xx}(\omega)$, the "Auto Power Spectral Density". The spectral densities indicate the relative magnitude of the frequency components in the correlation functions: the spectral density functions will be continuous functions if the correlation functions are non-periodic, whereas the spectral density functions will be line spectra if the correlation functions are periodic, which case only occurs when the test signals are periodic.

If x is a White Noise signal, then its Auto Spectral Density $S_{xx}(\omega)$ will be flat (meaning that all frequencies are equally probable) and its Auto Correlation Function $R_{xx}(\tau)$ will be an impulse at $\tau = 0$. Test signals having a flat spectrum over a prescribed frequency range can be generated, with suitable hardware, and alternative waveforms are shown in Figure 26.

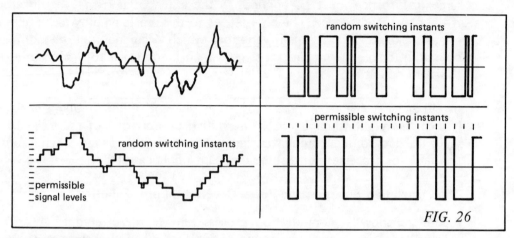

FIG. 26

14.7.2 The Application to Characterisation

Figure 27 illustrates, in a generalised form, the application of the procedure to plant characterisation. The noise generator may be an external noise source connected to inject noise into the plant, or it may be a source of noise occurring naturally within the plant. The following relationships, proofs for which may be found in the literature, are relevant in this context:

A.　　$R_{xy}(\tau) \propto g(\tau)$ if $R_{xx}(\tau)$ = an impulse at $\tau = 0$ (that is, if $S_{xx}(\omega)$ is a flat spectrum).

Thus, if the input noise is suitable, the process impulse response, with τ substituted for t, (that is, $g(\tau)$) is proportional to the Cross Correlation Function (input delayed), $R_{xy}(\tau)$.

B.

$$G(j\omega) = \frac{S_{xy}(j\omega)}{S_{xx}(\omega)}$$

Thus, gain magnitude and phase data can be obtained, for the transfer function, by dividing the Cross Density Spectrum (input delayed) by the input Auto Density Spectrum. If the latter is a flat spectrum, this reduces to　　$G(j\omega) \propto S_{xy}(j\omega)$

C.

$$\left| G(j\omega) \right| = \sqrt{\frac{S_{yy}(\omega)}{S_{xx}(\omega)}} \text{, provided that } z(t) = 0.$$

Thus, gain magnitude data can be obtained, for the transfer function, by dividing the output Auto Density Spectrum by the input Auto Density Spectrum, and square-rooting the result. If the input spectrum is flat, then this reduces to　　$\left| G(j\omega) \right| \propto \sqrt{S_{yy}(\omega)}$.

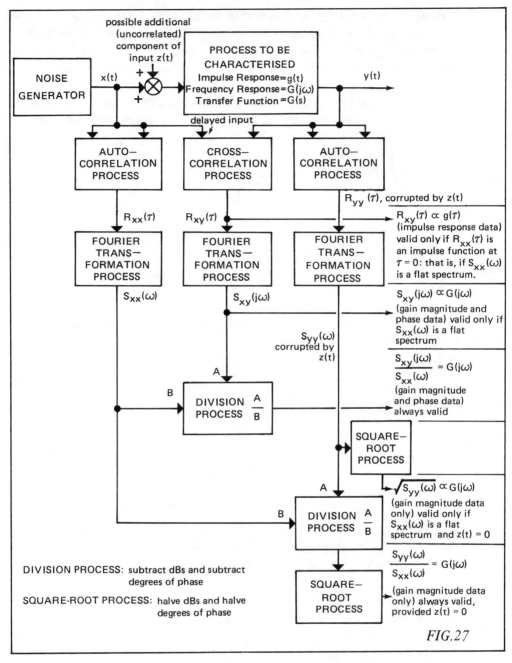

FIG.27

The various relationships provide a duplication of data, so that not all of them would be used, for any particular application. The procedure is completed by characterising either impulse response data (method A) or frequency response data (method B or method C), using the techniques of Sections **14.5** and **14.6** respectively.

14.7.3 The Hardware

Random noise generators are commercially available, but only those which generate a noise spectrum of significant magnitude down to DC are suitable: this requirement rules out most commercial noise generators.

Correlators are commercially available, as dedicated instruments, for the processing of analog noise signals, and they are normally constructed using microprocessor technology. Alternatively, a general purpose digital computer with a suitable real time interface may be programmed to function as a correlator.

Fourier Transform Analysers are also commercially available, as dedicated instruments interfaceable to a specified correlator. Normally, they can only transform data supplied by a correlator. Again, they are usually constructed using microprocessor technology. Alternatively, again, a suitable digital computer may be programmed to perform Fourier transformation.

14.7.4 PRBN Correlation

A highly specialised noise generator-correlator combination may be constructed cheaply, either around integrated circuit devices or using a microprocessor with a real time interface: the former version will now be described, making reference to Figure 28.

The noise generator is constructed by means of a shift register, synchronised to a clock pulse train, with the first bit being set from logic which is gated by the states of certain other bits. The output signal from any element can be shown to switch between the 1 and 0 levels, synchronously with the clock, in an apparently random sequence. However, the sequence will normally repeat itself every $(2^n - 1)T$ seconds, where n is the register word length and T is the clock interval: for this reason, it is called a "Pseudo-Random Binary Sequence" (PRBS) or "m-Sequence". This signal can then be level shifted, so that it now switches between $+V$ and $-V$ volts: such a signal is called "Pseudo Random Binary Noise" (PRBN), and its auto correlation function can be shown to approximate an impulse at $\tau = 0$.

Delayed versions of the sequence can be generated, for integer multiples of T, by combining the outputs of the shift register elements in specified combinational logic, each combination yielding a different delay τ.

Multiplication of the plant process output (which is analog) by the delayed PRBS (which is digital) is easily implemented by solid state analog switches and analog inverting and summing amplifiers; averaging over a whole number of sequences can be undertaken, for example, using an analog integrator gated from the shift register clock. Thus, a PRBN correlator is easily, and cheaply constructed. It yields the process cross correlation function (input delayed) which is, with the test signal used, approximately proportional to the process impulse response, which can now be characterised. The advantages of this type of correlator include the following:

- it is easily and cheaply constructed;
- the test signal bandwidth is proportional to the clock frequency and is therefore readily adjusted;
- the spectrum of the test signal extends down to DC;
- the sequence repeats exactly, so that the test data should be repeatable;

- the test signal is easily arranged to actuate the plant, since it simply switches between two levels.

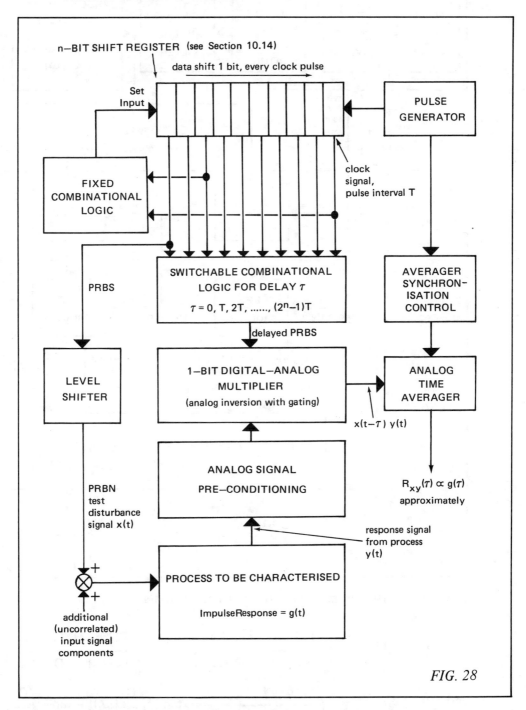

FIG. 28

14.7.5 PRBN and Frequency Response Computation

A PRBN generator also may be used with a real time digital computing system to compute directly the frequency response of a process, provided that a Fast Fourier Transform (FFT) software package is available for the computer. Figure 29 shows a typical set up, which includes both hardware and software elements.

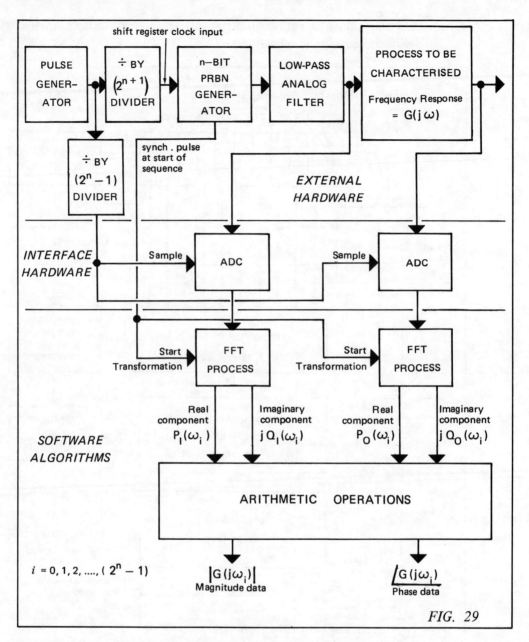

FIG. 29

It can be shown that, at any given frequency ω_i rad/s:

$$\left| G(j\omega_i) \right| = \left| \frac{P_o(\omega_i) + j\,Q_o(\omega_i)}{P_I(\omega_i) + j\,Q_I(\omega_i)} \right| = \left[\frac{P_o^2(\omega_i) + Q_o^2(\omega_i)}{P_I^2(\omega_i) + Q_I^2(\omega_i)} \right]^{1/2}$$

and $\;\;\underline{/G(j\omega_i)} = \underline{/\frac{P_o(\omega_i) + j\,Q_o(\omega_i)}{P_I(\omega_i) + j\,Q_I(\omega_i)}} = \tan^{-1}\!\left(\frac{Q_o}{P_o}(\omega_i)\right) - \tan^{-1}\!\left(\frac{Q_I}{P_I}(\omega_i)\right).$

The computer is used to generate values for these expressions at each of the set of specified frequencies, corresponding to the set of values of the variable i. The data will be corrupted by the presence of extraneous signals, so that this type of testing preferably is undertaken off-line.

14.8   THE USE OF CORRELATION FOR DIRECT FREQUENCY RESPONSE MEASUREMENT

A general purpose type of correlator, as referred to in Section 14.7.3, may be adapted to the direct measurement of frequency response data. To do this, it is necessary to synchronise the averaging process to a sinewave signal generator, as shown in Figure 30.

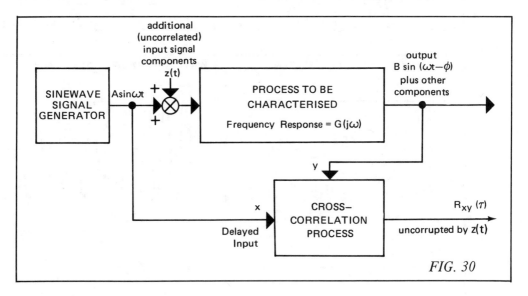

FIG. 30

Provided that the correlation averaging is undertaken over a whole number of cycles of the input sinewave, it is readily shown that

$$R_{xy}(\tau) = \frac{1}{2\pi n} \int_0^{2\pi n} A \sin \omega(t - \tau) \, B \sin (\omega t - \phi) \, d(\omega t)$$

$$= \frac{AB}{4\pi n} \int_0^{2\pi n} [\cos (\omega \tau - \phi) - \cos (2\omega t - \omega \tau - \phi] \, d(\omega t)$$

$$= \frac{AB}{2} \cos (\omega \tau - \phi), \quad n = 0, 1, 2 \dots\dots\dots \text{ etc.}$$

A plot of this function is shown in Figure 31.

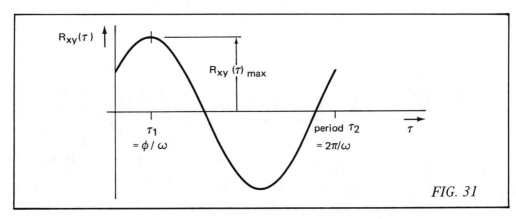

FIG. 31

From this, it can be seen that

$$\left|G(j\omega)\right| = \frac{B}{A} = \frac{2}{A^2} R_{xy}(\tau)_{max} \quad \text{and} \quad \underline{\angle G(j\omega)} = \phi = \frac{\tau_1}{\tau_2} 2\pi$$

The combination of a dedicated cross-correlator and sinewave signal generator would typically form the basis of the type of proprietary Transfer Function Analyser referred to in Section 14.6.1.

14.9 SPECIAL TECHNIQUES FOR THE TESTING OF AC-CARRIER SYSTEMS

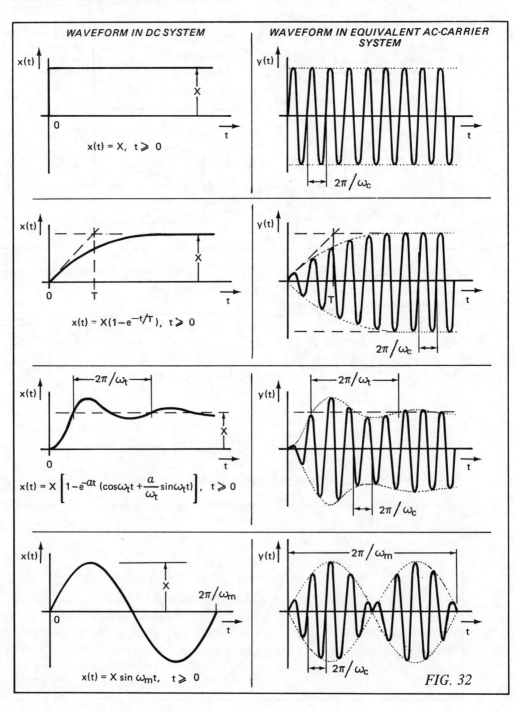

FIG. 32

The types of waveform which characterise the dynamic behaviour of DC control systems are transposed to become the envelopes of amplitude-modulated carrier waveforms, in the corresponding AC-Carrier systems. Examples are presented in Figure 32.

Note that, in general, either $y(t) = x(t) \sin\omega_c t$ or $y(t) = \sin[x(t)] \sin\omega_c t$, depending on the nature of the hardware used in the AC system. Note also that the envelope of each modulated waveform cannot be displayed directly.

The data represented by the AC-Carrier waveform are thus embodied in the envelope of the waveform, together with the phase of the carrier, measured relative to the carrier reference supply. The types of test signal which the system will require will therefore need to take this form, as will the types of signal representing the system response. Figure 33 indicates the hardware which could be required in order to characterise the system.

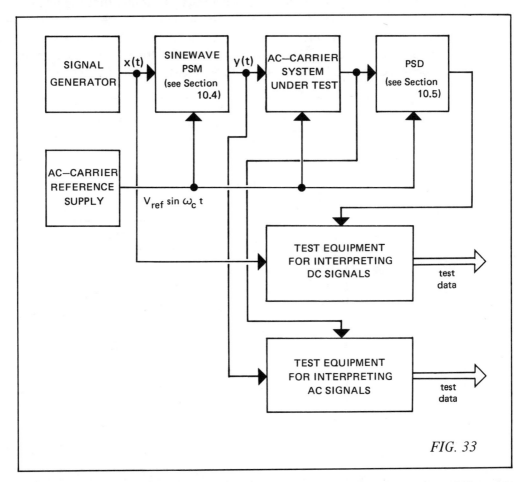

FIG. 33

Whether the AC signals or their DC counterparts are actually measured depends on the nature of the available test equipment. An alternative to using the phase-sensitive demodulator would occasionally be the temporary coupling of a DC transducer (assuming an appropriate type to be available) to the plant, purely for the purpose of characterisation. Certainly, the waveform from a DC device is more easily interpreted than its amplitude modulated counterpart.

14.10   SPECIAL TECHNIQUES FOR THE TESTING OF DIGITAL SYSTEMS

In most instances, it will be necessary to use a conventional type of signal generator, in order to generate the required disturbance functions. Occasionally, a signal generator may be digitally based, in which case it may have a digital output port: here, it may be feasible to input the digital output word directly into the control system, provided that the word is of the correct format and signal level; if this is not the case, then signal conversion (for example, from TTL levels to CMOS levels) and/or code conversion (see Section 10.15) may be necessary properties of the interfacing hardware. Another exceptional case would be where a digital controller is computer based, so that it is conceivable that the required variations in set point value (for example) might be generated by means of suitable program statements.

If the output data from the system are digital, then normally it would be necessary to convert the data to an equivalent DC voltage, assuming that the test equipment required an analog type of input signal. Some digitally based test equipment can process digital signals directly, assuming the input word to be of the correct format and signal level: if this is not the case, then signal conversion and/or code conversion could be necessary before processing could proceed.

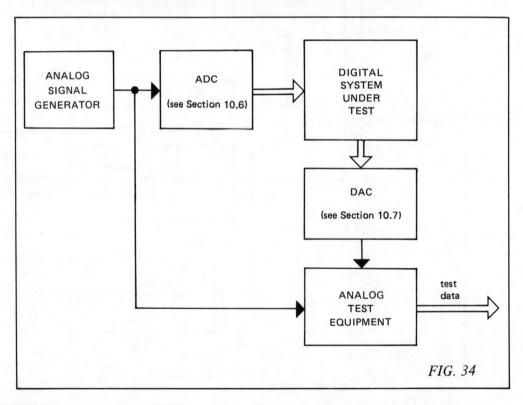

FIG. 34

Figure 34 represents the situation in which the control system requires digital input and output data and the signal generator and measuring instrument are both analog. The ADC and DAC will need to be chosen for both digital and analog compatibility with the equipment to which they are interfaced, and the sampling frequencies must be high in relation to the bandwidth of the control system by a factor preferably in excess of 10.

For simple on-off disturbances and for steady state calibration, the digital input word to the control system might be set up manually, using a suitable set of switches connected to an appropriate DC voltage source: contact bounce can be a problem, although this can be obviated by the use of special "switch debouncer" integrated circuits or bistable elements (see Section 10.14) connected to perform the same task.

14.11 SPECIAL TECHNIQUES FOR THE TESTING OF PNEUMATIC SYSTEMS

In most cases, it will be necessary to use an electronic signal generator in order to generate the required disturbance functions: signals may need to be given a DC offset, because they will have to be converted to pressures, which obviously can only be positive. Figure 35 shows a typical arrangement for testing a pneumatic system, using electronic instrumentation.

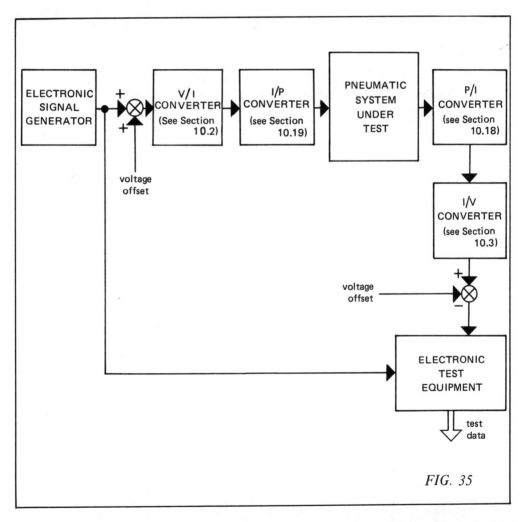

FIG. 35

Pneumatic strip chart (Y — T) recorders are available for operation from 3 — 15 psi (20 — 100 kPa) signals and these can be used to record the system output response. On these, the pen mechanism is directly actuated by the pneumatic signal, with a bellows or diaphragm (see Section 4.4) acting as the displacement transducer, connected to the pen mechanism by means of linkages.

However, the application of electronic test instruments will afford much greater versatility, although these will necessitate the use of an air-to-current converter together with a current-to-voltage converter (for which a resistor of appropriate value should suffice) and optional provision for offsetting the voltage dropped, since this will be unipolar.

It must be understood that, whenever I/P and P/I converters are used, the relatively slow response times of these converters may have a significant effect on the dynamic response data collected. It may well be necessary to measure the time constants of the converters and subsequently to remove the effect of the associated dynamic lag terms from the transfer functions deduced from the characterisation procedure.

For applying pressure step signals to the control system, it would be sufficient to use on-off pressure valves connected to suitable pressure-regulated pneumatic sources. The valves could be operated either manually or electrically, by means of solenoids.

Steady state calibration of pneumatic systems may be undertaken using a manually adjusted pressure-regulated air supply, together with a large-scale precision pressure gauge for indicating system input and output pressures: a small manually operated manifold could be useful as a pneumatic multiplexer for the pressure gauge.

15

CONTROL SYSTEM
PERFORMANCE
AND COMMISSIONING

15.1   THE NEED FOR SPECIFICATION FORMULATION

The ultimate function of a control system is the control of a property of an item of plant. The final control element and the feedback transducer become an integral part of the plant and must be selected on the basis of the criteria listed in Chapters 1 and 13; similar criteria also apply to the selection of the reference transducer and its network, if the controller is to be custom designed. Finally, it is necessary for the control engineer to either design or at least select the controller.

The completion of the design involves the selection and mechanisation of the control law for the controller. In essence, the engineer must be able to predict the performance which the system would achieve in the absence of this control law and then select the law in order that the performance consequently is improved sufficiently to meet the specification. When the completed system is commissioned, the responsible engineer will be required to demonstrate that the system can perform adequately the task for which it has been designed.

In order that the user shall be supplied with a system which will satisfy his needs, it becomes essential for the required performance to be specified very carefully and unambiguously. Inadequate formulation of performance specifications inevitably will lead to much dissatisfaction, recrimination, and possibly litigation, so that the importance of this aspect cannot be overstressed.

The performance of the final control element, plant process, and feedback transducer can be tested and identified, using the techniques described in Chapter 14. This performance then will be defined in terms of static characteristics, frequency (domain) responses, transient (time domain) responses, differential equations, transfer functions, etc. In some cases, it may be possible to identify individually the properties of the final control element, plant process, and feedback transducer but, in most instances, only the combination will be identifiable.

The performance of the completed control system normally is defined in terms of a combination of parameters relating to the following four areas of system performance:

- steady state accuracy in the presence of a steady applied disturbance, after all transient components of response have decayed to insignificance;
- frequency domain behaviour, which implies the response to a sequence of specified applied sinusoidal disturbances, after all transient components of response in each case have decayed to insignificance;
- time domain behaviour, which implies the transient response to a specified non-periodic disturbance, which usually will take the form of either an impulse, step, ramp, or square law (parabolic function);
- noise performance, which implies the effect, on either the controlled variable or the error variable, of specified noise disturbances which typically would be defined in statistical terms.

With all stable systems being operated within a region of linear behaviour, the transient components of response will decay to insignificance, if sufficient time is permitted to elapse for this to occur (assuming, of course, that a new disturbance is not applied in the meantime). In some systems containing significant nonlinearities, the transient response following the application of a disturbance may diverge or converge to a bounded oscillatory condition, which implies that the oscillation has a limiting amplitude and frequency. This condition is referred to as "limit cycling" or, more simply, as "cycling" and it may be acceptable if the amplitude and frequency are within tolerable proportions: such a situation is undesirable but it may prove to be a condition which has to be tolerated. In Sections 15.2 to 15.5, inclusive, the parameters most commonly used to define the four different domains of system performance will be detailed. In any practical case, not all of the parameters would be used, because to do so would represent an undesirable duplication of information which could be conflicting.

15.2   STEADY STATE ACCURACY

15.2.1 Factors Affecting Steady State Accuracy

There are many factors which can contribute to a steady state error (that is, a steady discrepancy between the actual and the desired values of the controlled variable), and many or all of these will be applicable to a particular control system. Generally speaking, a global limit will be placed upon the tolerable steady state error and the apportionment of this figure to the various factors contributing to it is largely at the discretion of the control engineer.

The factors which can contribute to steady state error are the following:

- reference and feedback transducer imperfections, such as curvature, deadband, quantisation, output signal offset, etc.;
- component tolerances and output signal offsets in the signal combination networks;
- nonlinearities, in the loop forward path components, such as deadband, hysteresis, backlash, static friction, coulomb friction, etc.;
- signal offsets in the loop forward path components;
- steady components of load on the plant;
- the nature of the reference variable, taken in conjunction with the system Type Number (see Section 15.2.2).

This last factor can be of significant importance but, at the same time, the engineer should not lose sight of the effect of the other factors listed. All texts dealing with the analysis of the behaviour of linear systems will show that the steady state error arising from a specified type of reference variable disturbance will be related to that disturbance, in the manner shown in Table 1.

TABLE 1. RELATIONSHIP BETWEEN STEADY STATE ERROR AND THE REFERENCE VARIABLE DISTURBANCE CAUSING THAT ERROR.

TYPE OF REFERENCE VARIATION	STEADY STATE ERROR, FOR THE NUMBER OF FORWARD PATH INTEGRATIONS SHOWN		
	0	1	2
step	$\dfrac{\text{input step size}}{1 + \text{system loop gain}}$	0	0
ramp	no steady state: controlled variable cannot track reference variable	$\dfrac{\text{ramp gradient}}{\text{system loop gain}}$	0
parabola (square law)	no steady state: controlled variable cannot track reference variable	no steady state: controlled variable cannot track reference variable	$\dfrac{\text{parabola second derivative}}{\text{system loop gain}}$

Immediately, it will be obvious that the number of forward path integrations and the value of the system loop gain are critical parameters, when system steady state error is being considered, and further discussion on these parameters will ensue.

The following are examples of steady component of load on a plant:

- a mass being raised or lowered by a pulley-cable combination, with the pulley drive being controlled by a position control or a speed control loop;
- a steady stator load current being drawn from a turbine-alternator set with loops for voltage control by manipulation of alternator excitation and frequency control by manipulation of turbine steam inflow rate;
- a steady outflow rate from a storage vessel subjected to liquid level control by manipulation of liquid inflow rate.

Essentially, there are nine different techniques available for the minimisation of steady state error: these are listed below and some will be elaborated upon in the sections which follow. In any particular system, some or most of these methods may be used.

A.   *Increasing the Loop Gain*

An increase in system loop gain will reduce the steady state error, in most instances. However, exceptions to this rule will arise where:

- the source of the error is in either the reference transducer, the feedback transducer, or the signal combination hardware;

- the source of the error is in any loop forward path component upstream of the point where the added gain is being incorporated, which suggests that it is preferable to increase the gain within the signal combination network(s).

In most practical cases, an increase in loop gain will result in a reduction in the degree of system stability; it will also tend to result in the transient saturation of forward path elements by reduced levels of reference variation.

B.   Increasing the Number of Forward Path Integrations

The effects of inserting an integration in the system forward path will be as follows:

- steady components of load disturbing the loop downstream of the added integration will no longer generate steady state error;
- signal offsets and nonlinearities occurring in forward path components downstream of the added integration will no longer generate steady state error, but signal offsets and certain nonlinearities occurring upstream of the added integration still will do so, which suggests that integration is best added immediately after, or even incorporated into, the signal combination network(s);
- the addition of integration will always result in a reduction in the degree of system stability, unless suitable transfer function terms are incorporated for compensation purposes;
- the addition of integration close to the signal combination network(s) will reduce any tendency towards transient saturation of the forward path elements.

C.   Replacing Components with Others Possessing Greater Precision

Obviously, there will be a trade-off between the resulting reduction in steady state error and the capital cost of the components, so that performance considerations need to be weighed against commercial considerations.

D.   Incorporating Additional Nonlinearities

In some instances, the effect of an unavoidable nonlinearity can be minimised or even nullified by cascading, with the offending element, an intentionally introduced nonlinearity, so that the combination has an overall static characteristic which, ideally, is linear. Curvature is a particular type of distortion which is amenable to this approach, and the cancellation of the orifice plate square law with a square-root extractor law is a commonplace application of the technique. Nonlinearities such as saturation, deadband, hysteresis, and granularity are not amenable readily to this approach. In some instances, the introduced nonlinearity may be placed in parallel with the offending element. Chapter 11 deals at length with the alternative techniques available for the construction of nonlinear networks.

E.   Adjusting the Calibration of the Reference Transducer

Where precise control is required, it is preferable that the calibration of the reference transducer should be left until the commissioning stage. In this manner, the calibration can be used to accommodate the effects of such imperfections as single-valued nonlinearities, signal offsets, and steady components of load. Inevitably, this adjustment will remain precise only if these imperfections are invariable.

F.   *Introducing Signal Offset into the Controller*

In some controllers, especially general purpose process controllers, provision is included for the adjustment of the offset of the output signal. This facility can be used to cancel out the effects of parasitic signal offsets and steady components of load, but the adjustment will remain precise only if these imperfections remain invariable.

G.   *Use of Minor Negative Feedback around Nonlinear Elements*

This application for minor negative feedback has been discussed at length in Section 5.5. The possible results of this technique can be summarised as follows:

- all nonlinearities except saturation can be disguised by negative feedback;
- the speed of response of an element can be increased by negative feedback;
- the incorporation of minor negative feedback probably will result in a loss in sensitivity, which may need to be restored by additional amplification inserted outside the minor loop.

The design of negative feedback loops around elements possessing significant nonlinearities may require the application of nonlinear system design techniques (see Section 15.6), in order that the minor loop shall have adequate stability margins.

H.   *Introducing Feedforward Control*

Where feedback control cannot cope adequately with components of load on the plant, it may be feasible to augment the feedback action with feedforward action. (General purpose feedforward controllers are discussed in Section 8.3.2). The mechanisation of feedforward control will necessitate the installation of a load transducer, the controller hardware, and possibly an additional final control element. This technique should provide the cancellation of the effect of steady components of load and will have the advantage that this cancellation will track long term changes in these components. In addition, the feedforward control law may be designed to provide some cancellation of the dynamic effects of transient components of load.

I.   *Reducing the Effect of Gear Backlash by Means of Divided Reset*

If the amplitude of gear backlash in a position servosystem is unacceptably large and the replacement of the gearbox with an improved version proves to be impracticable, a technique which sometimes is used involves the mounting of displacement transducers on the input and output shafts of the gearbox and mixing, in appropriate proportions, the two position feedback signals generated: sometimes this is known as "divided reset".

15.2.2 System Type Number

The Type Number (or Class Number) of a system is defined as the number of integrations in the loop transfer function or, in the case of systems with minor feedback loops, the effective transfer function of the outer (principal) loop. Loop integrations will occur always in the forward path of a loop and they will arise as listed in Table 2, in relation to the type number shown.

TABLE 2. THE CONTRIBUTION OF OUTER LOOP INTEGRATIONS TO SYSTEM TYPE NUMBER

SYSTEM TYPE NUMBER	TOTAL NUMBER OF FORWARD PATH INTEGRATIONS IN THE OUTER LOOP	FORWARD PATH INTEGRATIONS INHERENT IN THE PLANT TRANSFER FUNCTION	FORWARD PATH INTEGRATIONS INTRODUCED BY THE CONTROLLER TRANSFER FUNCTION
0	0	0	0
1	1	0	1
		1	0
2	2	0	2
		1	1
		2	0

Type 2 systems are relatively uncommon, because of the difficulties experienced with achieving reasonable stability margins for these systems (see Section 15.3); such a system is most likely to be achieved with one integration in the plant and the other in the controller.

An integration exists in a plant process if a steady applied value of the manipulated variable results in a steady state ramping of the controlled variable (and the measured variable). An example is where the liquid inflow rate to a tank is manipulated in order to vary the liquid level in the tank: a steady inflow rate will result in a steady rate of increase in liquid level, assuming no outflow to occur at the same time and that the surface area remains constant. A second example is where the hydraulic oil flow into, and out from, a cylinder is manipulated in order to vary the displacement of the piston: a steady flow rate will result in a steady rate of change in piston position, provided that leakage past the piston is insignificant. A third example is an electric motor, when the control input voltage (or current) is manipulated in order to vary the angular displacement of the shaft: a steady control signal ultimately will result in a steady rate of change in angular displacement. It is extremely unusual for two integrations to be present in a plant transfer function.

An integration can be introduced into a controller using either electronic means (see Sections 12.3 and 12.7) or pneumatic means (Section 7.2). In the case of the general purpose process controller (Section 8.3), the incorporation of integral action (reset action) into the control law will result in the addition of an integral term to the controller transfer function, as shown in Table 3. There is no provision made in process controllers for more than a single integration.

TABLE 3.   PROCESS CONTROLLER TRANSFER FUNCTIONS INVOLVING INTEGRAL ACTION

ACTION	TRANSFER FUNCTION
I	$\dfrac{1}{sK_pT_I}$
P I	$\dfrac{1}{K_p}\left(1+\dfrac{1}{sT_I}\right) = \dfrac{1+sT_I}{sK_pT_I}$
P I D	$\dfrac{1}{K_p}\left(1+\dfrac{1}{sT_I}+sT_D\right) = \dfrac{s^2T_IT_D+sT_I+1}{sK_pT_I}$

In all cases, the s in the denominator of the rationalised transfer function signifies that the control law will increase by 1 the type number of the loop in which the controller is installed.

Minor negative feedback can be applied for the elimination of an undesirable integration, present in the main system forward path, by making the integration part of the forward path of the minor loop, for which the closed loop transfer function will not include an integration term: this technique establishes the means whereby the type number of a system may be reduced. The stability of the complete system will be enhanced by this additional feedback loop.

15.3   FREQUENCY DOMAIN BEHAVIOUR

In those systems in which it is feasible to characterise the final control element, plant process, and feedback transducer in terms of frequency response data, the design of the compensation can be undertaken in the frequency domain. The types of frequency domain parameter which are specified assume linear behaviour, so that they may need to be specified in terms of small (sinusoidal) signal analysis, in the event that loop behaviour is affected significantly by non-linearities. The frequency domain parameters which appear in specifications can be subdivided into open loop and closed loop categories, as shown overleaf.

Parameters applying to open loop frequency response data are:

- gain crossover frequency ω_c;
- phase crossover frequency;
- gain margin, which typically is specified to lie between 8 and 20 dB;
- phase margin, which typically is specified to lie between 30° and 60°;
- low-frequency magnitude gradient, which is related directly to the system type number.

These various parameters are defined in Figure 1, using alternative representations of the data.

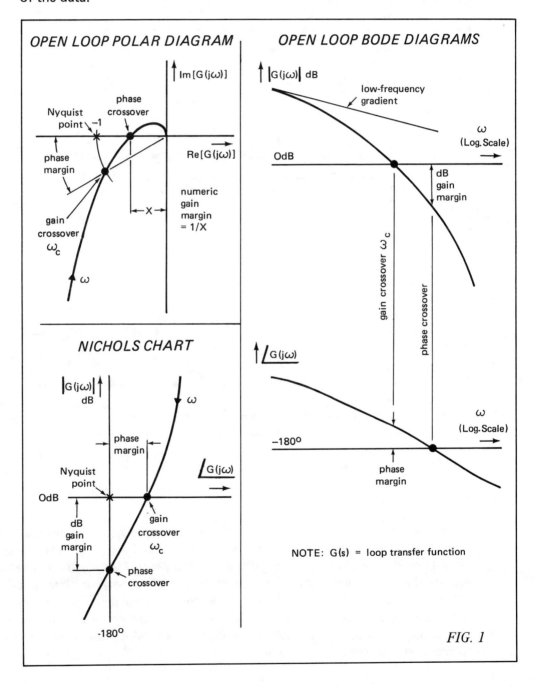

FIG. 1

Parameters applying to closed loop frequency response data are:

- peak gain magnitude M_m (if resonance occurs), measured relative to the magnitude at $\omega = 0$ – a typical specification is 1.3 to 1.5 numeric = 2.3 dB to 3.5 dB;
- resonant frequency ω_r, if resonance occurs;
- bandwidth ω_b ;
- high-frequency roll-off gradient, which is related to noise rejection capability.

These various parameters are defined in Figure 2.

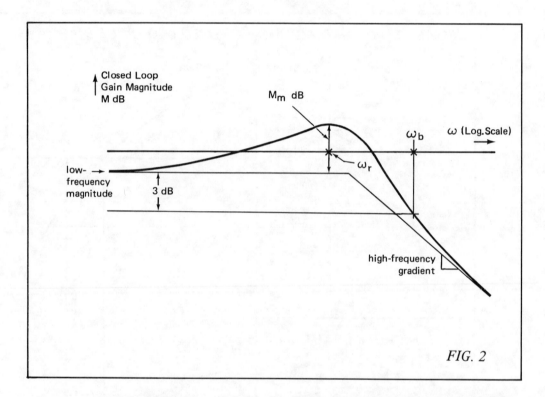

FIG. 2

Open loop and closed loop frequency domain parameters are interdependent. Thus, ω_c, ω_r, and ω_b will all have the same order of magnitude and usually occur in the sequence $\omega_c < \omega_r < \omega_b$. Similarly, relatively low stability margins will yield a high value for M_m.

15.4 TIME DOMAIN BEHAVIOUR

Time domain parameters, when they are used in specifications, normally refer to step response behaviour. The step in question may be applied to the reference variable or it may be applied to the load on the plant. Most of these parameters assume linear behaviour, but some (notably rise time, settling time, peak overshoot, and decrement) may also be applied to nonlinear behaviour. If behaviour is affected significantly by nonlinearities, it may be preferable to apply the parameters in terms of responses to small steps, for which the transient is likely to approach that for a linear model.

In plant processes involving the physical transportation of material (solid, liquid, or gas), the phenomenon of pure time delay (dead time, transport delay) is likely to occur between the point to which the manipulation is applied to the plant and the point at which the effect of the manipulation is instrumented. A notable exception to this occurs in liquid flow processes for which, provided that compressibility effects are minimal, the flow sensor should respond immediately the flow is manipulated at a different point in the line. Plant dead time can only be reduced by redesign of the plant, because it is not "disguised" by negative feedback: it will emerge, unaffected in value, in the system closed loop response.

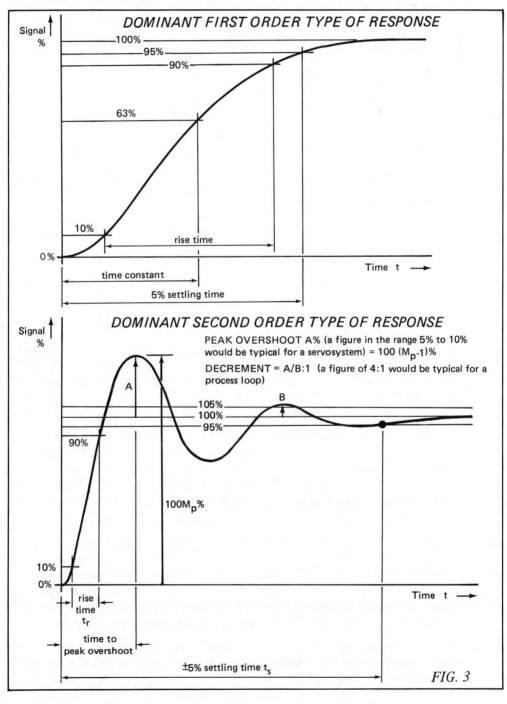

FIG. 3

The nature of a particular step response largely determines which parameters are most appropriate for specifying that response. Many practical responses conform approximately to the simple linear first order and second order responses discussed in Sections 14.4.3 and 14.4.4 respectively: when this occurs, the responses are said to exhibit first order or second order "dominance". The parameters which are most relevant to these two types of dominance are defined graphically in Figure 3: possible dead time has not been shown in these diagrams.

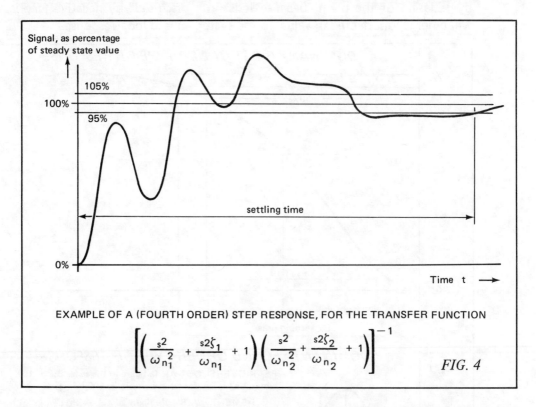

EXAMPLE OF A (FOURTH ORDER) STEP RESPONSE, FOR THE TRANSFER FUNCTION

$$\left[\left(\frac{s^2}{\omega_{n1}^2} + \frac{s2\zeta_1}{\omega_{n1}} + 1 \right) \left(\frac{s^2}{\omega_{n2}^2} + \frac{s2\zeta_2}{\omega_{n2}} + 1 \right) \right]^{-1}$$

FIG. 4

Where an actual response relates to a high system order and does not exhibit low order dominance, the definitions of some of the parameters shown in Figure 3 can easily become obscured. Settling time is still unambiguous, and therefore relevant, but the remaining parameters may need to be applied with caution. Figure 4 shows an example of a high order response for which the definitions of peak overshoot, time to peak overshoot, and decrement are not at all obvious. In a case such as this, a limit upon the oscillatory behaviour of the response is best imposed in terms of an upper bound on an appropriate "performance index": the index most commonly used for step responses is the "I T A E Criterion", which is defined as $\lim_{T \to \infty} \int_0^T t\,|e(t)|\,dt$ and which will penalise both long lived overshoots and long lived undershoots of the steady state value; e(t) is system error.

Where second order dominance is particularly strong, it may well be appropriate to use those parameters which apply specifically to second order responses:

- damping factor ζ — a figure in the vicinity of 0.707 would be typical;
- damped natural frequency $\omega_t = 2\pi/(\text{period of transient oscillations})$ rad/s;
- decay ratio $\alpha = \zeta\omega_n$, where $\omega_n = \omega_t/\sqrt{1 - \zeta^2}$.

Many control systems exhibit a nonlinear phenomenon known as "rate limiting". This is manifested as an upper limit on the rate at which the output signal can "slew" and should be demonstrated clearly by a large-signal step response, as shown in Figure 5. Where relevant, this parameter will have a marked influence upon large-signal settling time and, in addition, upon large-signal frequency response.

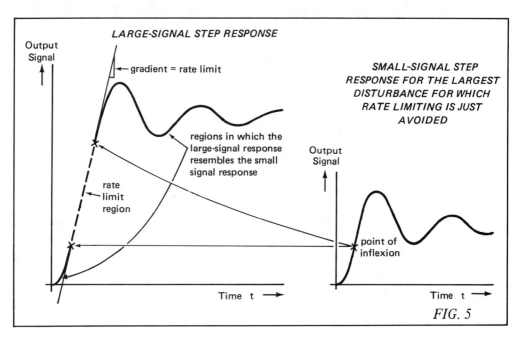

FIG. 5

15.5 NOISE PERFORMANCE

There are many potential sources of parasitic noise in control systems, amongst which feature the following:

- mains ripple due to imperfect smoothing of electric power supplies;
- pressure fluctuations due to imperfect smoothing of hydraulic power supplies;
- cutter reaction on machine tool drives;
- wind buffetting of antennae and aircraft;
- wind and wave buffetting of naval vessels;
- air and gas bubbles entering liquid flow lines;
- sediment in liquid flow lines;
- rumble in continuous belt drives, due to fluctuations in the mass being transported;
- imperfect smoothing in demodulation processes;
- quantisation and sampling in digital-analog conversion processes;
- crosstalk and self-induced high-frequency oscillations.

Where the noise enters the system with a significant amplitude, the system will need to be designed so as to minimise the effect of the noise upon the controlled variable. Some types of noise are random in nature, so that their effect can be specified only in statistical terms; other types of noise are periodic, so that it is practical to specify their effect in frequency domain terms.

The frequency response of the system between the noise source and the controlled variable will have a considerable bearing upon the noise performance and is best specified by parameters such as −3dB bandwidth, resonant gain magnitude, and roll-off gradient. If the frequency content of the noise input signal is known, the frequency content of the noise component of the controlled variable can be determined using a knowledge of this frequency response: this will apply to both periodic and nonperiodic noise signals, which exhibit line spectra and continuous spectra, respectively.

A commonly used performance index which can be applied in order to place a statistical amplitude limit upon the effect of noise is the "Root-Mean-Square Error Criterion", which is defined as

$$\left[\lim_{T \to \infty} \frac{1}{T} \int_0^T e^2(t)\, dt \right]^{\frac{1}{2}}$$, where e(t) is system error: this will penalise both large and long lived noise signal components.

15.6 ANALYTICAL DESIGN TECHNIQUES

Clearly, it is not the function of this volume to present the alternative analytical design techniques which are available for the design of control systems: these are covered more than adequately in the many excellent texts devoted to the analytical area. However, because the final stage of designing a control system involves either the design or the selection of a controller, including its control algorithm(s), it is considered relevant to provide a critical summary of the alternative methods which are in common industrial use.

15.6.1 Time Domain Analysis

Classical time domain analysis is suitable for designing systems which will exhibit first and second order behaviour. Since few practical systems will fall into these categories, it follows that this approach is largely unsuitable as a design method although, of course, the overall time domain performance of the designed system obviously will be of considerable significance.

State variable methods generate time domain performance but their complexity renders them appropriate mainly to high order systems being operated in a linear mode. Solutions are best generated by digital computer and, for low order linear systems, the labour involved will consume more time than is required using classical analysis. State variable methods have rarely been used, in practice, to compute the large-signal behaviour of those high order systems for which the nonlinearities normally present become significant. For the types of system for which they are most appropriate, state variable methods can be used to optimise simultaneously the values of a set of system parameters such as gain constants and time constants.

Large-signal behaviour of dominant first and second order systems containing significant nonlinearities can be undertaken using Phase Plane methods, which involve plots, to cartesian co-ordinates, of dx/dt versus x(t), where x(t) is a system variable of interest which typically is equated to system error e(t). Synthesis of phase portraits is not practicable for systems of order greater than two, but the format sometimes may be used to display experimentally-obtained response data, as an aid to the interpretation of time domain behaviour.

15.6.2 Frequency Domain Analysis

The frequency domain is a very powerful medium for the design of systems, although the collection of experimental data can be very time consuming. Experimentally derived frequency response data can be incorporated directly into the plots, without necessitating the derivation of the associated transfer functions. The effect of dead time is incorporated readily. The ultimate derivation of time domain performance data can be very involved, when the system order is high.

Frequency domain methods are most appropriate for systems behaving in a linear manner, which may imply small-signal behaviour. However, they can be extended to embrace large-signal nonlinear behaviour if Describing Functions are used although, without resorting to considerable complexity, this technique usually can yield data only on closed loop stability.

The merits of the alternative formats for displaying frequency response data are considered to be as follows:

Bode Diagram Format
- data values are well distributed;
- asymptotes can be used on magnitude plots, for both analysis and synthesis;
- compatible with Nichols chart format;
- does not provide open loop-closed loop transformation of data;
- multiplication of cascaded transfer functions transforms to the addition of data values;
- cannot incorporate describing function data usefully;
- can be used for the design of sampled data systems, if a new (dimensionless) frequency variable is defined.

Polar (Nyquist) Diagram Format
- data values are poorly distributed;
- provides open loop-closed loop transformation for linear operation;
- simple compensator transfer functions are represented by simple locus shapes — semicircles, circles etc.;
- multiplication of cascaded transfer functions transforms to vector multiplication, which is complicated to apply;
- can easily incorporate describing function data.

Inverse Polar (Inverse Nyquist) Diagram Format
- data values are poorly distributed;
- simple compensator transfer functions are represented by simple locus shapes;
- when used for feedback compensation, the manipulation of transfer functions transforms to vector addition, which is relatively straightforward

to apply;
- provides open loop-closed loop transformation for linear operation.

Nichols Chart Format
- data values are well distributed;
- compatible with Bode diagram format;
- provides open loop-closed loop transformation for linear operation;
- can easily incorporate describing function data.

Clearly, it can be seen that the alternative formats all have merits and demerits, which explains why they all have a place in design procedures. Frequency response methods are not amenable to rigorous optimisation of any particular parameter: each new trial value will generate a new set of frequency response curves.

15.6.3 s-Domain Analysis

The ability to design in the s-domain assumes that the final control element-plant process-feedback transducer combination can be represented accurately by a transfer function, which presupposes that a reliable characterisation procedure has been conducted: see Chapter 14. Analysis is suitable only for linear behaviour, so that it can be used only for small-signal behaviour when significant nonlinearities are present. Moreover, the method cannot incorporate the effect of dead time.

The principal merits of the root locus diagram are:
- it provides a means to optimise rigorously a particular parameter, which need not necessarily be the system loop gain;
- it gives a good indication of dominance in the closed loop behaviour;
- it readily indicates, in detail, closed loop time domain behaviour and, to a lesser extent, frequency domain behaviour and, moreover, shows how these behaviours change as the parameter being optimised is changed;
- the method is extended readily to the z-domain for the design of sampled data systems.

The Routh-Hurwitz stability criterion is a simple test which can be applied very rapidly in order to predict closed loop stability or instability, but it will not yield information on the degree of stability such as would be indicated, for example, by stability margins in the frequency domain.

15.6.4. Transformation of Data between Time and Frequency Domains

Closed loop performances in the time and frequency domains are interdependent. Where the behaviour can be regarded as being linear, one performance is predictable from the other, but the level of difficulty encountered in undertaking this transformation of data will depend upon the order of the system.

Where closed loop performance can be regarded as being second order dominant, the following *approximate* relationships can be used for ball-park estimates:

$t_s \cong \pi/\omega_c$ $M_p \cong 0.85 M_m$ $\zeta = 1/(2M_m)$, where M_m is numeric

$t_s \cong 3\sqrt{1 - \zeta^2}/\zeta\omega_t$ $\omega_t \cong \omega_r \cong 0.75\omega_c$ $t_r \omega_t \cong 1.3$.

Note that all of these parameters have been defined in Sections 15.3 and 15.4.

Certain researchers have compiled performance charts* which enable closed loop performance parameters to be read off, once specified open loop performance parameters are applied as input data. These charts have tended to concentrate either upon particular classes of servomechanism or upon particular classes of process loop, with the latter incorporating the effect of dead time: these can be useful for the classes of system covered, although their application may involve a considerable amount of graphical interpolation.

15.6.5 Computer Simulation

Computer simulation has been used extensively in the aerospace industry, in nuclear and thermal power generation, and in certain process industries for the optimisation of system designs. In addition to requiring the necessary computing equipment, technical expertise, and availability of time and finance, computer simulation cannot be successful unless the final control element-plant process-feedback transducer combination can be represented accurately in mathematical terms, using the characterisation procedures of Chapter 14. Because of all of the factors involved, it is hardly surprising that industries with limited resources have not invested heavily in computer simulation.

An interesting and recent phenomenon associated with microprocessor based process controllers is the provision of the capability to allocate temporarily some of the processor hardware to simulation functions, during the system commissioning stage. Thus, processor hardware may be "borrowed" from another loop and used to simulate the plant process in the loop presently being commissioned, so that the controller may first be tuned with the model before ultimately being connected to the plant. In this manner, controller tuning for optimum system performance may be undertaken off-line, in contrast to the more usual on-line tuning procedure. The technique assumes that the plant process can first be characterised and then modelled adequately by the controller algorithms available.

15.7   COMMISSIONING PROCEDURES

The procedures to be outlined here assume that the final control element and feedback transducer have been coupled to the plant and tested for correct functioning. The nature of the next stages of commissioning depends upon whether the

---

* Chestnut, H. and Mayer, R.W.: "Servomechanisms and Regulating System Design". Vol. 1, John Wiley, N.Y., 2/e 1959, pp. 515 to 532.

Wills, D.M.   :   "Control Engineering", April 1962, pp. 104 to 108.
             :   "Control Engineering:', August 1962, pp. 93 to 95.

controller has been custom designed or is general purpose. In the former case, the nature of the control law (that is, the compensation transfer function) may be subjected to last-minute modification; in the latter case, the control law will have been chosen from a small number of alternatives and the parameter values will be subjected to fine tuning as the commissioning proceeds. The descriptions which follow assume that a single feedback loop is being commissioned: obviously, the procedures will require further development when feedforward action and multiple, interacting, feedback loops are being commissioned.

15.7.1 Commissioning of Custom Designed Controllers

The following operations will need to be conducted, more or less in the sequence indicated:

- connect the controller to the final control element, to complete the forward path, whilst leaving the feedback disconnected;
- if not already present, temporarily instal means to attenuate the error signal and power up the hardware with minimum signal applied to the final control element;
- check that the signal from the feedback transducer has a polarity which is the reverse of that of the signal from the reference transducer, normally indicating that the feedback will be in the negative sense when it is connected — if the sense is incorrect, take suitable steps to cause a reversal (see overleaf);
- if open loop characterisation is to be undertaken, identify the final control element-plant process-feedback transducer combination, using one or more of the procedures described in Chapter 14;
- if characterisation is to be undertaken with the loop closed, reduce the reference signal to zero and increase the error attenuation to maximum, close the feedback connection, gently reduce the error attenuation until the system is reasonably responsive to reference disturbances (without approaching instability), and undertake the characterisation by using a suitable procedure (see Chapter 14);
- design and install the compensation hardware — typically, this would involve introducing a compensation transfer function in order to increase the system phase crossover frequency or reduce the gain crossover frequency, or both, together with means to achieve the desired figure for the system loop gain; occasionally, the compensation may be introduced as part of an additional feedback path ("feedback compensation"), as an alternative to the more usual introduction into the forward path ("forward path" or "cascade compensation");
- with the loop closed and a high level of error attenuation again present, apply small reference disturbances and monitor the system response;
- gently reduce the error attenuation and check that the system response progressively approaches the predicted behaviour as the loop gain approaches the design figure;
- fine tune the compensator parameters, as necessary;
- remove the error attenuator, if it was to be temporary;
- calibrate the reference transducer, in terms of corresponding steady state values of controlled variable, taking into account relevant loading condit-

ions on the plant;

- undertake comprehensive performance tests to corroborate compliance with the system performance specification.

If initially it is found that the principal feedback would be in the positive sense, reversal can be effected using one of the following techniques, noting that not all will be practicable in any particular situation:

- installing a sign inverting element in the forward path, within the controller;
- interchanging the signal connections from the controller to the final control element;
- reversing the action of the final control element;
- reversing the sense of the physical coupling of the final control element to the plant;
- reversing the sense of the physical coupling of the feedback transducer to the plant;
- interchanging the power supply connections to the feedback transducer;
- interchanging the signal connections from the feedback transducer to the controller;
- installing a sign inverting element in the feedback path, within the controller.

Note that, whenever a sign inversion is effected in the principal feedback path, the sense of the calibration of the reference transducer also becomes reversed and this may require correction.

15.7.2 Commissioning of General Purpose Process Controllers

Two types of empirical approach are used for predicting optimum settings for general purpose process controllers. They both involve time domain testing of the plant: in the first method, the final control element-plant process-feedback transducer combination is subjected to a step disturbance with the feedback signal disconnected; in the second method, a non-optimum feedback loop is completed and subjected to a step disturbance of the set point.

The Open Loop Response Method

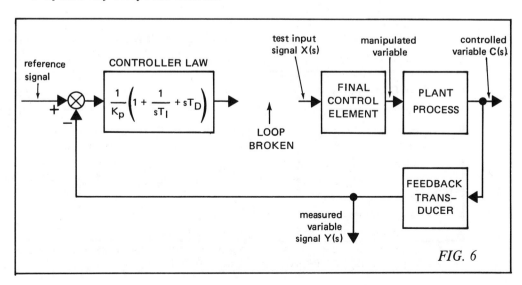

FIG. 6

The system hardware is connected to comply with the block diagram of Figure 6. The loop is open and the final control element is subjected to a step disturbance of magnitude X units. The response of the measured variable y(t) is recorded and analysed on the basis that it will assume the general form shown in Figure 7.

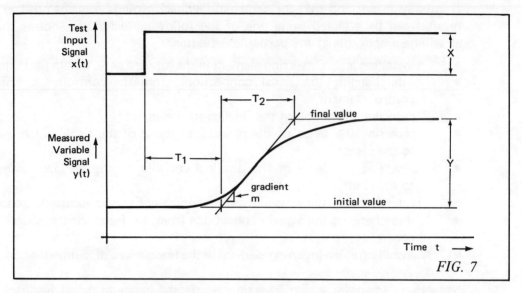

FIG. 7

The slope m corresponds to the maximum gradient of this "process reaction curve", T_1 is an equivalent dead time, and T_2 is an equivalent time constant. It is seen the response is being modelled mathematically by the transfer function

of the form $\frac{Y}{X}(s) = \frac{Ke^{-sT_1}}{(1 + sT_2)}$. In practice, the actual transfer function often is

somewhat more complicated than this. However, the assumption of the above form often is an acceptable approximation and provides a means for generating reasonable initial settings for the controller. These settings ultimately may be readjusted to obtain a more desirable closed loop response. The values of Y, T_1, T_2, and X are used to determine the recommended values for the controller settings for K_p, T_I, and T_D in accordance with Table 4.

TABLE 4.   ZIEGLER-NICHOLS RECOMMENDATIONS ON THE BASIS OF PROCESS REACTION CURVE DATA

TYPE OF CONTROL LAW	K_p	T_I	T_D
P	mT_1/X	—	—
PI	$mT_1/0.9X$	$3.33T_1$	—
PID	$mT_1/1.2X$	$2T_1$	$T_1/2$

Note: proportional band = $100K_p$% and m = Y/T_2.

Alternative coefficient values have been proposed by various researchers for the Table 4 entries but, since these formulae are to be used only for the initial controller settings, refinement of the coefficients must be of limited benefit.

In practice, it is necessary to measure the response curve for both positive and negative going input steps and for various magnitudes of input step X, in order to determine the most representative model of the above form. If the spread of values obtained for the parameters Y/X, T_1, and T_2 is within (say) 10 to 15%, the expressions for recommended controller settings should yield reasonable values: these settings ultimately may be readjusted to obtain a more desirable response, once the loop has been closed.

Reference to Table 4, and also to Table 5 below, shows that, when integral action is incorporated, the gain $1/K_p$ introduced into the loop has to be reduced, due to the fact that the introduction of an integration term tends to reduce system stability. Conversely, when derivative action is introduced, the gain may be increased, due to the stabilising effect of the derivative term.

Note that the open loop response method will not be suitable for use with plant processes which incorporate an integral term, because then the open loop response will be asymptotic to a ramp.

Note also that the loop should not be closed until it has been ascertained that the sense of the feedback is negative, as discussed in Section 15.7.1.

The Closed Loop Response Method

This method is based upon the closed loop step response of a non-optimised feedback loop. Having checked that the sense of the feedback will be negative, the system of Figure 6 is restored to closed loop operation; the controller is set initially for proportional action only ($T_1 = \infty$, $T_D = 0$) with a very high proportional band K_p. Using the set point control, a small step disturbance of reference input $r(t)$ is applied to the system and the closed loop response is obtained by recording the measured variable $y(t)$. The value of K_p then is reduced progressively until the input disturbance just triggers a continuous limit cycling of the measured variable. This value (K_{p_m}) of proportional band and the value T_u of the period of the oscillation are measured. The recommended initial trial values for the controller settings are determined in accordance with Table 5.

TABLE 5. ZIEGLER-NICHOLS RECOMMENDATIONS ON THE BASIS OF LIMIT CYCLING DATA

TYPE OF CONTROL LAW	K_p	T_I	T_D
P	$K_{p_m}/0.5$	—	—
PI	$K_{p_m}/0.45$	$T_u/1.2$	—
PID	$K_{p_m}/0.6$	$T_u/2$	$T_u/8$

The main disadvantage with the Ziegler-Nichols closed loop method is that it can be undesirable to introduce limit cycling into a plant, even for a short duration: cycling may cause practical problems, including danger to plant and personnel.

An alternative approach is initially to follow the above procedure but to stop reducing K_p when a 4:1 (or thereabouts) decrement is obtained for the currently non-optimised closed loop step response. If the decrement actually achieved for this initial response is given by A:1 and the period of the decaying oscillation is P seconds, a reasonable set of new trial values for the controller parameters will be given by

$$K_{p_{new}} \quad = \quad K_{p_{old}} / (0.5 + 2.27 \, \Delta) \; \%$$

$$T_{I_{new}} \quad = \quad P / (1.2 \sqrt{1 + \Delta^2}) \qquad \text{seconds for P I control}$$

or $\qquad\qquad = \quad P / (2 \sqrt{1 + \Delta^2}) \qquad \text{seconds for P I D control}$

and $\quad T_{D_{new}} \quad = \quad P / (8 \sqrt{1 + \Delta^2}) \qquad \text{seconds for P I D control}$

where $\Delta = \dfrac{1}{2\pi} \ln(A)$. The advantages with this type of procedure are that the plant

is not subjected to cycling and that the formulae may be reapplied iteratively, to implement an optimisation routine which can be undertaken even when the loop is in service.

16

INTERFACING CONTROL SYSTEMS TO DIGITAL COMPUTERS

16.1 INTRODUCTION

A digital computer or microprocessor may be interfaced to a number of control systems associated with a particular plant. The function of the computer may be data acquisition, or control, or a combination of the two. In the case of data acquisition, the computer is required to interrogate signals being transmitted by plant transducers and to process the data so gathered. The function of this processing may be one or more of the following:

- statistical analyses of the performance of the systems;

- cost analyses of the plant processes being controlled;

- logging of performance data defining plant behaviour leading up to, and subsequent to, a plant failure condition, in order to facilitate the inquest.

In the case of control, the computer may be involved either in a "supervisory" role or in direct digital control (DDC). Figure 1 illustrates these alternative modes.

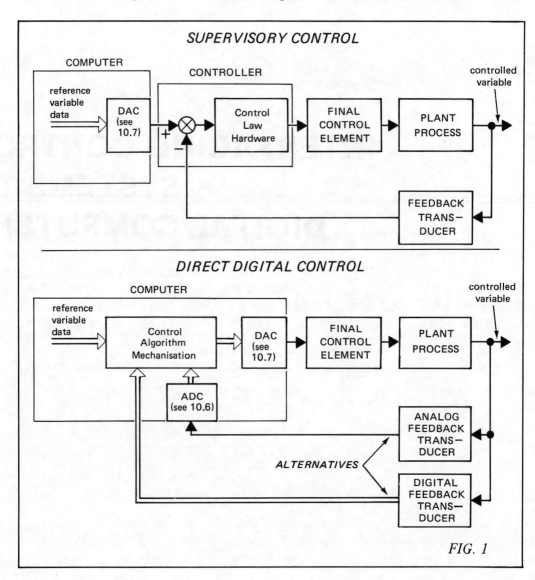

FIG. 1

In the case of supervisory control, the principal function of the computer is to generate a reference signal for an external controller, so that the computer hardware is outside the control loop. In the case of DDC, the principal function of the computer is both to generate reference variable data and to synthesise the controller, so that the computer hardware forms an integral part of the loop.

In the DDC case, therefore, the computer is required to:

- generate the reference variable;

- generate error data, by comparing the reference data and feedback data, which will be data input to the computer via its interface;

- generate output data to be converted, via the interface, to a driving signal for the final control element, the output data being related to the error data in terms defined by the chosen control algorithm, which is equivalent to the control law of the (conventional) controller in the supervisory control case.

The computer may compute absolute values of output or it may compute increments in output value, depending upon the nature of the final control element and its driving circuits.

Although, for both cases, the computer has been shown associated with only one control loop, it is common practice to timeshare the computer hardware between a multiplicity of control loops, in order to effect cost efficiency. This means that the input data to the computer and the output data from the computer must be processed by multiplexing hardware.

In addition to being concerned with the processing of data variables, the computer may also be required to perform decision making tasks related to the occurrence of specified events. Thus, a multiplicity of single on–off types of (digital) signal may also form part of the set of input and output signals to be handled by the computer interface.

The function of the interface is to enable the external system hardware to be associated with the processor section of the computer. A typical arrangement is for the interface components to be treated by the processor as sections of memory, with suitable memory addresses being reserved for these components, so that the transfer of data would be effected by means of sets of signals on the normal address and data buses of the computer. In cases where large quantities of data need to be transferred in very short periods of time, the interface data lines may be connected directly to the data lines of reserved sections of memory, with transfer then being effected independently of the operation of the central processing unit: such a scheme is known as "direct memory access" (DMA). In cases where external events are required to alter, as soon as possible, the current processing being undertaken by the computer, the event signal sources may be hardwired together into the computer's "priority interrupt" or "vectored interrupt" system, with the wiring sequence determining the order of precedence.

16.2 ANALOG INPUT CHANNELS

Analog input hardware often is divided into two categories: high level, in which the signal magnitudes range up to 10 V DC, and low level, in which the signal magnitudes range up to 1 V DC. Subdivision is necessary because the method of preamplification of the signal, prior to analog-digital conversion, is different for the two categories. The level of input signal experienced will depend upon the nature of the analog transducer which provides the signal source.

16.2.1 Signal Conditioning

Frequently, the analog signal from a transducer may be required to be "conditioned" before it can be processed by the ADC. The need for conditioning can arise because the signal level is inappropriate and/or because protection of the interface is required against excessive voltage or current transients. Conditioning of a particular signal can necessitate one or more of the following:

- attenuation;
- amplification;
- air-to-current conversion (see Section 10.18);
- current-to-voltage conversion (see Section 10.3);
- noise filtering (see Chapter 12);
- compensation for nonlinearities (see Chapter 11);
- electrical isolation;
- electrical protection.

Signal amplification and common-mode noise rejection often is effected by use of high quality special purpose encapsulated "Instrumentation Amplifiers". A typical internal organisation of one of these amplifiers is shown in Figure 2.

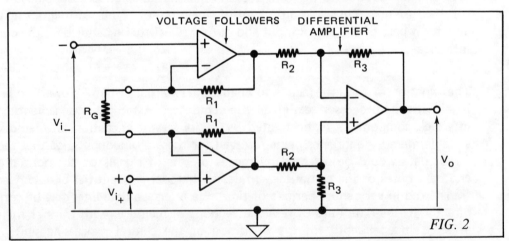

FIG. 2

For this arrangement, it can be shown that $V_o = \dfrac{R_3}{R_2}\left(1 + \dfrac{2R_1}{R_G}\right)(V_{i_+} - V_{i_-})$, provided that the amplifier imperfections are ignored, resistors are perfectly matched, and the amplifiers are unsaturated. The external (or sometimes internal) resistor R_G enables the overall voltage gain to be preset at the input terminals. The differential input network enables common-mode noise components to cancel, and the voltage follower arrangement at the input enables a very high input impedance to be presented to the signal source.

More elaborate versions of these amplifiers are known as "Isolation Amplifiers", and these effect electrical isolation up to a level of (say) 8 kV between the input and output networks. One type of isolation amplifier uses transformers to decouple the networks, and a typical arrangement is shown in Figure 3.

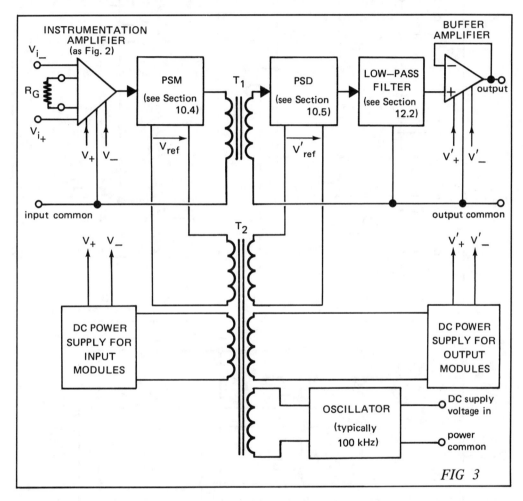

FIG 3

Several variations on this arrangement are marketed commercially as encapsulated modular devices, some of which use opto-couplers as alternatives to the transformers shown in Figure 3.

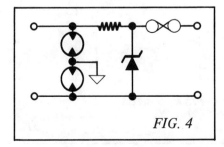

FIG. 4

Figure 4 shows a typical protection arrangement for a double-ended voltage input signal, involving a fuse, zener diode, and gas-discharge suppressors.

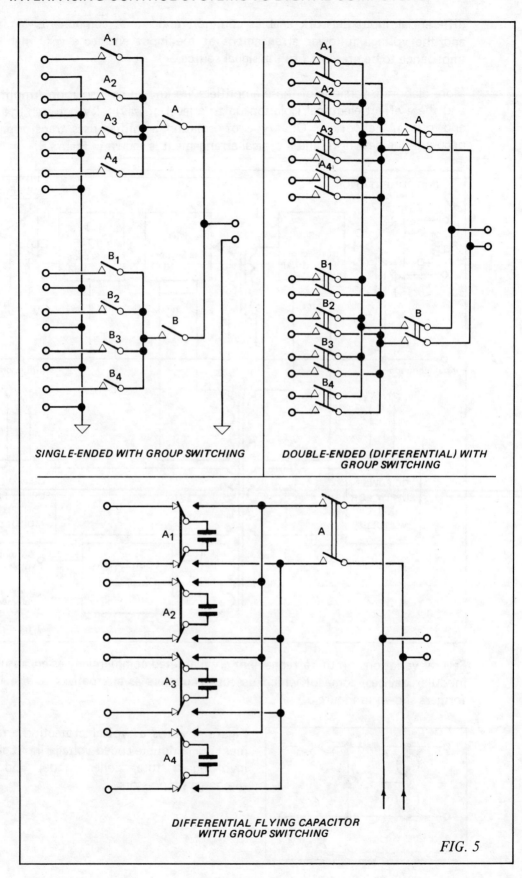

SINGLE-ENDED WITH GROUP SWITCHING

DOUBLE-ENDED (DIFFERENTIAL) WITH GROUP SWITCHING

DIFFERENTIAL FLYING CAPACITOR WITH GROUP SWITCHING

FIG. 5

16.2.2 Analog Multiplexers

A Multiplexer (MUX) is a selection switch which determines which analog input signal is to be connected to the ADC at any particular moment in time. The computer is programmed to address a specified input signal and this address is sent (via the address bus) to the multiplexer, which decodes the address and closes the appropriate switch. The speed at which the MUX can switch determines the maximum scanning rate (number of points/second) of the analog input system. Most MUX are composed of either electromechanical relays or metal oxide semiconductor field-effect transistors (MOSFETs).

Typically, the relay types used are either dry reed or mercury wetted. Because of the inherent time constant of the coil circuit, scanning rates are relatively low: typically, 300 samples/second; allowance must also be made for contact bounce, when dry reeds are used. Relays are rugged electrically and they can accept a high common-mode voltage: that is, a high common voltage on both inputs, when the voltage source is double-ended, the voltage usually being specified relative to earth potential. Relay MUX systems are more expensive than equivalent MOSFET MUX systems.

The MOSFET systems can switch with high scanning rates: typically, up to several thousand samples/second. These MUX need to be protected from parasitic voltage spikes and they can tolerate common-mode voltages only up to approximately 10V, with double-ended voltage sources.

MUX systems can also be classified in terms of the type of configuration used for the connections. Figure 5 shows typical configurations, in which the relay symbol should be replaced be a solid state switch symbol, if MOSFET switches are being used. Single-ended configurations involve a minimum number of connections but give relatively poor noise rejection; double-ended, differential, configurations yield improved noise rejection, because common-mode noise will virtually cancel out; differential flying capacitor configurations give the best noise rejection.

16.2.3 Analog Input Systems

The performance of an analog input system is a function of all of the components in that system, so that it is important to consider these components in relation to each other. In general, each ADC must be preceded by either a buffer amplifier or a sample-hold amplifier, in order to minimise the loading effect of the ADC input and to provide the ADC with a stationary signal during each conversion process: the sample-hold may form an integral part of the ADC. For low level signals (in the mV range), a high-gain amplifier usually precedes either the ADC or the MUX, in order to amplify the signal level to within the range of the ADC: this is the procedure of "scaling", which optimises the resolution of the analog-digital conversion process.

Figure 6 shows a variety of typical analog input configurations for both high-level and low-level input signals. Note that it is particularly difficult to multiplex low-level signals at high speeds, because of difficulties experienced with the design of satisfactory low noise low-level high speed MUX.

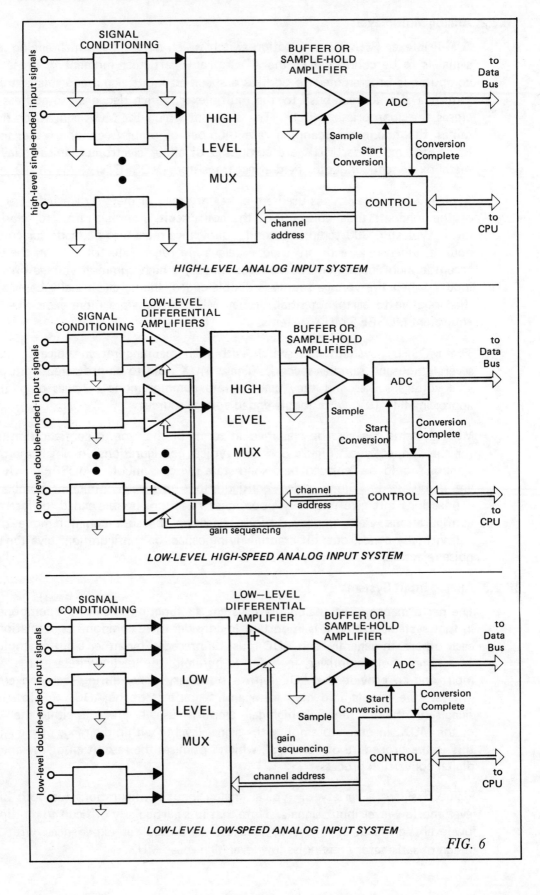

HIGH-LEVEL ANALOG INPUT SYSTEM

LOW-LEVEL HIGH-SPEED ANALOG INPUT SYSTEM

LOW-LEVEL LOW-SPEED ANALOG INPUT SYSTEM

FIG. 6

16.3 ANALOG OUTPUT CHANNELS

Analog output signals are generated by digital-analog converters, the digital data being supplied to each DAC from the processor data bus. Seldom are DACs multiplexed, so that normally one will be supplied for each analog output channel. The DAC usually generates a high-level single-ended voltage signal which, in some applications, will need to be converted to (say) a 4 to 20 mA current signal: refer to Section 10.2.

The output signal from the DAC normally would be used to drive either the remote set point input of an external controller (in supervisory control), a final control element (in DDC), or a recording instrument (for display purposes).

16.4 SINGLE DIGITAL INPUT CHANNELS

Digital inputs are used to communicate the occurrence of discrete events having a binary nature. Such events include the operation of an electromechanical relay, the mechanical activation of a limit switch on a plant, the manual activation of a pushbutton or toggle switch on a control console, etc. The interface will require to be supplied, via the contact in question, from a suitable voltage source and will need to include a detection network and addressing logic to interrogate this network. Whenever noise and/or contact bounce are present, it will be necessary to incorporate appropriate signal conditioning circuitry: this may take the form of a low-pass filter (see Section 12.2), a Schmitt trigger IC, or a contact debouncer IC. In addition, protection circuitry similar to that in Figure 4 may be required, in order to protect the interface from excessive input signals. Figure 7 shows a typical interface hardware arrangement for one switch contact.

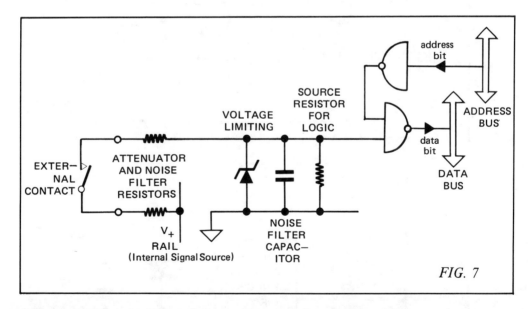

FIG. 7

Frequently, it is necessary to isolate electrically the external contact from the computer interface. This normally is a requirement whenever the signal being switched by the contact has a level which can potentially damage the interface hardware. Figure 8 illustrates a number of alternative arrangements for providing this isolation.

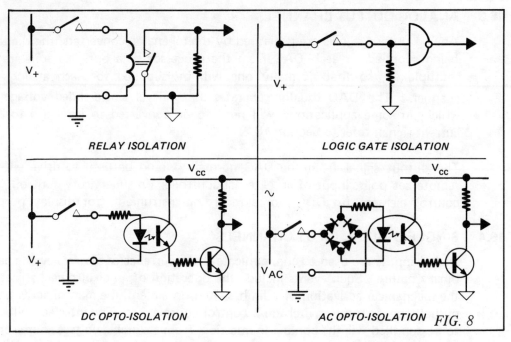

FIG. 8

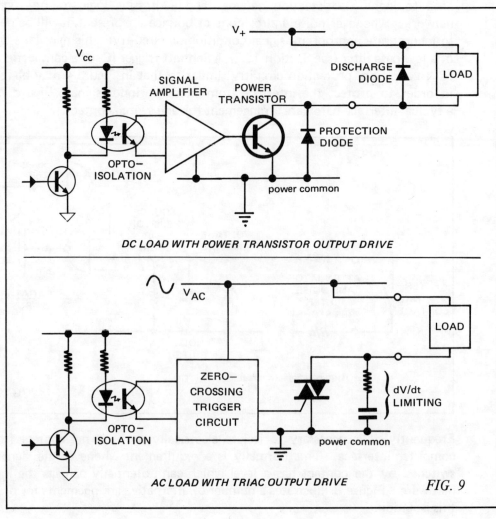

FIG. 9

In some applications, the data required by the processor may need to represent a count of a number of events: for example, representing the number of times a particular limit switch has closed. In this situation, after conditioning, the switch signal would be used as the serial input to a digital counter (see Section 10.14), the parallel output of which would represent the count size, to be supplied to the processor data bus.

16.5 SINGLE DIGITAL OUTPUT CHANNELS

Digital output signals are used to activate two-state actuators, in control applications, and to activate annunciators, in display applications. In some cases, the digital output may need to take the form of a pulse of variable width or, alternatively, a pulse train of variable frequency and/or duration. Like digital inputs, digital outputs can involve electromechanical (dry reed or mercury wetted relay), electronic (TTL logic), or electro-optical (opto-isolator) hardware, and no further discussion on these should be necessary. For switching high-power loads, relays of sufficient rating, power transistors, power – FETs, SCRs, and Triacs may be used as alternatives for driving the load. Figure 9 shows two of many possible configurations.

16.6 STANDARD BUS FORMATS

Figure 10 shows a typical complete data communication and control interface to a digital processor. This configuration assumes that all communication between the interface and the processor is undertaken in parallel format, by means of a common input/output bus which, alternatively, is known as a "Data Highway". Typical word lengths are alternatively 8, 12, 16, 24, and 32 bits, so that the number of data connections within the bus must be at least equal to this number, plus provision for signal common. With some sacrifice of speed, the same lines may be used for data transmission in the two directions (input and output), by using "tri-state line terminators". These terminators present a low-impedance source or sink, when enabled, and a very high impedance, when disabled, so that they can act as digital transmitters and receivers when enabled and behave as ineffective (very high impedance) loads when disabled.

With this type of configuration, the complete interface must be designed for full compatibility with the format for the data, address, and control bus connections as specified by the manufacturer of the processor. This militates against standardisation, because there is no one standard bus format in common use, and this therefore makes for complexity in the design of new interfaces.

An alternative adopted by some manufacturers is to use serial communication between the interface and the processor and possibly between different sections of the interface. This considerably reduces the number of interconnections required, so that it may become as little as, say, one or two co-axial cables: it makes for a much greater universality of connection, because of the limited number of alternative formats used with serial transmission, and for a significant reduction in cost, for long transmission paths. This techniques introduces the possibility of electrical portability, of interfaces, between different processors. The inevitable trade off is in speed, because it takes considerably longer to

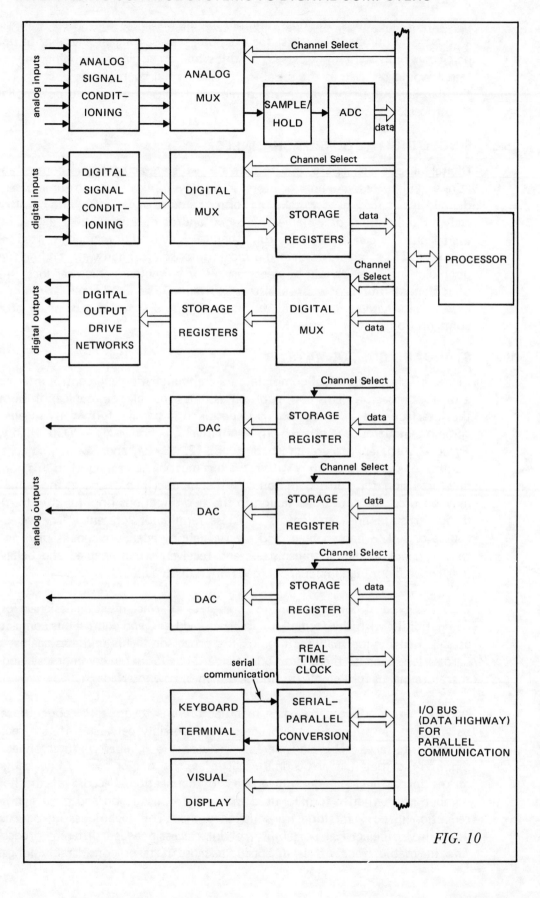

FIG. 10

transmit a sequential pulse train along a serial connection, compared with transmitting concurrently a set of pulses along a set of parallel connections, for the transmission of the same data.

16.6.1 Parallel Bus Standards

The four parallel bus standards in common use are:

- S100 bus
- 6800 bus
- IEEE-488 bus
- IEEE-583 CAMAC bus.

The S100 and 6800 buses are used mainly for communication between modules within a given computer system. The IEEE-488 bus is used principally for communication between several computer systems. The CAMAC standard is suitable for communication at all levels.

These bus systems have a certain degree of commonality, in that they all allocate 8 bidirectional lines or 16 unidirectional lines for data transfer, 16 unidirectional lines for addressing, and between 5 and 12 unidirectional lines for control.

Power supply and signal common connections also are present, although these are not included in the listings below.

S100 Bus

This bus system was developed for use with the Intel 8080 processor but since has been used with many other processor types. It is based upon 100 lines, with the following distribution:

data in	8 lines
data out	8 lines
address	16 lines
clocks	4 lines
control and status	36 lines
vectored interrupts	8 lines
unused (spare)	14 lines

6800 Bus

This bus system was developed for use with the Motorola 6800 processor. The distribution is as follows:

data in/out (bidirectional)	8 lines
address	16 lines
control and status	10 lines
clocks	3 lines

IEEE - 488 Bus

This bus system was developed by Hewlett-Packard to enable instruments to be connected to computers and to one another. Each device may take the form of a "Talker", enabling it to transmit data, a "Listener", enabling it to receive data, and a "Controller", enabling it to supervise the operation of the other devices as talkers and listeners. The distribution is as follows:

data, address, and device command (bidirectional)	8 lines
byte-transfer control	3 lines
general control	5 lines

IEEE - 583 CAMAC Bus

This bus system was developed by the European nuclear power industry. It is comprehensive and incorporates provision for both serial and parallel transmission of data, between racks of devices, at rates up to 24 million bits/second. The principal bus has the following distribution:

read	24 lines
write	24 lines
address	5 lines
control	3 lines
command	5 lines
status	4 lines
timing	2 lines

16.6.2 Serial Bus Standards

There are several serial bus standards in common use, and these include the following:

- EIA - RS232C bus
- EIA - RS422 bus
- EIA - RS423 bus
- current loop bus.

The RS232C standard specifies 25 pin connectors and uses ± 12 V pulses for data transfer. The distribution is as follows:

transmitted data	1 line
received data	1 line
control and status	9 lines
timing	3 lines

Data can be transmitted at one of many alternative rates, which range from 50 to 19200 bits/second. When voice-grade telephone lines form part of the communications link, the signals may be modulated and demodulated by "modems" sited at the two ends of the link, using either phase or frequency modulation, depending upon the bit rate required.

The RS422 and RS423 standards are similar to RS232 but the transmission hardware is configured slightly differently, resulting in an increase in the maximum permissible length of link.

For systems in which the length of the transmission path lies within the approximate limits of 6 m and 350 m, Current Loop transmission is used. For this, a transmitter at one end of the link is configured as a 20 mA current source and a receiver at the other end behaves as a current sink. The transmitter and receiver circuits include means to convert voltage signals to current signals and vice-versa.

Serial data may be sent synchronously or asynchronously, depending upon the nature of the device being interfaced. With synchronous transmission, a clock signal must be transmitted simultaneously, to effect synchronisation of the hardware at the two ends of the link. With asynchronous transmission, start and stop bits must be sent, respectively, before and after each data word, for identification purposes.

17

ON-STREAM ANALYSERS

17.1   INTRODUCTION

Analysers are required for the assessment of the quality of the gaseous, liquid, and solid products of manufacturing processors.   It is preferable always to measure directly the value of the property of interest but often this is impracticable, so that frequently it is necessary to infer the value of this variable by measuring related properties. Thus, for example, electrical conductivity may be measured in order to infer chemical composition. Off-line analysis in the laboratory may be undertaken to measure the property of interest but such a procedure is inappropriate for feedback control. Thus, here we require analytical instruments which function as feedback transducers, so that they must operate on-line and must generate electrical (or pneumatic) feedback signals, to be used by the relevant process controllers.

Analysers which function, automatically, on-line are referred to as "On-Stream Analysers" and these can take many forms, some of which will have off-line laboratory analyser counterparts.   An on-stream analyser may be extremely expensive (say, in the order of several $10,000), when compared with other feedback transducers, and this expense means that such an analyser must be selected with great care and must be maintained meticulously. Some on-stream analysers perform their analysis on a sequence of samples of the test product, because by their nature the analytical procedure is a batch process: whenever such an analyser is used as a feedback transducer, the resulting control system will respond with the type of behaviour associated with sampled-data control systems.   Another characteristic of some of these analysers, especially the sampling types, is the significant dead time which may be inherent in the analytical process: this dead time will affect adversely the stability of the associated closed loop control system.

The number of varieties of analyser falling into the on-stream category is considerable and, for this reason, only the most commonly used types can be covered here in detail. The alternative operating principles considered in this volume are as follows:

- thermal conductivity, measured in terms of the cooling effect of the test medium upon a heated filament;

- combustibility, measured in terms of the heating effect of the test medium when it is ignited by a hot filament;

- chromatography, which involves decomposing a mixture into its component parts, by passing it through a porous material;

- spectrometry, which involves decomposing a mixture into its component parts, by ionising the mixture and then separating the different types of ion;

- ultra-violet photometry, which involves measuring the degree of absorption of UV radiation by the test medium;

- visible light photometry, which involves measuring the degree of absorption of visible light by the test medium;

- infra-red photometry, which involves measuring the degree of absorption of IR radiation by the test medium;

- colorimetry, which involves measuring the spectrum of visible light transmitted through, or reflected by, the test medium;

- turbidimetry, which involves measuring the intensity of visible light transmitted through the test medium;

- paramagnetism, which involves measuring the flowrate of those gases which are capable of being attracted by magnetic fields;

- refractometry, which involves measuring the degree of refraction of light beams transmitted through the test medium;

- density measurement, which involves measuring the density or specific gravity of the test medium;

- pH measurement, which involves measuring the degree of acidity or alkalinity of the test medium;

- humidity measurement, which involves measuring the moisture content in gases and vapours;

- moisture measurement, which involves measuring the moisture content in solid materials;

- radiation measurement, using radioisotope radiation sources, which involves measuring the intensity of radiation transmitted through, or reflected by, the test medium.

Table 1 lists these principles and relates them to the type of test medium to which they can be applied, and also indicates whether the analysis can be continuous or must be made upon samples.

TABLE 1.
APPLICABILITY OF ANALYTICAL PRINCIPLES TO DIFFERENT TEST MEDIA

Analytical Principle	Type of Test Medium			Continuity		Reference Section
	Gas/Vapour	Liquid	Solid	Continuous	Sampled	
thermal conductivity	•			•		17.2
combustibility	•			•	•	17.2, 17.7
chromatography	•	•			•	17.2
mass spectrometry	•	•	•		•	17.3
UV photometry	•	•		•		17.4
visible photometry	•	•		•		17.4
IR photometry	•	•		•		17.5
colorimetry	•	•	•	•		17.6
turbidimetry	•	•	•	•		17.6
paramagnetism	•			•		17.7
refractometry		•		•		17.8
density		•		•		4.7
pH		•		•		4.8
humidity	•			•		4.9
moisture content			•	•		4.10
radioactivity		•	•	•		4.6, 4.7.5, 4.11, 17.9

17.2   CHROMATOGRAPHS

Chromatographs are used generally for the analysis of gases and vapours, but versions are available also for the analysis of liquids. They are amongst the most expensive on-stream analysers.

17.2.1 Gas Chromatographs

These are the most widely used types of on-stream analyser. They are capable of analysing up to one hundred or more individual components in a gas or vapour stream; they can separate complex mixtures into their components and measure the concentration of these components. Gas chromatographs are used on such processes as catalytic cracking, distillation, ammonia production, sulphur recovery, etc. The following factors are relevant:

- one must know how beforehand the components to be expected in the sample and (approximately) their relative concentration;

- concentrations ranging from a few parts per million to approximately 60% can be measured;

- variables such as flowrate and temperature must be regulated carefully, because they will affect the measurements;

- vapours formed from liquids having boiling points up to 450°C may be analysed.

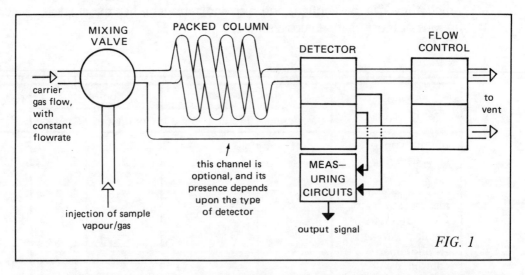

FIG. 1

Figure 1 shows the principle of operation of the chromatograph. A sample of the test vapour/gas is injected into a stream of a carrier gas : this carrier gas is controlled to have a constant flowrate and, typically, the gas is helium. If the test medium is in the liquid phase, it may be vaporised, beforehand, by means of a small flash heater.

The vapour/gas mixture is passed through a packed column, which typically takes the form of a long coil of stainless steel tube packed with appropriate adsorbing or absorbing material. A wide range of suitable materials is available, taking the alternative forms of granules and coated meshes. The rates at which individual components flow through the column depend upon their relative affinities for the column material, and each component is identifiable by its position in the time based sequence, as the decomposed sample emerges from the column and enters the detector.

The time required to perform an analysis with a single column typically ranges from 1 to 20 minutes, including any time required for subsequent flushing, so that the corresponding sample rates will range from 1 per minute to 3 per hour. However, high speed chromatographs employing up to ten columns, each handling (typically) fifteen different components, have been produced, and these can perform an analysis in as little as 10 seconds, yielding a rate of 6 samples per minute : such an instrument requires a computer to control the complex sequencing required by the mixing valves and detectors.

The techniques which have been used for detectors for gas chromatographs include the following:

- thermal conductivity
- electron capture
- helium ionisation
- ultrasonic
- microcoulometry
- dielectric

- flame ionisation
- flame photometry (see Section 17.4)
- gas density balance
- argon ionisation
- thermionic
- infra-red (see Section 17.5).

Thermal conductivity and flame ionisation detectors are by far the most commonly used, and these will be described in Sections 17.2.3 and 17.2.4 respectively. Figure 2 shows typical variations in the output signal from the detector, when the sample contains four measurable components.

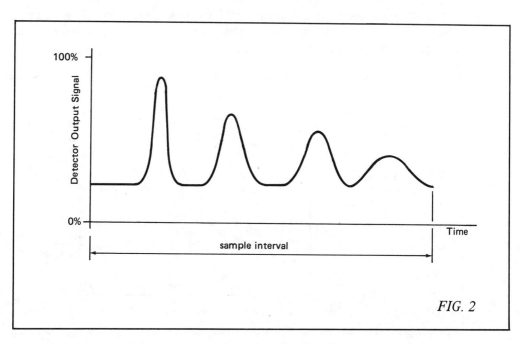

FIG. 2

17.2.2 Liquid Chromatographs

Where a liquid sample cannot be vaporised because of excessively high boiling point, it is possible sometimes to pass the liquid directly through the column. Such liquid chromatographs are similar in design and operation to gas chromatographs and usually are used with liquid samples having temperatures up to 200°C. They are suitable also for samples which are unstable or corrosive at high temperatures.

The choice of alternative packing materials for liquid chromatographs is presently rather limited, with the result that cycle times between 15 and 30 minutes are typical.

The detectors most commonly used with liquid chromatographs employ the following alternative techniques:

- flame ionisation (see Section 17.2.4)
- UV and visible light photometry (see Section 17.4)
- refractive index detection (see Section 17.8)
- fluorescence detection
- spray impact detection
- flame emission detection
- atomic absorption detection
- detection of electrochemical properties
- detection of chemically reactive properties.

17.2.3 Thermal Conductivity Detector

The temperature of a heated electrical filament, exposed to an atmosphere of a gas or vapour being measured, will depend upon the heat transferred from the filament to the gas and subsequently conducted away by the gas flow.

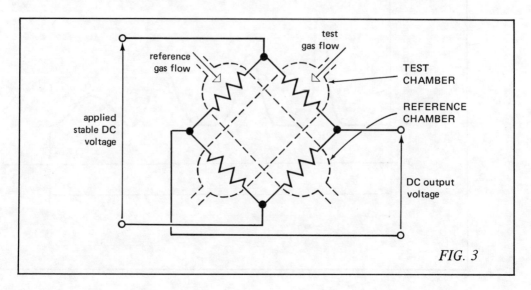

FIG. 3

Figure 3 shows a typical Wheatstone bridge network of four heated filaments (or thermistors), mounted in pairs within two chambers enclosed by a common temperature-controlled metal heat sink. The change in temperature and consequent change in resistance of the test chamber filaments will depend upon the prevailing composition of the test gas, and this will be reproduced as a change in the DC output voltage from the bridge.

17.2.4 Flame Ionisation Detector

The sample flow is passed into a burner assembly where it is mixed with hydrogen gas. The mixture is ignited by a heated platinum wire and is permitted to burn in an atmosphere of air or oxygen which is diffused around the burner. The temperature of the flame is such that ionisation of the sample occurs, and this results in a measurable electrical potential difference between the burner and an electrode located above the burner. This potential difference can be shown to be proportional to the number of carbon atoms currently present in the flame.

17.3 MASS SPECTROMETERS

Mass spectrometers are comparable to gas chromatographs, in terms of general performance, but the former are both more expensive and faster. To function, the most sophisticated spectrometers use a computer which preferably should be dedicated to the one task; the simpler spectrometers will require some basic digital hardware for analysis and read-out. Mass spectrometers are used principally to determine the concentration of elemental components, and discrimination between the same type of ion from different compounds is possible, with special conditioning or signal processing. Instruments are reported to be capable of measuring the concentrations of ten to twelve components in less than two seconds, although sample preconditioning may add to this timespan; however, the majority of instruments will measure fewer components and will require a longer processing time. Figure 4 illustrates the principle of operation.

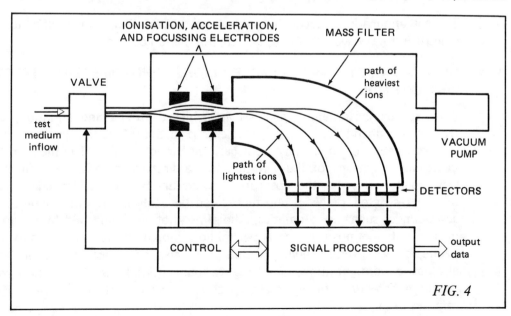

FIG. 4

Samples of test gas/vapour are drawn in by suction established by the vacuum pump: in the case of test media which are solids or liquids, the sample should first be vaporised. Each sample is ionised by one of a number of alternative means, and the ion beam produced is accelerated and focussed by suitable electric fields. The high speed beam enters a mass filter, in which electromagnetic and/or electrostatic fields cause the ions to deviate from a straight path : the trajectory taken by each ion will depend upon its mass/charge ratio, so that each type of ion will follow a different trajectory. The detectors are ion capture devices, such as electron multipliers, located behind narrow slits : they are capable of sensing concentrations ranging from several parts per billion to several tens of percentage.

Alternative methods of ionisation use the following means :

- electron bombardment using heated filaments
- spark generation
- optical techniques
- chemical techniques.

Mass filters can involve the following :

- magnetic fields
- magnetic and electric fields in tandem
- sets of four charged parallel rods which produce fields having superimposed constant and time-varying components
- a series of grids polarised alternately at high frequencies.

Materials admitted to the ionisation chamber must be gases or vapours free from contaminating particles and, in the case of sophisticated spectrometers, held within narrow temperature and pressure limits. Samples may require pretreatment.

Typical applications occur in natural gas production, coal gasification, PVC manufacture, sewage treatment, and environmental control.

17.4   ULTRA–VIOLET AND VISIBLE LIGHT PHOTOMETERS (SPECTRO–PHOTOMETERS)

With spectrophotometers, analysis is achieved by passing radiation, usually from a broadband source with wavelengths in the 0.1 to 0.4 μm range, through the test medium, which may be a gas, vapour, or liquid. The medium then is identified by means of the variation in transmitted radiation as a function of wavelength. Because the absorption bands are broad and limited in number, only a restricted range of substances can be analysed in this manner: organic compounds such as aromatics, diolefins, ketones, and aldehydes may be measured to within a few parts per million; inorganic gases and vapours such as ozone, chlorine, and mercury vapour may also be measured. There are five alternative configurations, involving various orientations of radiation sources, radiation detectors, filters, beam splitters, and the test cell. These types are referred to as:

- opposed beam
- split beam
- dual beam with single detector
- dual beam with dual detector
- flicker.

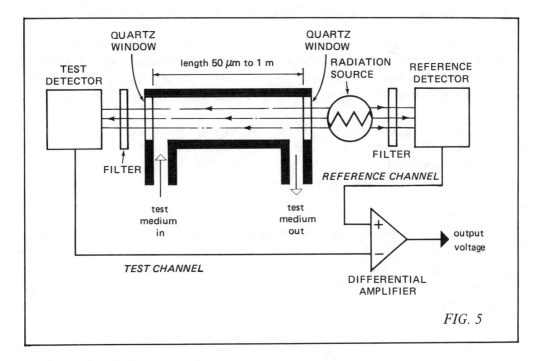

FIG. 5

Figure 5 shows the construction of a typical opposed beam photometer. In this, the function of the reference channel is to cause compensation for variations in the spectrum of the radiation source. This source, together with the filters (which isolate specific wavelengths), will be chosen on the basis of the chemical for which analysis is sought. Occasionally, the radiation source may be pulsed at a specific frequency; also, a sequence of filters may be rotated through the beams, in order to extend the range of the instrument. The response of the instrument is reasonably linear and the 90% response time is in the order of 1 second, typically.

Alternative radiation sources include:

- hydrogen discharge lamp (broadband)
- tungsten lamp (broadband)
- tungsten-iodine lamp (broadband)
- mercury vapour lamp (0.2537 μm wavelength)
- tunable diode laser (narrow band).

Alternative radiation detectors include:

- vacuum phototube

- photomultiplier

- photo-voltaic (solar) cell

- photodiode

- phototransistor.

17.5 NON—DISPERSIVE INFRA—RED (NDIR) ANALYSERS

These analysers function along similar principles to UV and visible light photo-meters, but operate in the 1 to 2.5 μm wavelength range. Usually, they are used to determine the concentration of only one component, although exceptions have been cited which can analyse up to nineteen different components.

NDIR analysers are suitable for a range of gases and liquids exhibiting good infra-red absorption: typical examples are carbon dioxide, carbon monoxide, ethylene, isobutane, etc. Specifically excluded are elemental diatomic gases such as oxygen, hydrogen, nitrogen, chlorine, etc., and inert gases, such as helium and argon.

These analysers operate on the principle that radiation energy is absorbed and converted to kinetic energy by those molecules which respond to the wave-lengths of interest: it therefore is necessary to find a wavelength at which only the component of interest responds. However, overlapping effects due to other components sometimes can be accommodated, by means of appropriate compen-sation and filtering.

The absorption bands in the IR region tend to be narrow, so that NDIR analysers exhibit good selectivity; however, they are less sensitive than spectrophotometers. 90% response times range from 0.5 to 10 seconds.

The radiation source must be capable of radiating energy over a wide band of infra-red wavelengths and, for this reason, glass envelopes are not practicable. Alternative sources include:

- a coil or helix of metal alloy wire heated, by electric current, to the 400 to 900°C temperature range;

- a rod of silicon carbide heated, by direct current, to the 1100 to 1370°C temperature range;

- a rod of zirconium oxide heated, by direct current, to 1930°C;

- tunable diode laser.

Radiation detectors can be divided into three categories:

- thermal — thermopiles (thermocouple stacks) and bolometers (large thermistors);

- pneumatic—microphones and diaphragms;

- photosensitive—phototubes, photomultipliers, photo-voltaic cells, photo-diodes, and phototransistors.

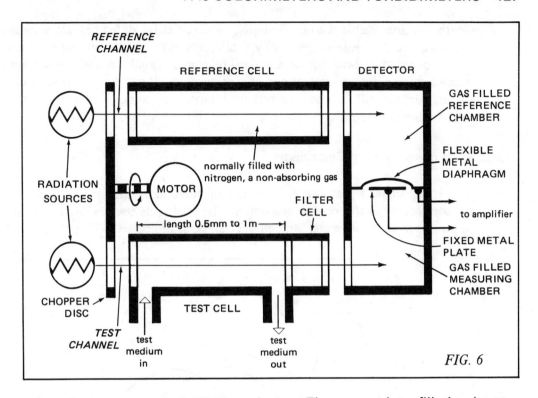

REFERENCE
CHANNEL

REFERENCE CELL

DETECTOR

GAS FILLED
REFERENCE
CHAMBER

RADIATION
SOURCES

MOTOR

normally filled with
nitrogen, a non-absorbing gas

FLEXIBLE
METAL
DIAPHRAGM

|←——length 0.5mm to 1m——→|

FILTER
CELL

to amplifier

FIXED METAL
PLATE

GAS FILLED
MEASURING
CHAMBER

CHOPPER
DISC

TEST CELL

*TEST
CHANNEL*   test
medium
in

test
medium
out

FIG. 6

Figure 6 shows a typical NDIR analyser. The gas used to fill the detector chambers is chosen to absorb energy at the wavelength of interest, and therefore usually is the same gas as the component of interest in the test medium: this detector gas absorbs energy and expands as a result. Unequal energy in the two chambers results in displacement of the metallic diaphragm. This diaphragm and the fixed metal plate together act as a capacitance microphone, which is connected into an amplifier. The filter cell is filled with selected gases, to remove energy at specific wavelengths from the test channel beam, in order to inhibit overlap: it is filled, therefore, with the component responsible for the overlap.

17.6 COLORIMETERS AND TURBIDIMETERS

Colorimeters and turbidimeters measure the intensity of transmitted or reflected visible light. The test medium may be a gas, vapour, liquid, or solid, depending upon the construction of the instrument. Colorimeters are concerned with the precise measurement of specific colours and are used for the control of dyeing processes, the detection of parasitic substances (having specific colours) in stream flows, the measurement of chemical reactions in terms of the colours generated by the reaction processes, etc. Turbidimeters are concerned with the precise measurement of the clarity or opacity of the test medium. There are two categories of instrument: the Spectrophotometric type and the Tristimulus type, of which the latter is the more accurate.

17.6.1 Spectrophotometric Types of Colorimeter

These instruments are constructed along the lines of visible light photometers, as described in Section 17.4. Interference filters are selected for specific wavelengths in the visible band. Similarly, the radiation detectors are selected for operation in the visible region. Typically, the test medium would be compared with a one-dimensional colour standard reference, which normally is chosen from a series of specific concentrations of platinum-cobalt solutions. The output from the instrument will indicate the relative intensity of colour in the test medium, at the selected wavelengths.

17.6.2 Tristimulus Types of Colorimeter

These instruments measure transmitted or reflected light on the basis of comparison with specific colour standards. The standards usually used have spectral responses in the blue, green, and amber bands, as indicated in Figure 7.

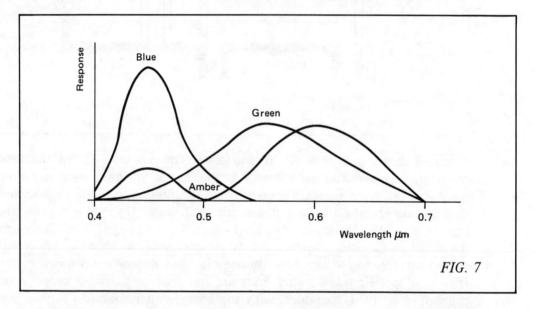

FIG. 7

The instrument depicted in Figure 8 produces a rapid, sequential, comparison between the test medium and the reference standard, on the basis of the measurements made by the three different colour channels. The instrument measures directly the percentage difference in light energy between the test medium and the reference. Because the measurement is in terms of ratio determination, the flicker technique reduces the effect of drift caused by long term variations in the light source and photodetectors.

17.6.3 Turbidimeters

Turbidimeters are constructed along the same lines as colorimeters. The light sources and filters in colorimeters are chosen to enhance specific wavelengths of interest; in turbidimeters, however, the light sources and filters are chosen to be non-specific: that is, no particular wavelength should be favoured. Thus, the photodetector used will be sensing the intensity of broadband light received, and this will be a measure of the clarity or opacity of the test medium. A common application for turbidimeters is in smoke level detection in the smoke stacks of power stations and other plant.

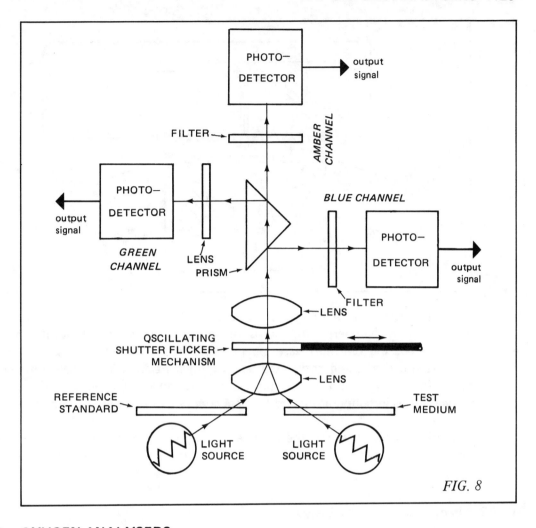

PHOTO—DETECTOR → output signal

FILTER →

AMBER CHANNEL

PHOTO—DETECTOR ← output signal

GREEN CHANNEL

LENS

PRISM →

BLUE CHANNEL

PHOTO—DETECTOR → output signal

FILTER → LENS

QSCILLATING SHUTTER FLICKER MECHANISM →

← LENS

REFERENCE STANDARD →

TEST MEDIUM ←

LIGHT SOURCE   LIGHT SOURCE

FIG. 8

17.7   OXYGEN ANALYSERS

There are many applications in which it is required to sense oxygen levels. One example is the measurement of oxygen level in smoke stacks, because this represents a good indication of boiler combustion efficiency. Another example is the measurement of oxygen level in water, because this represents a good indication of the level of possible pollution.

Most types of oxygen analyser use either the combustible property or the "paramagnetic" property of oxygen, but there are a few based upon other principles. All types have a 90% response time no greater than one minute. The paramagnetic property of oxygen refers to the fact that oxygen molecules are attracted by a magnetic field; other gases, with the exception of a few oxides of nitrogen, either are repelled by magnetic fields, and are referred to as "diamagnetic", or are unaffected.

17.7.1 Combustion Type Oxygen Analysers

With these analysers, the oxygen content in a gaseous test sample is used to oxidise a fuel, and the heat so generated from subsequent combustion is measured.

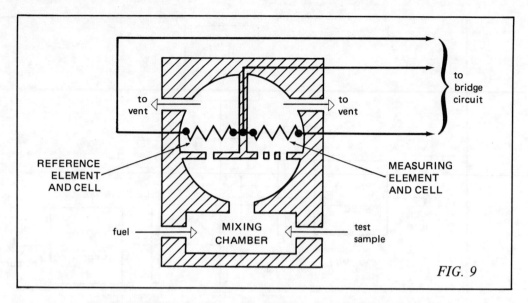

FIG. 9

In the configuration of Figure 9, the test sample and a measure of fuel are mixed in the mixing chamber, and combustion in the measuring cell is stimulated by a catalytic coating on the measuring filament. The two filaments serve to sense temperature rise, being connected as two adjacent arms in a Wheatstone bridge network. The function of the (uncoated) reference filament is to compensate for variations in temperature and thermal conductivity of the test sample.

The bridge network senses the relative changes in filament resistance, which will be related to combustion temperature and hence to oxygen level in the test sample.

17.7.2 Paramagnetic Oxygen Analysers

Paramagnetic analysers are distinctive from the combustion type of analyser in that the test medium is not destroyed in the measurement process. Paramagnetic analysers can be subdivided into two categories: the deflection type, which requires the paramagnetic property to be constant during the measurement, and the thermal type, which depends upon the decrease in pagamagnetic effect which results from an increase in the temperature of the oxygen content in the test medium.

The deflection type of analyser operates on the torque balance principle, and seeks to balance magnetically and electrostatically derived torques arranged to act upon a body suspended in the gas stream, as indicated in Figure 10. Typically, the body is a small dumbbell suspended, by a filament, between the poles of a magnet; the electrostatic field is established by electrodes sited close to one end of the dumbbell.

When the instrument settles to a steady state, a torque balance will exist and the amplifier output will be a measure of the torque due to the magnetic field system, which will be a known function of the oxygen concentration around the magnet and dumbbell.

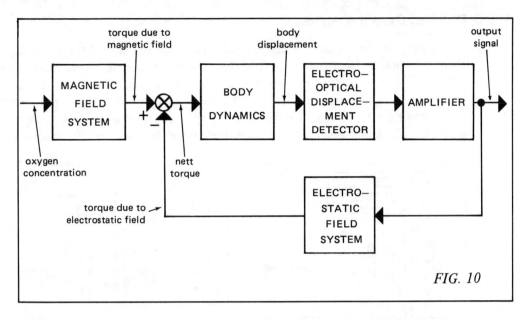

FIG. 10

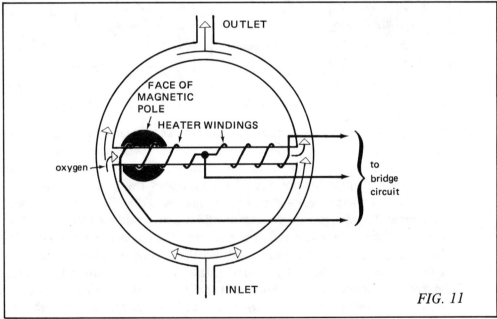

FIG. 11

Figure 11 shows the construction of a thermal type of analyser. The oxygen component in the gas stream passing through the glass vessel is attracted by the magnetic field, and tends to pass down the central glass tube, where it is heated by the heater windings. These windings form two adjacent limbs of a Wheatstone bridge network, and the change in resistance sensed will be a function of the conduction of heat by the oxygen flow. The oxygen loses much of its paramagnetic property as it becomes heated, and convection causes more oxygen to be drawn in past the pole face. The rate at which oxygen is able to flow past the pole face will be a measure of its concentration, and this will be indicated by the output from the bridge network: the left-hand winding tends to be cooled by the entry of fresh oxygen, whilst the right-hand winding tends to be heated by the heat drawn from the left-hand winding by the oxygen flow.

17.7.3 Dissolved Oxygen Analysers

The most commonly used analysers for measuring the concentration of dissolved oxygen in liquid streams are the Polarographic and Galvanic types. Note, however, that analysers normally used for measuring the oxygen content in gas flows may be adapted to the measurement of dissolved oxygen, if the oxygen is removed beforehand from the liquid stream, using appropriate means; also, polarographic and galvanic analysers may be used for the measurement of gaseous oxygen.

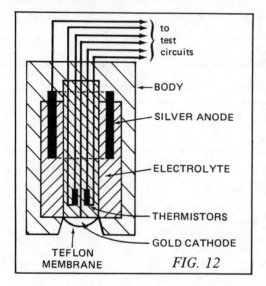

FIG. 12

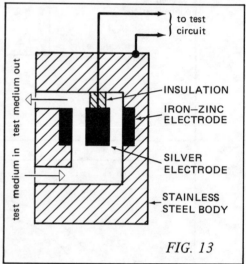

FIG. 13

Figure 12 shows a cross section through a typical polarographic probe. The probe incorporates two noble metal electrodes, which are separated from each other by an electrolyte of potassium chloride solution or gel. The probe face is covered by a permeable Teflon membrane, which separates the gold cathode from the test medium. A constant voltage of approximately 0.8 V DC is applied between the electrodes. The oxygen in the test medium permeates the membrane and diffuses to the cathode, where it is reduced, causing a flow of ions to the anode. The current flow around the circuit formed by the voltage source, electrodes, and electrolyte is proportional to the oxygen concentration and is amplified by a suitably configured instrumentation amplifier. The calibration is sensitive to temperature, and thermistors embedded in the probe are used to generate a signal which is applied to compensate for temperature variations.

Figure 13 shows a cross section through a typical galvanic cell, through which the test medium flows, making contact with two electrodes, one of noble metal and the other of base metal alloy. The two electrodes are polarised by an externally connected DC voltage source. The liquid stream serves as the electrolyte and the dissolved oxygen becomes ionised, resulting in a drift of ions between the electrodes. The current flow is measured by a suitably configured instrumentation amplifier, and is proportional to the oxygen concentration. The cell is sensitive to temperature and pressure variations, which must be either controlled or measured and compensated. The liquid medium must have a minimum conductivity for the cell to function, so that a suitable chemical might need to be added to the stream, upstream of the cell, in order to achieve this requirement.

17.8   REFRACTOMETERS

Refractometers are used for measuring the relative concentrations in liquids composed of two principal components, and the measurement will be degraded by the presence of trace impurities.

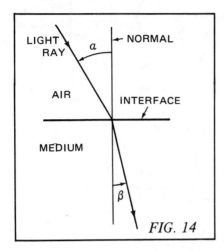

FIG. 14

Figure 14 shows how the refractive index n is defined, on the basis of the refraction of a light ray at the interface between air and a test medium:

$$n \overset{\Delta}{=} \frac{\sin\alpha}{\sin\beta}$$

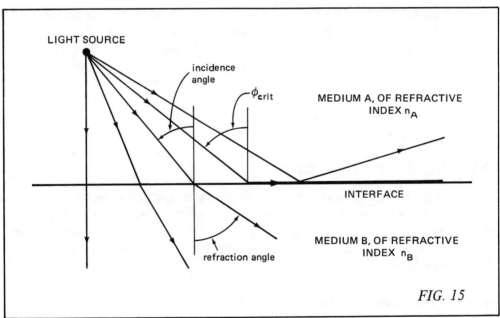

FIG. 15

Figure 15 shows alternative paths for light rays impinging on the interface between two media, with the light source being sited on the side occupied by the medium having the larger refractive index. Total internal reflection just occurs when the angle of incidence is equal to the critical angle ϕ_{crit} as shown, and this value is given by $\phi_{crit} = \sin^{-1}(n_B/n_A)$.

One type of refractometer, which is used with clean translucent liquids, is based upon changes in refraction angle. The other type, which is used with clean or turbid liquids or slurries, is based upon changes in critical angle. In each case, medium A would be a fixed reference and medium B would be the test medium.

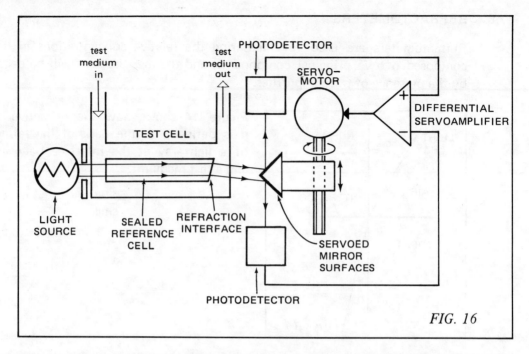

FIG. 16

Figure 16 shows a typical arrangement for a refraction angle type of refracto-meter, which operates on an illumination balance principle. The reference cell is filled with a liquid having a refractive index which is approximately mid-scale for the test medium. The servomotor drives the beam splitter until the two photodetectors sense equal incident illumination. In the steady state the position of the beam splitter will be a measure of the refraction angle of the beam, which will be representative of the composition of the test medium. The typical 90% response time for refractometers is in the 10 to 30 second range.

17.9 RADIATION TECHNIQUES

Where radioactivity is to be used for measurement purposes, the choice of radiation source will depend upon the type of radiation to be used, which in turn will depend upon the test medium and its surroundings. The choice of detector for sensing the intensity of radiation transmitted through the test medium also will depend upon the type of radiation, in addition to other factors.

17.9.1 Radiation and Radioactive Sources

In some cases, radioactivity can be defined in terms of the emission of specific subatomic particles. In other cases, it is convenient to regard electromagnetic radiation as a stream of small packets (quanta) of energy, travelling at the velocity of light.

The α particle is the nucleus of the Helium-4 atom, and therefore is a body consisting of two protons and two neutrons, bound together. The α particle is characteristic of very heavy elements; the energy level associated with it can occur within the 2 to 9 MeV range, but the level lies within a very narrow band of MeV for any particular radioisotope. The α particle will be stopped completely even by very thin material, so that it has a very limited industrial use.

The β particle is the electron ejected from an atomic nucleus, when an excess neutron decays into a proton plus an ejected electron. The energy level associated with the β particle can cover a wide MeV band for each radioisotope, with the maximum level lying between 18 keV and 3.6 MeV, typically. The β particle can pass through steel up to 3mm in thickness.

γ radiation is an electromagnetic radiation emitted when an atomic nucleus in an excited state reverts to a more stable state. The radiation can occur with a number of simultaneous specific quantum energy levels lying between 100 keV and 3 MeV. γ radiation can pass through steel more than 30 cm thick and concrete more than 100 cm thick. The intensity of a beam of γ radiation is diminished by solid matter in inverse proportion to the distance travelled through that matter: the more dense the material, the more effective it is in attenuating the radiation.

X radiation is an electromagnetic radiation emitted when an electron transfers from a higher to a lower atomic energy state. X radiation is similar to γ radiation but has much lower energy levels associated with it.

Other types of electromagnetic radiation are emitted by certain radioisotopes, but normally these other types are not significant as far as industrial measurements are concerned.

Artificial radioisotopes are produced by exposing target material to bombardment by high velocity particle streams, in cyclotrons and nuclear reactors. Over 700 types of artificial radioisotope have been made, emitting a variety of radiation (α, β, γ, X, etc.) and having half lives ranging from 2 minutes to 5×10^{10} years. Certain radioisotopes emit only one type of radiation, whilst others emit several types simultaneously. For any given radioisotope, the energies of the emitted radiations are constant and specific to that radioisotope.

The extent of the energy loss occurring when a test medium is exposed to radiation depends upon the type of radiation. Consequently, the choice of a radioisotope to be used as the radiation source in any particular application will be based upon the properties and physical dimensions of the test medium.

17.9.2 Radiation Detectors

In the industrial applications of radiation techniques considered in this volume, the type of radiation involved and the energy levels associated with it will be specific for the radioisotope chosen to be the radiation source: this information therefore will represent known data. The function of the detector therefore can usually be confined to the measurement of the quantity of radiation arriving at the detector; in addition, some applications may necessitate the measurement of the spatial distribution of this radiation.

The range of radiation detectors used industrially includes Ionisation Chambers, Proportional Counters, Geiger Muller Counters, Scintillation Counters, and Solid State Detectors, together with other less common types.

Ionisation Chambers

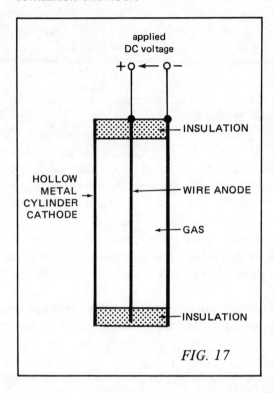

applied
DC voltage

+○ ←○ −

INSULATION

HOLLOW
METAL
CYLINDER
CATHODE

WIRE ANODE

GAS

INSULATION

FIG. 17

Figure 17 shows a cross section through a typical ionisation chamber. In industrial applications, it would be used most widely for the detection of β and γ radiation: in the former case, the β particles would enter through a quartz or glass window inserted in the wall of the chamber; in the latter case, γ radiation would be able to pass through the metal wall without difficulty, so that a window would not be required. Typically, the gas filling would be argon, and could be highly pressurised for the detection of γ radiation. The applied DC voltage will have a value of several hundred volts. Radiation entering the chamber causes ionisation of the gas molecules, and positive ions will migrate to the cathode whilst electrons will migrate to the anode.

The resulting current circulating in the circuit is detected by a suitably configured instrumentation amplifier. Each ionising event will generate a minute current pulse: these pulses may either be counted individually, to yield a total count size, or integrated to produce a measure of the frequency with which the events occur.

Proportional Counters

The proportional counter is a special form of ionisation chamber operated at rather higher levels of applied DC voltage. At such levels, secondary ionisation occurs, with the result that the chamber can establish (internally) charge amplification factors as high as 10^4. The filling may be argon, hydrogen, methane, or some other gas, at various alternative pressures. This type of detector always is used for pulse counting, and is particularly suitable for high pulse frequencies and for distinguishing between different types of radiation; generally, it is used for α and β particle detection.

Geiger Muller Counters

The Geiger Muller counter is another special form of ionisation chamber, but it is excited by voltage levels well in excess of 1000 V. At these levels, an avalanche breakdown occurs, generating charge amplification factors as high as 10^8. Because of the high signal levels generated, external amplification rarely is necessary. Typically, the filling is a mixture of argon and an organic vapour. This type of detector always is used for pulse counting, but it is unsuitable for very high pulse frequencies; generally, it is used for α and β particle detection.

Scintillation Counters

A range of materials, which may be crystals, liquids, gases, plastics, or certain types of glass, behave as phosphors: that is, they emit photons when impacted by quanta of radiation. A scintillation counter uses a mass of one of these phosphor materials, and the light emitted as a result of exposure to radiation is converted to a current and amplified, using a photomultiplier, which can achieve current gains as high as 10^6. This type of detector may be used for sensing either pulse count or pulse height, so that it is able to distinguish between different radiation energy levels. It can operate at very high frequencies and is suitable for the detection of α, β and γ radiation.

Solid State Detectors

A Semiconductor radiation detector is based upon a silicon or germanium p-n junction, across which a small DC voltage is applied. The incidence of radiation upon the junction causes an increase in hole-electron pairs, so that a pulse of current is generated in the external circuit, which can be configured to count such pulses. These detectors are suitable for detecting α and β particles.

An alternative type is the Photoconductive detector, which is based upon a crystal of high purity. The incidence of radiation causes an increase in the conductivity of the crystal, so that a current pulse is generated in the external circuit, which is configured to count such pulses. These detectors are suitable for the detection of β and γ radiation.

BIBLIOGRAPHY

Bibliographic entries have been listed by author in alphabetical order. In many instances, a reference is relevant to the material in several chapters of this volume: the numbers of the most appropriate chapters are shown at the end of each entry. In other instances a reference is considered to be of general interest: such an entry is terminated with the letter G.

ADAMS, Leslie Frank. Engineering measurements and instrumentation. London, English Universities Press, 1975. — G

AHEARN, Arthur John. Trace analysis by mass spectrometry. New York, Academic Press, 1972. — 17

AHRENDT, William Robert and TAPLIN, J.F. Automatic feedback control. New York, McGraw-Hill, 1951. — G

AHRENDT, William Robert and SAVANT, C.J. Servomechanism practice. 2nd ed. New York, McGraw-Hill, 1960. — G

ALPERT, Nelson L., KEISER, William E. and SYMANSKI, Herman A. IR theory and practice of infrared spectroscopy. New York, Plenum Pub., 1973. — 17

ANALOG DEVICES, INC. Analog-digital conversion handbook, edited by Daniel Sheingold. Norwood, Mass., Analog Devices, 1972. — 10

ANALOG DEVICES, INC. Analog-digital conversion notes, edited by Daniel Sheingold. Norwood, Mass., Analog Devices, 1977. — 10

ANAND, Davinder K. Introduction to control systems. Elmsford, N.Y., Pergamon Press, 1974. — G

ANDERSON, Brian D.O., and VANGPANITLERD, Sumeth. Network analysis and synthesis: a modern systems theory approach. Englewood Cliffs, N.J., Prentice-Hall, 1973. — 9, 10, 11, 12

ANDERSON, Brian D.O. and MOORE, John B. Optimal filtering. Englewood Cliffs, N.J., Prentice-Hall, 1979. — 12

ANDREW, William G. Applied instrumentation in the process industries. 2nd ed. Houston, Gulf Publishing Co., 1979. — G

ARORA, Y.L. Flow measurement techniques. Bombay, Universal Book Corporation, 1978. — 4

ARTWICK, Bruce A. Microcomputing interfacing. Englewood Cliffs, N.J., Prentice-Hall, 1980. — 16

ATKINSON, Peter. Feedback control theory for engineers. 2nd ed. London, Heinemann, 1972. — G

AUSLANDER, David M., TAKAHASHI, Y. and RABINS, M.J. Introducing systems and control. New York, McGraw-Hill, 1974. — G

BAECK, H.S. Practical servomechanism design. New York, McGraw-Hill, 1968. — G

BAIULESCU, George and ILIC, V.A. Stationary phases in gas chromatography. Oxford, Pergamon, 1975. — 17

BALDWIN, Clifford Thomas. Fundamentals of electric measurements. 2nd ed. London, Harrap, 1973. — G

BANNON, Edward. Operational amplifiers: theory and servicing. Reston, Va., Reston Pub. Co., 1975. — 5, 9, 10, 11, 12

BAREE, Edwin C. Linear control systems. Scranton, Pa., International Textbook Co., 1963. — G

BARNA, Arpad. Operational amplifiers. New York, Wiley-Interscience, 1971. — 5, 9, 10, 11, 12

BARRY, B. Austin. Engineering measurements. New York, Wiley, 1964. — G

BASIC INDUSTRIAL MEASUREMENT AND CONTROL: programmed course. Cleveland, Ohio, Penton Pub. Co., 1973.　　　　G

BASS, H.G. Introduction to engineering measurements. New York, McGraw-Hill, 1971.　　　　G

BATESON, Robert. Introduction to control system technology. Columbus, Ohio, Merrill, 1973.　　　　G

BECKWORTH, Thomas G. and BUCK, N.L. Mechanical measurements. 2nd ed. Reading, Mass., Addison-Wesley, 1971.　　　　9, 14

BEDFORD, Burnice Doyle and HOFT, R.G. Principles of inverter circuits. New York, Wiley, 1964.　　　　5, 8

BELL, David A. Fundamentals of electric circuits. Reston, Va., Reston Pub. Co., 1978.　　　　5, 9, 10, 11, 12

BELL AND HOWELL COMPANY. CEC/Instruments Division. Pressure transducer handbook. Pasadena, Calif., The Company, 1974.　　　　4

BELLAMY, Lionel John. The infra-red spectra of complex molecules. London, Chapman Hall, 1975.　　　　17

BENDAT, Julius S. Principles and applications of random noise theory. New York, Krieger, 1978.　　　　14

BENDAT, Julius S. and PIERSOL, A.G. Random data; analysis and measurement procedures. New York, Wiley-Interscience, 1971.　　　　14

BENNETT, Stuart. A history of control engineering, 1800 − 1930. Stevenage, Peregrinus for the Institution of Electrical Engineers, 1979.　　　　1

BENSON, Frank Atkinson and HARRISON, D. Electric-circuit theory. 3rd ed. London, Arnold, 1978.　　　　5, 9, 10, 11, 12

BENSOUSSAN, A. and LIONS, J.L. New trends in system analysis. International Symposium, Versailles, 1976. Berlin, Springer Verlag, 1977.　　　　G

BERLIN, Howard M. Design of phase-locked circuits with experiments. (The phase-locked loop bugbook). Indianapolis, Ind., H.W. Sams, 1978.　　　　11

BERTABANFFY, Ludwig Von. General system theory: foundations, development, application. New York, G. Brazilier, 1973.　　　　G

BETTS, John Arthur. Signal processing, modulation and noise. London, English Universities Press, 1970.　　　　14

BIRD, Gordon Joseph Alexander. Design of continuous and digital electronic systems. London, McGraw-Hill, 1980.　　　　G

BISHOP, Albert Bentley. Introduction to discrete-linear controls: theory and application. New York, Academic Press, 1975.　　　　G

BISHOP, George Daniel. Linear electronic circuits and systems. London, MacMillan, 1974.　　　　G

BLANCHARD, Alain. Phase-locked loops; application to coherent receiver design. New York, Wiley, 1976.　　　　12

BLASCHKE, W.S. The control of industrial processes by digital techniques: the organisation design and construction of digital control systems. New York, Elsevier Scientific Pub. Co., 1976.　　　　G

BOYLESTEAD, Robert L. and NASHELSKY, Louis. Electronic devices and circuit theory. 2nd ed. Englewood Cliffs, N.J. Prentice-Hall, 1978.　　　　5, 9, 10, 11, 12

BRISTOW, Paul Anthony. Liquid chromatography in practice. Handforth, Hetp, 1976.　　　　17

BRITISH VALVE MANUFACTURERS ASSOCIATION. Valve users manual: a technical reference book on industrlal valves for the control of fluids, edited by J. Kempley. London, Mechanical Engineering Publications, 1980.　　　　7

BUCKLEY, Ruth Victoria. Control engineering: theory, worked examples and problems. London, MacMillan, 1976.   G

BUDAK, Aram. Circuit theory fundamentals and applications. Englewood Cliffs, N.J., Prentice-Hall, 1978.   5, 9, 10, 11, 12

BUDAK, Aram. Passive and active network analysis and synthesis. Boston, Houghton Mifflin, 1974.   5, 9, 10, 11, 12

BUKSTEIN, Edward J. Basic servomechanisms. New York, Holt, Rinehart & Winston, 1963.   G

BURROWS, C.R. Fluid power servomechanisms. London, Van Nostrand Reinhold, 1972.   6

BUTUSOV, I.V. Automatic control measuring and regulating devices. Oxford, Pergamon Press, 1965.   G

CADZOW, James A and MARTENS, Hinrich R. Discrete — time and computer control systems. Englewood Cliffs, N.J., Prentice-Hall, 1970.   G

CADZOE, James A Discrete — time systems: an introduction with interdisciplinary applications. Englewood Cliffs, N.J., Prentice-Hall, 1973.   G

CALDWELL, William I. et al. Frequency response for process control. New York, McGraw-Hill, 1959.   14, 15

CARROLL, Grady C. and RHODES, Thomas J. Industrial process measuring instruments. New York, McGraw-Hill, 1962.   G

CARROLL, Grady C. and RHODES, Thomas J. Industrial instruments for measurement and control. 2nd ed. New York, McGraw-Hill, 1972.   G

CERNI, R.H. and FOSTER, L.E. Instrumentation for engineering measurement. New York, Wiley, 1962.   G

CHEN, Chi-Tsong. Introduction to linear system theory. New York, Hold, Rinehart & Winston, 1970.   G

CHESTNUT, Harold and MAYER, R.W. Servomechanisms and regulating system design. New York, Wiley, 1979 reprint.   G

CHIRBIAN, Paul M. Basic network theory. New York, McGraw-Hill, 1969.   5, 9, 10, 11, 12

CHIRONIS, Nicholas P. Gear design and applications. New York, McGraw-Hill, 1967.   9

CHIRONIS, Nicholas P. Mechanisms, linkages and mechanical controls. New York, McGraw-Hill, 1969.   9

CHUBB, Bruce A. Modern analytical design of instrument servomechanisms. Reading, Mass., Addison-Wesley Pub. Co., 1967.   G

CLARK, Frank James. The data recorder. Reston, Va., Reston Pub. Co., 1973.   14

CLARKE, A. Bruce and DISNEY, R.L. Probability and random processes for engineers and scientists. New York, Wiley, 1970.   14

CLAY, Richard. Nonlinear networks and systems. New York, Wiley-Interscience, 1971.   11

CLAYTON, C.G. Modern developments in flow measurement. London, Peregrinus, 1972.   4

CLAYTON, George Burbridge. Operational amplifiers. 2nd ed. London, Butterworths, 1979.   5, 9, 10, 11, 12

CLULEY, John Charles. Computer interfacing and on-line operation. New York, Crane Russak, 1975.   16

COLLETT, Charles Vincent and HOPE, A.D. Engineering measurements. London, Pitman, 1974.   14

COLLOQUIUM on the design, application and maintenace of large industrial drives, Institution of Electrical Engineers, 1978.   5, 8

CONDER, John R. and YEUNG, C.L. Physicochemical measurement by gas chromatography. Chichester, Wiley, 1979.   17

CONFERENCE ON SERVOCOMPONENTS, London, 1967. London, Institution of Electrical Engineers, 1967.   2, 5

CONNOR, Frank Robert. Networks. London, Edward Arnold, 1972.   9, 10, 11, 12

CONSIDINE, D.M. Encyclopedia of instrumentation and control. New York, McGraw-Hill, 1971   G

CONSIDINE, D.M. Process instruments and controls handbook. 2nd ed. New York, McGraw-Hill, 1974.   G

COOMBS, Clyde F. Basic electronic instruments handbook. New York, McGraw-Hill, 1972.   G

COOPER, George R. and McGILLAN, Clare D. Probabilistic methods of signal and system analysis. New York, Holt, Rinehart & Winston, 1971.   14

COOPER, William David. Electronic instrumentation and measurement techniques. 2nd ed. Englewood Cliffs, N.J., Prentice-Hall, 1978.   G

COUGHLIN, Robert F. and DRISCOLL, Frederick F. Operational amplifiers and linear integrated circuits. Englewood Cliffs, N.J., Prentice-Hall, 1977.   5, 9, 10, 11, 12

CROW, Leonard Ray. Synchros: self-synchronous devices and electrical servomechanisms. Vincennes, Ind., Scientific Book Pub. Co., 1953.   G

CRUZ, Jose Bejar. Feedback systems. New York, McGraw-Hill, 1971.   G

CSAKI, Frigyes. Modern control theories: nonlinear, optimal, and adaptive systems. Budapest, Akademia Kiado, 1972.   G

DANIELS, Richard W. Approximation methods for electronic filter design. New York, McGraw-Hill, 1974.   12

DARYANANI, Gobind. Principles of active network system and design. New York, Wiley, 1976.   10, 11, 12

DAVENPORT, Wilbur B. Probability and random process; an introduction for applied scientists and engineers. New York, McGraw-Hill, 1970.   14

DAVIES, Rex Mountford. Power diode and thyristor circuits. Stevenage, Peregrinus for the Institution of Electrical Engineers, 1979.   5, 8

DAVIES, W.D.T. System identification for self adaptive control. New York, Wiley, 1970.   14

DAVIS, Sidney A. & LEDGERWOOD, B.K. Electromechanical components for servomechanisms. New York, Mc-Graw Hill, 1961.   G

DAVIS, Wilfred Owen. Gears for small mechanisms. 2nd ed. London, N.A.G., 1970.   9

D'AZZO, John J. and HOUPIS, C.H. Feedback control system analysis and synthesis. 2nd ed. New York, McGraw-Hill, 1966.   G

D'AZZO, John J. and HOUPIS, C.H. Linear control system analysis and design: conventional and modern. New York, McGraw-Hill, 1975.   G

DE BARR, Albert Edward. Automatic control: in introduction to the theory of feedback and feedback control systems. London, Chapman and Hall, 1962.   G

DEBOO, Gordon J. & BURROUS, C.N. Integrated circuits and semiconductor devices; theory and application. 2nd ed. New York, McGraw-Hill, 1977.   5, 9, 10, 11, 12

DEPIAN, Louis. Linear active network theory. Englewood Cliffs, N.J., Prentice-Hall, 1962.   10, 11, 12

DERTOUZOS, Michael L. Systems, networks and computation: basic concepts. New York, McGraw-Hill, 1972.   G

DESOER, Charles A. & KUH, E.S. Basic circuit theory. New York, McGraw-Hill, 1969.   G

DESOER, Charles A. and VIDYASAGAR, M. Feedback systems: input-output properties. New York, Academic Press, 1975.   G

DEWAN, S.B. & STRAUGHEN, A. Power semiconductor circuits. New York, Wiley, 1975.   5, 8

DIJKSMAN, E.A. Motion geometry of mechanisms. Cambridge, Cambridge University Press, 1976.   9

DIFFENDERFER, A. James. Principles of electronic instrumentation. 2nd ed. Philadelphia, W.S. Saunders & Co., 1979.   G

DIRECTOR, Stephen W. Circuit theory: a computative approach. New York, Wiley, 1975.   G

DI STEFANO, Joseph J., STUBBERUD, A.R. and WILLIAMS, J. Theory and problems of feedback and control systems. New York, McGraw-Hill, 1967.   G

DOLEZAL, Vaclav. Nonlinear networks. Amsterdam, Elsevier Scientific, 1977.   11

DOOLEY, Daniel J. Data conversion integrated circuits. New York, IEEE Press, 1980.   10, 13, 16

DOUCE, John Leonard. Introduction to the mathematics of servomechanisms. London, English Universities Press. 1963.   G

EARLEY, Bert. Practical instrumentation handbook. Stamford, Lincs., Scientific Era Pubs., 1976.   G

ECKMAN, Donald P. Principles of industrial process control. New York, Wiley, 1965.   G

EIMBINDER, Jerry. Application considerations for linear integrated circuits. New York, Wiley-Interscience, 1976.   5, 9, 10, 11, 12

ELECTRO-CRAFT CORPORATION. DC Motors, speed controls, servo systems: an engineering handbook. 3rd ed. Oxford, Pergamon Press, 1977.   G

ENGINEERING EQUIPMENT USERS ASSOCIATION. A guide to the selection of automatic control valves. Rev. ed. London, 1971.   7

ERWALL, Lars G., FORSBERG, H.G. and LJUNGGREN, K.L. Industrial isotope techniques. Copenhagen, Munksgaard, 1964.   17

ESPOSITO, Anthony. Fluid power with applications. Englewood Cliffs, N.J., Prentice-Hall, 1980.   6, 13

EVELEIGH, Virgil W. Adaptive control and optimization techniques. New York, McGraw-Hill, 1967.   G

EVELEIGH, Virgil W. Introduction to control systems design. New York, McGraw-Hill, 1971.   G

FARAGO, Francis T. Handbook of dimensional measurement. New York, Industrial Press, 1968.   G

FAULKENBERRY, Luces M. An introduction to operational amplifiers. New York, Wiley, 1977.   5, 9, 10, 11, 12

FAURRE, Pierre & DEPEYRET, Michel. Elements of system theory. Amsterdam, North-Holland, 1977.   G

FAWCETT, John Reginald. Hydraulic servo-mechanisms and their applications. Morden, Eng., Trade and Technical Press, 1970.   6, 13

FESTO-PNEUMATIC PTY LTD. Pneumatic elements for automation. 16th ed. Melbourne, Festo Pneumatic, 1972.   6

FINKEL, Jules. Computer-aided experimentation: interfacing to minicomputers. New York, Wiley, 1975.   16

FISHER GOVERNOR CO. Fisher control valves. Marshalltown, Iowa. (n.d.)   7

FORTMAN, T.E. & HITZ, K.L. Introduction to linear control systems. New York, Dekker, 1977.   G

FOX, Harry W. Master op-amp applications handbook. Blue Ridge Summit, Pa., G/L Tab Books, 1978. 5, 9, 10, 11, 12

FRIBANCE, Austin E. Industrial instrumentation fundamentals. New York, McGraw-Hill, 1962. G

GABEL, Robert A. & ROBERTS, Richard A. Signals and linear systems. New York, Wiley, 1973. 14

GARDNER, Floyd. Phaselock techniques. 2nd ed. New York, Wiley, 1979. 12

GARNER, Kenneth Charles. Introduction to control system performance measurements. Oxford, Pergamon, 1968. 14

GENERAL ELECTRIC (U.S.A.) Semiconductor Products Department. Silicon controlled rectifier manual. 4th ed. New York, General Electric, 1967. 5, 8

GHAZNAVI, Couros and SEIDMAN, Arthur H. Electronic circuit analysis. New York, MacMillan, 1972. 5, 9, 10, 11, 12

GILLE, Jean Charles, PELEGRIN, M.J. and DECAULNE, P. Feedback control systems: analysis, synthesis and design. New York, McGraw-Hill, 1959. G

GLASS, Carter M. Linear systems with applications and discrete analysis. St. Paul, West Pub. Co., 1976. G

GOLDMAN, Stanford. Frequency analysis, modulation and noise. New York, Dover Pubs., 1967. 14, 15

GOODWIN, Alfred Bernard. Fluid power systems: theory, worked examples and problems. London, MacMillan, 1976. 6, 13

GORSKI-POPIEL et al. Frequency synthesis: techniques and applications. New York, IEEE Press, 1975. 14, 15

GRAEME, Jerald G. Applications of operational amplifiers: third generation techniques. New York, McGraw-Hill, 1973. 5, 9, 10, 11, 12

GRAEME, Jerald G. Designing with operational amplifiers: applications, alternatives. New York, McGraw-Hill, 1977. 5, 9, 10, 11, 12

GRAEME, Jerald G. Operational amplifiers: design and applications. New York, McGraw-Hill, 1971. 5, 9, 10, 11, 12

GRAY, Bernard Francis. Measurements, instrumentation and data transmission: a text for the OND in technology (engineering). London, Longman, 1977. G

GREGORY, Jack Norman. The world of radioisotopes. Sydney, Angus and Robertson, in association with the Australian Atomic Energy Commission, 1977. 17

GUPTA, S.C. Transform and state variable methods in linear systems. New York, Wiley, 1971 reprint. G

GYUGYI, L. & PELLY, B.R. Static power frequency changers: theory, performance, and applications. New York, Wiley, 1976. 5, 8

HAINES, Roger W. Control systems for heating, ventilating and air conditioning. 2nd ed. New York, Van Nostrand Reinhold, 1977. 8

HALE, Francis J. Introduction to control system analysis and design. Englewood Cliffs, N.J., Prentice-Hall, 1973. G

HARNDEN, John Davis and GOLDEN, Forest B. Power semiconductor applications. New York, IEEE Press, 1972. 5, 8

HARRISON, Howard L. and BOLLINGER, J.G. Introduction to automatic controls. 2nd ed. Scranton, Pa., International Textbook Co., 1969. G

HASEBRINK, J.P. & KOBLER, R. Control engineering 1, fundamentals of pneumatics/electropneumatics. Berkheim, W. Germany, Festo, 1975. 6

HAYKIN, S.S. Active network theory. Reading, Mass., Addison-Wesley, 1970. 9, 10, 11, 12

HAYWARD, A.T.J. Flowmeters: a basic guide and source-book for users. London, MacMillan, 1979. 4

HEALEY, Martin. Principles of automatic control. 3rd ed. London, English Universities Press, 1975.   G

HEARN, Edwin John.   Strain gauges. Watford, Eng., Merrow, 1971.   3

HEDGES, Charles S.   Industrial fluid power. 2nd ed. Dallas, Wormack Educational Pubs., 1972.   6, 13

HEDGES, Charles S.   Practical fluid power control — electrical and fluidic. Dallas, Wormack Educational Pubs., 1971.   6

HELFFERICH, Friedrich and KLEIN, Gerhard.   Multicomponent chromatography: theory of interference. New York, 1970.   17

HERCEG, Edward E.   Handbook of measurement and control: an authoritative treatise on the theory and application of the LVDT. Pennsauken, N.J., Schaevitz Engineering, 1972.   2

HERRICK, Clyde N.   Instruments and measurements for electronics. New York, McGraw-Hill, 1971.   14

HILBURN, John L. and JOHNSON, David E.   Manual of active filter design. New York, McGraw-Hill, 1973.   12

HNATEK, Eugene R.   A user's handbook of D/A and A/D convertors. New York, Wiley, 1976.   10

HOESCHELE, David F.   Analog-to-digital, digital-to-analog conversion techniques. New York, Wiley, 1968.   10

HOUGEN, Joel O. Measurements and control applications. 2nd ed. Pittsburgh, Instrument Society of America, 1979.   G

HOUGHTON, Philip Stephen.   Gears: spur, helical, bevel, internal epicyclic and worm. 3rd ed. London, Technical Press, 1970.   9

HUANG, Thomas S. and PARKER, Ronald R.   Network theory: an introductory course. Reading, Mass., Addison-Wesley, 1971.   9, 10, 11, 12

HUELSMAN, Laurence P.   Active Filters: lumped, distributed, integrated, digital and parametric. New York, McGraw-Hill, 1970.   12

HUELSMAN, Laurence P.   Theory and design of active RC circuits. New York, McGraw-Hill, 1968.   12

HUMPHREY, William M. Introduction to servomechanism system design. Englewood Cliffs, N.J., Prentice-Hall, 1973.   G

HUNTER, Richard Sewall.   The measurement of appearance, New York, Wiley, 1975.   17

HYDRAULIC HANDBOOK, compiled by the editors of Hydraulic Pneumatic Power. 5th ed. Morden, Trade and Technical Press, 1972.   6, 13

IFAC Symposium on Control in Power Electronics and Electrical Devices; proceedings of the 2nd IFAC Symposium, Dusseldorf, 3 — 5 October 1977, edited by W. Leonhard. Oxford, published for IFAC by Pergamon Press, 1978.   5, 8

INTERNATIONAL ATOMIC ENERGY AGENCY.   Isotopes in day to day life. Vienna, I.A.E.A., 1977.   17

INTERNATIONAL ATOMIC ENERGY AGENCY.   Radioisotope applications in industry: a survey of radioisotope application, classified by industry or economic activity. Vienna, I.A.E.A., 1963.   17

INTERNATIONAL Conference on Power Electronics — Power semiconductors and their applications. (1974 Institution of Electrical Engineers). Papers. London, IEE, 1974.   5, 8

INTERNATIONAL Symposium on Nuclear Techniques in Exploration, Extraction and Processing of Mineral Resources, (1977, Vienna). Vienna, I.A.E.A., 1977.   17

ISA handbook of control valves: a comprehensive reference book containing application and design information; edited by J.W. Hutchinson and A.R. Merwick. 2nd ed. Pittsburgh, Instrument Society of America, 1976.   7

JENSEN, Randall W. & WATKINS, Bruce O. Network analysis, theory and computer methods. Englewood Cliffs, N.J., Prentice-Hall, 1974.   9, 10, 11, 12

JOHNSON, Curtis D. Process control instrumentation technology. New York, Wiley, 1976.   G

JOHNSON, David E. Introduction to filter theory. Englewood Cliffs, N.J., Prentice-Hall, 1976.   12

JOHNSON, Edward Lee & STEVENSON, Robert. Basic liquid chromatography. Palo Alto, Calif., Varian, 1978.   17

JOHNSON, Eric R. Servomechanisms. Englewood Cliffs, N.J., Prentice-Hall, 1963.   G

JOHNSON, James E. Electrohydraulic servosystems. 2nd ed. Cleveland, Ohio, Hydraulics & Pneumatics, 1977.   6, 13

JONES, Ernest Beachcroft. Instrument technology, vol. 1: Measurement of pressure, level, flow and temperature. 3rd ed. Newnes-Butterworth, 1974.   4

JONES, Ernest Beachcroft. Instrument technology, vol.2: Analysis instruments. 2nd ed. Newnes-Butterworth, 1976.   4, 17

JONES, Ernest Beachcroft. Instrument technology, vol.3: Telemetering and automatic control. 2nd ed. Newnes-Butterworth, 1957.   G

JONES, Martin Hartley. A practical introduction to electronic circuits. Cambridge, Cambridge University Press, 1977.   5

KALVODA, Robert. Operational amplifiers in chemical instrumentation. Chichester, Eng., E. Horwood; New York, Halsted Press: 1975.   5

KARNI, S. Network theory: analysis and synthesis. Boston, Mass., Allyn & Bacon, 1965.   9, 10, 11, 12

KARTASCHOFF, P. Frequency and time. New York, Academic Press, 1978.   14, 15

KEITZ, H.A.E. Light calculations and measurements: an introduction to the system of quantities and units in light technology, and to photometry. 2nd rev. ed. London, MacMillan, 1971.   17

KERR, Robert Blackburn. Electrical network science. Englewood Cliffs, N.J., Prentice-Hall, 1977.   9, 10, 11, 12

KINARIVALA, B.K., KUO, F.F. and TSAS, N.K. Linear circuits and computation. New York, Wiley, 1973.   9, 10, 11, 12

KIVER, M.S. Transistor and integrated electronics. 4th ed. New York, McGraw-Hill, 1972.   5, 9, 10, 11, 12

KLAPPER, Jacob and FRANKLE, John J. Phase-locked and frequency-feedback systems: principles and techniques. New York, Academic Press, 1972.   12

KNAPMAN, C.E.H. Developments in chromatography. London, Applied Science Pubs., 1978.   17

KOPPE, H. Thyristor and triac power control using 61-series modules. Eindhoven, Phillips' Gloelampen fabrieken, 1973.   5, 8

KORN, G.A. Random-process simulation and measurements. New York, McGraw-Hill, 1966.   14

KOSOW, Irving L. Control of electric machines. Englewood Cliffs, N.J., Prentice-Hall, 1973.   5, 8

KU, Yu-Hsiu. Analysis and control of linear systems. Scranton, Pa., International Textbook Co., 1962.   G

KUO, Benjamin Chung-i. Automatic control systems. 3rd ed. Englewood Cliffs, N.J., Prentice-Hall, 1975.   G

KUO, Benjamin C.   Discrete-data control systems. Englewood Cliffs, N.J., Prentice-Hall, 1970.   G

KUO, Benjamin C. and TAL, J.   Incremental motion control, vol.1: DC motors and controls. SRL Pub. Co., 1978.   5, 8, 13

KUO, Benjamin C.   Incremental motion control, vol.2: Step motors and controls. SRL Pub. Co., 1979.   5, 8, 13

Laboratory handbook of chromatographic and allied methods, chief editor O. Mikes. Chichester, Eng., Ellis Horwood, 1979.   17

LAM, Harry Y.F.   Analog and digital filters. Englewood Cliffs, N.J., Prentice-Hall, 1979.   12

LANGLEY, Billy C.   Electric controls for refrigeration and air conditioning. Englewood Cliffs, N.J., Prentice-Hall, 1974.   8

LAREW, Walter B.   Fluid clutches and torque convertors. Philadelphia, Chilton, 1968.   9

LATHI, B.P.   Signals, systems, and controls. New York, Intext Educational Pubs., 1974.   G

LEATHARD, D.A. & SHURLOCK, B.C.   Identification techniques in gas chromatography. London, Wiley-Interscience, 1970.   17

LENT, Deane.   Analysis and design of mechanisms. 2nd ed. Englewood Cliffs, N.J., Prentice-Hall, 1970.   9

LESEA, Austin & ZAKS, Rodney.   Microprocessor interfacing techniques. 2nd ed. Berkeley, Calif., Sybex, 1978.   16

LEVSON, Karsten.   Fundamental aspects of organic mass spectrometry. New York, Verlag Chemie, 1978.   17

LEWIS, John Barkley.   Analysis of linear and dynamic systems: a unified treatment for continuous and discrete time and deterministic and stochastic signals. Champaign, Ill., Matrix Publications, 1977.   G

LEWIS, Laurel J.   Linear systems analysis. New York, McGraw-Hill, 1969.   G

LIGHTBAND, D.A. and BICKNELL, D.A.   The direct current traction motor. London, Business Books, 1970.   5

LINDSEY, William C. & SIMON, Marvin K.   Phase-locked loops and their applications. New York, IEEE Press, 1978.   12

LINDSEY, William C.   Synchronization systems in communication and control. Englewood Cliffs, N.J., Prentice-Hall, 1972.   G

LION, Kurt Siegfied.   Elements of electrical and electronic instrumentation: an introductory textbook. New York, McGraw-Hill, 1975.   G

LIPTAK, Bela G.   Instrument engineers' handbook. Philadelphia, Chilton, 1969-72.   G

LITTLEWOOD, A.B.   Gas chromatography: principles, techniques and applications. 2nd ed., New York, Academic Press, 1970.   17

LIU, Chung Laung & LIU, J.W.S.   Linear systems analysis. New York, McGraw-Hill, 1975.   G

LUBKIN, Yale Jay.   Filter systems and design: electrical, microwave and digital. Reading, Mass., Addison-Wesley, 1970.   12

LUENBERGER, David G.   Introduction to dynamic systems: theory, models and applications. New York, Wiley, 1979.   G

LYTHALL, Reginald Tarlton.   AC motor control: a guide to the basic methods of starting, controlling, sequencing and protecting AC induction motors. London, Iliffe, 1971.   5, 8

MAAS, J.H. Van der.   Basic infrared spectroscopy. 2nd ed. London, Heyden & Son, 1972.   17

MABIE, Hamilton Horth, and OWIRK, Fred W. Mechanisms and dynamics of machinery. 3rd ed. New York, Wiley, 1975.   9

McCLOY, D. and MARTIN, H.R. Control of fluid power. 2nd ed. Chichester, Eng., Halstead Press, 1980.   6, 13

McFADDEN, William H. Techniques of combined gas/chromatography/mass spectroscopy: applications on organic analysis. New York, Wiley, 1973.   17

MacFARLENE, Alistair G.J. Frequency-response methods in control systems. New York, IEEE Press, 1979.   12, 14, 15

McINTYRE, R.L. Electric motor control fundamentals. 3rd ed. New York, McGraw-Hill, 1974.   5, 8

McLAFFERTY, Fred Warren. Interpretation of mass spectra. 2nd ed. Reading, Mass., Benjamin, 1973.   17

McMURRAY, William. Theory and design of cycloconvertors. Cambridge, Mass., M.I.T. Press, 1972.   8

McNEIL, Ian. Hydraulic power. London. Longman, 1972.   6, 13

MANSFIELD, P.H. Electrical transducers for industrial measurement. London, Butterworths, 1973.   2, 3, 4, 17

MARCUS, Abraham and LENK, John D. Measurements for technicians. Englewood Cliffs, N.J., Prentice-Hall, 1971.   G

MARSHALL, S.A. Introduction to control theory. London, MacMillan, 1978.   G

MAZDA, F.F. Thyristor control. London, Butterworths, 1973.   5, 8

MEADOW, Charles T. Man-machine communication. New York, Wiley-Interscience, 1970.   16

MERRITT, Henry Edward. Gear engineering, London, Pitman, 1971.   9

MICHALEC, George W. Precision gearing; theory and practice. New York, Krieger, 1979.   9

MIDDLEDITCH, Brian S. Practical mass spectrometry: contemporary introduction. New York, Plenum Press, 1979.   17

MILES, Victor Chesney. Thermostatic control; principles and practice. 2nd ed. London, Newnes-Butterworths, 1975.   3, 8

MILLER, J.T. A revised course in industrial instrument technology. London, United Trade Press, 1964.   2, 3, 4, 17

MILLER, Richard W. Servomechanisms: devices and fundamentals. Reston, Va., Reston Pub. Co., 1977.   G

MIRTES, Bohmil. D.C. amplifiers. London, Iliffe, 1971.   5

MITRA, Sanjit Kumar. Active inductorless filters. New York, IEEE Press, 1971.   12

MODERN developments in flow measurement: proceedings of the international conference held at Harwell, 21st — 23rd September, 1971. London, Peter Perigrinus, 1972.   4

MOLTGEN, Gottfried. Line commutated thyristor converters. Berlin: Siemens Aktiengesellschaft, 1972.   5, 8

MORRIS, Noel Malcolm. Electrical circuits and systems. London, MacMillan, 1975.   G

MULLARD LIMITED. Industrial Electronics Division Power engineering using thyristors. Sydney, Mullard Ltd., 1970.   5, 8

MUNRO, N. Modern approaches to control system design. Stevenage, Eng., Perigrinus for the Institution of Electrical Engineers, 1979.   G

MURPHY, John M.D. Thyristor control of A.C. motors, Oxford, Pergamon, 1973.   5, 8

NAGRATH, I.J. and GOPAL, M.   Control systems engineering. New York, Wiley, 1977.   G

NATIONAL MEASUREMENT LABORATORY.   Tests and measurements. 2nd ed. Melbourne, C.S.I.R.O., 1977.   14

NATIONAL SEMICONDUCTOR CORPORATION. The pressure transducer handbook. Santa Clara, Calif., the Corporation, 1977.   4

NATIONAL SEMICONDUCTOR CORPORATION. Special functions databook. Santa Clara, Calif., the Corporation, 1979.   4

NEUBERT, Herman Karl Paul. Instrument transducers: an introduction to their performance and design. 2nd ed. Oxford, University Press, 1976.   2, 3, 4, 17

NEWMAN, Louis B. Friction material: recent advances. Park Ridge, N.J., Noyes Data Corporation, 1978.   9

NORTON, Harry N. Handbook of transducers for electronic measuring systems. Englewood Cliffs, N.J., Prentice-Hall, 1969.   G

OGATA, Katsuhiko. Systems dynamics. Englewood Cliffs, N.J., Prentice-Hall, 1978.   G

O'HIGGINS, Patrick J.   Basic instrumentation: industrial measurement. New York, McGraw-Hill, 1966.   G

O'KEEFE, William.   Valves. New York, Power, 1971.   7

OLIVER, Frank J. Practical instrumentation transducers. London, Pitman, 1972.   2, 3, 4, 17

OPEN UNIVERSITY. Control Engineering Course Team. Controllers and compensators and multiloop strategies. Milton Keynes, Eng., Open University Press, 1978.   8, 12, 15

OPEN UNIVERSITY. Control Engineering Course Team. Control strategies. Milton Keynes, Eng., Open University Press, 1977.   G

OPEN UNIVERSITY. Control Engineering Course Team. Nonlinearities and controllers and computers. Milton Keynes, Eng., Open University Press, 1978.   G

OPEN UNIVERSITY. Control Engineering Course Team. Root locus and transient response; introduction to design. Milton Keynes, Eng., Open University Press, 1978.   15

OPEN UNIVERSITY. Instrumentation Course Team. Introduction to instrumentation and the measurement of strain. Milton Keynes, Eng., Open University, 1974.   3

OPEN UNIVERSITY. Instrumentation Course Team. Numerical control of machine tools. Milton Keynes, Eng., Open University Press, 1974.   2, 5, 8, 13

OPEN UNIVERSITY. Instrumentation Course Team. Transducers. 1, temperature, displacement, force, torque, pressure. Milton Keynes, Open University Press, 1974.   2, 3, 4

OPEN UNIVERSITY. Instrumentation Course Team. Transducers. 2, acceleration, vibration, velocity, flow. Milton Keynes, Open University Press, 1974.   2, 3, 4

OPERATIONAL AMPLIFIERS. design and applications. New York, McGraw-Hill, 1971.   5, 8, 9, 10, 11, 12

PANTER, Philip F. Modulation, noise, and spectral analysis applied to information transmission. New York, McGraw-Hill, 1965.   14

PARRIS, N.A. Instrumental liquid chromatography: a practical manual on high-performance liquid chromatographic methods. Amsterdam, Elsevier Scientific, 1976.   17

PATRANABIS, D. Principles of industrial instrumentation. New Delhi, Tata McGraw Hill, 1976.   2, 3, 4, 17

PATTISON, James Bulmer. A programmed introduction to gas-liquid chromatography. 2nd ed. London, Heydon, 1973.   17

PEARSON, George Harold. Valve design; manually operated patterns. London, Pitman, 1972.   7

PEARSON, George Harold. Valve design. London, Mechanical Engineering Publications, 1978.   7

PELLY, B.R. Thyristor phase-controlled converters and cycloconverters; operation control and performance. New York. Wiley-Interscience, 1971.   5, 8

PERRY, Sidney George, AMOS, R. and BREWER, P.J. Practical liquid chromatography. New York, Plenum Press, 1972.   17

PHELAN, Richard M. Automatic control systems. Ithaca, N.Y., Cornell University Press, 1977.   G

PHILCO CORPORATION. Philco Technological Center. Servomechanism fundamentals and experiments. Englewood Cliffs, N.J., Prentice-Hall, 1964.   G

PIPPENGER, John L. and HICKS, Tyler G. Industrial hydraulics. New York, McGraw-Hill, 1970.   6, 13

PIRAUX, Henry. Radioisotopes and their industrial applications. Eindhoven, Philips Technical Library, 1964.   17

POUCHER, George Howard. Introduction to control techniques. Amsterdam, Elsevier Scientific, 1977.   G

PRECISION MONOLITHICS INC. Full line catalogue: linear wonderland. Santa Clara, Calif., Precision Monolithics Inc., 1979.   5, 8, 9, 10, 11, 12

PRESSMAN, Abraham I. Switching and linear power sypply, power converter design. Rochelle Park, N.J., Hayden Book Co., 1977.   5, 8

PROKES, Josef. Hydraulic mechanisms in automation. Amsterdam, Elsevier, 1977.   6

PRYDE, Andrew and GILBERT, M.T. Applications of high performance liquid chromatography. London, Chapman Hall, 1979.   17

PUN, Lucas et al. Integrated automation practice. New York, American Elsevier, 1976.   G

RAMAMOORTY, M. An introduction to thyristors and their applications. London, MacMillan, 1978.   5, 8

RAMOUS, Arthur J. Applied kinematics. Englewood Cliffs, N.J., Prentice-Hall, 1972.   9

RAMSHAW, Raymond Southern. Power electronics: thyristor controlled power for electric motors. London, Chapman and Hall, 1975.   5, 8

RAVEN, Francis Harvey. Automatic control engineering. 3rd ed., New York, McGraw-Hill, 1978.   G

RCA power devices. Somerville, N.J. RCA Solid State, 1978.   5, 8

RHODES, John David. Theory of electrical filters. London, Wiley, 1976.   12

RHODES, Thomas J. Industrial instruments for measurement and control. 2nd ed. New York, McGraw-Hill, 1973.   2, 3, 4, 17

RICHARDS, R.J. An introduction to dynamics and control. London, Longman, 1979.   G

ROBERGE, James K. Operational amplifiers: theory and practice. New York, Wiley, 1975.   5, 8, 9, 10, 11, 12

RONY, Peter R. LARSEN, David G. and TITUS, Jonathon A. The 8080A bugbook: microcomputer interfacing and programming. Indianapolis, H.W. Sams, 1977.   16

RUBIS, J.E. The theory of linear systems. New York, Academic Press, 1971.   G

RUTKOWSKI, George B. Handbook of integrated circuit operational amplifiers. Englewood Cliffs, N.J., Prentice-Hall, 1975.   5, 8, 9, 10, 11, 12

SAVANT, C.J. Control system design. 2nd ed. New York, McGraw-Hill, 1964.   G

SAY, Maurice George. Performance and design of alternating current machines; transformers, three-phase induction motors and synchronous machines. 3rd ed. London, Pitman, 1968.   5

SAY, Maurice George. Alternating current machines. 4th ed. London, Pitman, 1976.   5

SCHMID, Hermann. Electronic analog/digital conversions. New York, Van Nostrand-Reinhold, 1970.   10

SHEPHERD, W. Thyristor control of AC circuits. Bradford, Bradford University Press; London, Crosby Lockwood Staples, 1976.   5, 8

SHIGLEY, Joseph Edward. Kinematic analysis of mechanisms. 2nd ed. New York, McGraw-Hill, 1969.   9

SHINNERS, Stanley M. Modern control system theory and application. 2nd ed. Reading, Mass., Addison-Wesley, 1978.   G

SHINSKEY, F. Greg. Process-control systems; application, design, adjustment. New York, McGraw-Hill, 1967.   G

SHUMILOVSKII, Nilolai Nickolaevich. Radioactive isotopes in instrumentation and control. Oxford, Pergamon Press, 1964.   17

SIMPSON, C.F. Practical high performance liquid chromatography. London, Heyden for Continuing Education Committee of the Chemical Society, 1976.   17

SKILLING, H.H.   Electric networks. New York, Wiley, 1974.   9, 10, 11, 12

SMITH, Otto J.M. Feedback control systems. New York, McGraw-Hill, 1958.   G

SMITH, J.I. Modern operational circuit design. New York, Wiley-Interscience, 1971.   5, 8, 9, 10, 11, 12

SMYTH, Michael P. Linear engineering systems: tools and techniques. New York, Pergamon Press, 1972.   G

SNELL, Foster D. Photometric and fluorometric methods of analysis: metals. New York, Wiley, 1978.   17

SNYDER, Lloyd R. and KIRKLAND, J.J. Introduction to modern liquid chromatography. 2nd ed. New York, 1979.   17

SOCIETY FOR EXPERIMENTAL STRESS ANALYSIS. Technical Committee on Strain Gages. Strain gage accuracy: proceedings of technical session. Boston, Mass., October 23, 1970. Westport, Conn., Society for Experimental Stress Analysis, 1970.   3

SOCIETY FOR EXPERIMENTAL STRESS ANALYSIS. Technical Committee on Strain gages. Practical applications of strain gages: proceedings of technical session, Salt Lake City, Utah, May 18, 1971. Westport, Conn., Society for Experimental Stress Analysis, 1971.   3

SOCIETY FOR EXPERIMENTAL STRESS ANALYSIS. Technical Committee on Strain Gages. Strain gages in extreme environments: proceedings of technical session, Seattle, Wash., October 17, 1972. Westport, Conn., Society for Experimental Stress Analysis, 1972.   3

SPINK, Leland Kenneth. Principles and practice of flow meter engineering. 9th ed. Foxboro.   4

STEIGLITZ, Kenneth. An introduction to discrete systems. New York, Wiley, 1974.   G

STEWART, Harry L. and STORER, J.M. ABC's of hydraulic circuits. Indianapolis, H.W. Sams, 1973.   6, 13

STEWART, Harry L. and STORER, J.M. ABC's of pneumatic circuits. Indianapolis, H.W. Sams, 1973.   6

STEWART, Harry L. and STORER, J.M. Fluid power. 2nd ed. Indianapolis, H.W. Sams, 1973.   6, 13

STEWART, Harry L. Pneumatics and hydraulics. 3rd ed. Indianapolis, T. Audel, 1976.   6, 13

STEWART, J.L. Fundamentals of signal theory. New York, McGraw-Hill, 1960.   G

STIMSON, Allen. Photometry and radiometry for engineers. New York, Wiley, 1974.   17

STOCK, Ralph and RICE, C.B.F. Chromatographic methods. 3rd ed. London, Chapman and Hall, 1974.   17

STRINGER, John. Hydraulic systems analysis: an introduction. London, MacMillan, 1976.   6, 13

SUN, H.H. Synthesis of R.C. networks. New York, Hayden Book Co., 1967.   12

SUY, Chung Ha and RADCLIFFE, C.W. Kinematics and mechanisms design. New York, Wiley, 1978.   9

SYDENHAM, P.H. Measuring instruments: tools of knowledge and control. Stevenage, Eng., Peregrinus, 1979.   G

SYMPOSIUM on Incremental Motion Control Systems and Devices. University of Illinois at Urbana — Champaign, 1972 — 73.   2, 8, 13

SYMPOSIUM on Radioisotope Instruments in Industry and Geophysics, 1965, Warsaw. Vienna, I.A.E.A., 1966.   17

SYMPOSIUM on Radioisotope Tracers in Industry and Geophysics. 1966, Prague. Vienna, I.A.E.A., 1967.   17

SZABO, Marianne. Fluid motors: for profit-making designs. Cleveland, Ohio, Hydraulics and Pneumatics, 1977.   6

TAYLOR, Philip Lester. Servomechanisms; an introduction to the practice and theory of closed-loop position-control systems, with an account of methods of data transmission and computation. 2nd ed. London, Longmans, 1969.   G

TEMES, Gabor C. and MITRA, Sanjit K. Modern filter theory and design. New York, 1973.   12

THALER, George Julius. Automatic control: classical linear theory. New York, Academic Press, 1975.   G

THALER, George Julius. Design of feedback systems. Stroudsburg, Pa., Dowden, Hutchinson & Ross, 1973.   G

THOMSON, John et al. Frequency conversion. London, Wykeham, 1969.   5, 8

TRETTER, Steven A. Introduction to discrete-time signal processing. New York, Wiley, 1976.   G

TRUXAL, John G. Automatic feedback control system synthesis. New York, McGraw-Hill, 1955.   G

TURNBULL, D.E. Fluid power engineering. London, Newnes-Butterworth, 1976.   5, 8

TUTTLE, David F. Circuits. Tokyo, McGraw-Hill, 1977.   5, 8, 9, 10, 11, 12

UPSON, Arthur Richard & BATCHELOR, J.H. Synchro engineering handbook. Beckenham, Eng., Muirhead & Co., 1965.   2

VAN DER ZIEL, Albert. Noise in measurements. New York, 1976.   14

VAN VALKENBURG, M.E. Network analysis. 3rd ed. Englewood Cliffs, N.J., Prentice-Hall, 1974.   5, 8, 9, 10, 11, 12

VANZETTI, Riccardo. Practical applications of infrared techniques: a new tool in a new dimension for problem solving. New York, Wiley-Interscience, 1972.   17

VERKHOVSKII, Boris Isaakovich. The use of radioactive isotopes for checking production processes. Oxford, Pergamon Press, 1963.   17

VIERSMA, T.J. Analysis, synthesis and design of hydraulic servosystems and pipelines. Amsterdam, Elsevier Scientific, 1980.   6, 13

VOROB'EVA, Tamara Mikhailovna. Electromagnetic clutches and couplings. Oxford, Pergamon, 1965.   9

WADE, James T., EDWARDS, P.L. & CLARK, J.E. Electronic circuit analysis: a first course. Sydney, Wiley, 1973.   5, 8, 9, 10, 11, 12

WAIT, J.V., HUELSMAN, L.P. & KORN, G.A. Introduction to operational amplifier theory and applications. New York, McGraw-Hill, 1975.   5, 8, 9, 10, 11, 12

WALLER, William Frederick. Fluid control. West Wickham, Eng., Morgan-Grampian, 1970.   6, 13

WATSON, H.J. Modern gear production. Oxford, Pergamon Press, 1970.   9

WEAVER, Graham George. Electric controls. West Wickham, Eng., Morgan-Grampian, 1970.   G

WEBER, Samuel. Circuits for electronic engineers. New York, McGraw-Hill, 1977.   5, 8, 9, 10, 11, 12

WEBER, Thomas W. An introduction to process dynamics and control. New York, Wiley-Interscience, 1973.   G

WEISKE, Wolfgang. How the thyristor works. Berlin, Siemans Aktiengesellschaft, Heyden, 1978.   5, 8

WEYRICK, Robert C. Fundamentals of automatic control. New York, McGraw-Hill, 1975.   G

WHALEN, Anthony D. Detection of signals in noise. New York, Academic Press, 1971.   14

WHITE, Robert Gordon. Handbook of ultraviolet methods. New York, Plenum, 1965.   17

WIGHTMAN, Eric Jeffrey. Instrumentation in process control. London, Butterworths, 1972.   3, 4, 17

WILKINSON, Barry & HORROCKS, David. Computer peripherals. London, Hodder and Stoughton, 1980.   16

WILLIAMS, Arthur Bernard. Active filter design. Dedham, Mass., Artech House, 1975.   12

WILLIAMS, Jacques Leopold. Stability theory of dynamical systems. New York, Wiley-Interscience, 1970.   G

WILLSON, Alan N. Nonlinear networks: theory and analysis. New York, IEEE Press, 1975.   11

WILSON, Derek Robert. Modern practice in servo design. Oxford, Pergamon, 1970.   G

WOLANSKY, William D., NAGOHOSIAN, John & HENKE, Russell W. Fundamentals of fluid power. Boston, Houghton Mifflin, 1977.   6, 13

WOLSEY, Willem Harry. Basic principles of automatic control: with special reference to heating and air conditioning. London, Hutchinson, 1975.   G

WONG, Yu Jen & OTT, William E. Function circuits: design and applications. New York, McGraw-Hill, 1972.   12

WOOD, Peter. Switching power converters. New York, Van Nostrand Reinhold, 1981.   5, 8

WOOLVET, G.A. Transducers in digital systems. Stevenage, Peregrinus for the IEE, 1977.   2, 8, 13

WRIGHT, William David. The measurement of colour. 4th ed. London, Hilger & Watts, 1969.   17

YANG, Wen-Jei & MASABUCHI, M. Dynamics for process and system control. New York, Gordon & Breach, 1970.   G

YOUSEFZADEH, B. Basic control engineering. London, Pitman, 1979.   G

ZWEIG, Gunter and SHERMA, Joseph. CRC handbook of chromatography. Cleveland, CRC Press, 1972.   17

INDEX